Samuel Brown

and

Union Chain Bridge

GORDON MILLER

and

The Chainworks of Brown Lenox

STEPHEN K JONES

THE FRIENDS OF THE UNION CHAIN BRIDGE

THE FRIENDS OF THE UNION CHAIN BRIDGE
Horncliffe, Berwick-upon-Tweed TD15 2XT
Registered as a Charity in England and Wales (No 1162687) and Scotland (No SC046208)
The Friends of the Union Chain Bridge is a Charitable Incorporated Organisation constituted under the Charities Act 2011
www.unionbridgefriends.com

First published 2017

A CIP catalogue record for this book is available from the British Library.

ISBN: 978 1 5272 1616 7

Imperial measures and symbols are used throughout.

Front cover: *Detail from* Union Chain Bridge over the River Tweed by Alexander Nasmyth (The Paxton Trust)

Set in Times New Roman
Designed and typeset by Printspot, Berwick-upon-Tweed TD15 1BN
Printed by Martins the Printers, Spittal, Berwick-upon-Tweed TD15 1RS

Fig 1 - Snow and ice 1967 - view from Horncliffe over Tweedhill and Paxton House (Mrs. E. Curle)

Dedicated to the memory of

Francis 'Cockle' Cowe

(1931-2016)

Berwick Historian

who introduced me to the Union Bridge

GM

Fig 2 - View towards Scottish side

Contents

Fig 3 - English bank pier in 1975

Forewords

Professor Roland Paxton

There is no technical triumph in bridge building more worthy of appreciation than Union Chain Bridge, which united England and Scotland by road over the River Tweed in 1820. Essentially, this feat comprised the development and application of long iron eye-bar links in the main chains of a suspension bridge to replace an often dangerous ford. This was achieved by what was then, a world record span, four times longer than would have been practicable in stone, with a huge saving in time and cost. It led, in the infancy of 'strength of materials' design, to a new era in bridge building. The bridge is now the world's longest-serving of its type.

The bridge's example and significance clearly justify this book. It is the brain child of local architect Gordon Miller, with a contribution by engineering historian Stephen Jones on the iron industry of Wales, where the bridge's ironwork was made. Their book effectively highlights its importance to a wider public, visitors, researchers and its custodians. Miller's attention was drawn to this subject in 1970, since when he has periodically engaged in research and inspection and created the manuscript off which he has recently blown the dust!

Much that is new or long-forgotten about the key roles of Capt. Brown and John Rennie CE is revealed. Not least that of William Molle, Chairman of the Road Trustees, for his vision, zeal and key personal contacts. As well as the bridge's direct benefits he saw it 'promoting mutual friendship and esteem between the two ancient nations now happily united' [Molle 1819]

In providing this fascinating story of Brown's masterpiece in context, the authors are to be congratulated on their wide-ranging dedication to detail from prime sources. It is undoubtedly the definitive history of the Union Bridge to date.

Prof/Dr Roland Paxton MBE, FICE, FRSE
Hon Professor, Institute for Infrastructure and Environment, Heriot Watt University;
ICE Panel for Historical Engineering Works;
Co-Patron, Friends of Union Chain Bridge.

Hans Seland

As the first Industrial Revolution got under way in Britain, new iron bridges crossed ever-wider waterways to speed transport of people and goods. An American innovation by James Finley in 1802, the level suspension bridge, broke the 100 feet span limitation that had hampered development of long bridges for so long. British engineer Thomas Telford and industrialist Samuel Brown caught on to the new prospects. Telford verified by experiment the basic relationship between stress and strain in a catenary chain and Brown built a working full-scale model of a suspension bridge at his London factory of wrought iron anchor chains. Telford and Brown both collaborated and competed to propose the best design for Runcorn Bridge near Liverpool, but the 1000 feet main span proved too ambitious for its time. Telford accepted a commission to design and build Menai Bridge in Wales while Brown was invited to construct the superstructure of a suspension bridge to cross the river some five miles west of Berwick upon Tweed. When Brown's Union Chain Bridge opened in 1820, it spanned ca. 360' between its two pylons and was the first level bridge in service of its kind in Europe.

Robert Stevenson's account of the opening ceremony was translated into French and German and soon European governments sent their best scholars and engineers to inspect and report on the new opportunities. Most famous were perhaps Charles Dupin and Claude Navier who both came from France to Berwick in the early 1820s. Navier hit upon the early work of Telford's associate, the mathematician Davies Gilbert, and in his report to the French government in 1823 Navier refined the mathematics of suspension bridges to a high standard. Navier was charged with the opportunity to apply his theory to a new suspension bridge across River Seine in Paris, but the project failed for geotechnical reasons.

In Denmark Professor G.F. Ursin published digests of contemporary polytechnic reports in his new "Magazin" in the years from 1826 until 1842. Norwegian regional roadmaster, Georg D.B. Johnson (1794–1872) read Ursin's publications and decided to see for himself. In 1838 he went on a government mission to Britain and around the North Sea to study modern roads and bridges, harbours and the new railroads. Johnson came to The Borders region to look for the solution to a definite river crossing at Aabel on the main highway some miles east of the city of Kristiansand. As it were, Union Bridge was too long and Brown's Kalemouth Bridge crossing River Teviot to the west of Kelso, was too short. The no-nonsense military engineer decided to keep the old ferry working at Aabel, and to copy Kalemouth Bridge "lock, stock and barrel" for another highway river crossing at Bakke some 100 miles further west on the south coast. Back home, Johnson was granted permission to build Scandinavia's first suspension bridge and he awarded the contract for the wrought iron superstructure to the Iron Works at Tvedestrand. Jacob Aall, the owner, envisaged new business opportunities and did his best to make the bridge a success. He even engaged his British agents Dahl & Thompson in Newcastle upon Tyne to travel to Kelso to check on construction details. But the project went sour because Johnson's notes were not always accurate or based on sight. Thus the diameter of the main chains at Bakke was smaller than at Kelso, the pylons were lower, the bridge deck was heavier and the allowance for live load was not in line with the state of the art. Neither approximation was very inaccurate, but it all added up to an inferior end product. Johnson's young assistant, C.V. Bergh, saw what was happening and tried to advice his senior master, but he was brushed off. Bergh then reported over Johnson's head to central Government and after a winter of ugly debate, Johnson was relieved of his bridge duty. Bergh was promoted project manager and finished Bakke Suspension Bridge to his own design according to Navier in 1844. The bridge stands proudly to this day.

The harsh realities of technology transfer hit both Navier and Johnson with full force some 200 years ago. Navier never got another commission to build a bridge after his Pont des Invalides failed, but his theoretical work dominated Continental bridge design for many years to come. Johnson moved on to a position as national Director of Canals and Harbours. He spent the next few years advocating the use of stone tramways according to Telford as an alternative to the iron railway that Robert Stephenson sold to the Norwegian government around 1850. He never admitted his failure at Bakke and in his writings he totally ignored his former assistant. Bergh became recognized as Norwegian expert of suspension bridges and rose to be the country's first Director of the Norwegian Public Roads Administration.

Concrete development of new industry and associated transport infrastructure in continental Europe began in earnest around 1840. Even smaller countries on Europe's periphery saw the need to modernize and joined in the search for new technologies. Norway was one of them. In spite of occational setbacks and personal cost to some actors, the pioneers of The Industrial Revolution laid the foundations for the modern society, as we know it. Sam Brown and his Union Chain Bridge made notable contributions to that process.

Hans Seland (BSc) CEng.
Norwegian Public Roads Administration, Senior Principal Engineer (Retired)

Author's Note

Sometime during the first week of June 1970, seeing Samuel Brown's Union Chain Bridge for the first time, like thousands before, I was enchanted and intrigued. The fact that the bridge was there at all engendered even more excitement, as there seemed to be so much original 'structure' surviving.

A bronze plaque on the face of the English side anchorage pier *(fig 130)* gave some information:

UNION SUSPENSION BRIDGE
DESIGNED AND EXECUTED BY CAPT S. BROWN. R.N.
OPENED IN 1820
IMPROVED AND STRENGTHENED IN 1902-3
BY THE
TWEED BRIDGES TRUSTEES
WATSON ASKEW ROBERTSON, ESQ. D.L. OF
PALLINSBURN AND LADYKIRK, CHAIRMAN.
S. SANDERSON, D.L. CLERK TO TRUSTEES
J. A. BEAN, ENGINEER TO THE TRUSTEES.

As Trustees controlled the administration and maintenance of the bridge it suggested that a great deal of caring had run parallel with the passing years, and it seemed that the bridge history must have been thoroughly recorded, also that of its creator Samuel Brown. To my subsequent astonishment this was not so, beyond the simple facts of its existence and brief physical descriptions in published works.

Fig 4 - Royal Tweed Bridge 1928

Although some five miles up the Tweed from Berwick-upon-Tweed, where the river then divides England from Scotland, Brown's bridge may historically be regarded as one of a unique bridge foursome; the other three spanning the river at Berwick. They are all well known, documented, cared for and revered by the authorities responsible, for they are:

The 'Old Bridge' or Berwick Bridge having fifteen arches spanning over 1,164 feet and built by James Burrell in 1634.

Robert Stephenson's Royal Border Bridge opened by Queen Victoria in 1850; of 2,152 feet length in a gracious curve over land and water, having twenty eight towering stone arches which completed the London - Edinburgh link for the North Eastern Railway

The Royal Tweed Bridge in reinforced concrete by L.G.Mouchel and Partners, opened by the Prince of Wales in 1928 to carry the Great North Road over the Tweed.

They are all monuments in civil engineering history and, without doubt, Brown's suspension bridge ranks among them and their respective creators, and deserves to be better known and respected. After a very cursory examination it was sad to find that it was severely dilapidated, and being ill-treated by excessively heavy and fast driven traffic, and under these conditions, how was it to survive?

Out of no more than irresistible curiosity, and memories of childhood spent fishing on the banks of the Hundred Foot Drain in the Fens by Samuel Brown's Earith Bridge, certain cussed determination of my thoughts concentrated upon discovery and very soon started upon a survey of record drawings and photography, which led to other related researches, and all that follows is the prying result.

Gordon Miller 1975

Fig 5 - The Old Bridge (1634) Royal Tweed Bridge (1928) and Robert Stephenson's Royal Border Bridge (1850) in the background

Fig 6 - Robert Stephenson's Royal Border Bridge (1850)

Introduction and Notes on Sources

Samuel Brown revelled in challenging problems; he was imaginative, had a great capacity for work, and was blessed with a driving ambition to succeed and prove his ideas. A practical resourcefulness, coupled with a natural sense of line and beauty, stamps all his creations. Seventeen years in the Navy provided him with a thorough insight and testing ground concerning the behaviour of materials, and his involvement with wrought-iron, both in manufacture and application, ultimately secured his total interest. He made two important contributions to the art of engineering - first the idea of using iron to replace hempen cables for ships' ground tackle, and secondly the invention and improvement of iron bar linking techniques that made possible the first 'Chain Bridge of Suspension' in Britain, completed in 1820, that was capable of carrying carts and wagons. Both ideas were adopted and developed by other engineers, but the merit of invention was Samuel Brown's, and his chain linking methods paved the way for the popularity that suspension bridges have ultimately enjoyed.

In 1973 the Union Chain Bridge had reached the fourth critical point in its history, and its useful life was again threatened. It had faced crises in the years 1871, 1891 and 1902, but in those instances the bridge was part of an important road system and it was therefore repaired and strengthened. In 1973 the situation was different. The existing bridges at Berwick and Norham were considered to be adequate for a community whose mobility was self-sufficient, and there was no really serious agricultural or other need for the bridge. However, local feeling ran high at the suggestion that the bridge might be restricted in use, and the Northumberland County Council, in agreement with the Tweed Bridges Trustees, decided to check the actual bridge use with an electronic traffic counter.

Upon the evidence obtained, the fate of the bridge was to be decided, and the results were very surprising, for they proved to be much higher than had been anticipated. This turned the scales in favour of restoration rather than a de-classification, which may have meant use only by pedestrians. Such a de-classification would have meant eventual extinction, since continuous ageing without repair would naturally lead, in time, to the bridge being declared unsafe for any use.

Although the structure is listed this does not imply an automatic grant of money for maintenance to keep the bridge in use, but any idea of pulling it down was another matter, and a dilemma therefore existed as to its future.

With the traffic count record providing high figures of vehicle use per day, the Surveyor of Bridges, Northumberland County Council, was instructed to prepare a detailed report about necessary repairs and estimated costs; and to recommend stages for carrying out such works. The Surveyor's findings were accepted by both the Tweed Bridges Trustees and the County Council, and the bridge was closed to vehicle traffic during the summer and autumn of 1974 for essential repairs to be carried out. This first stage work was concentrated upon the road platform and suspension bars, and in future stages the catenary chains, their respective pier bearings and the ground hold-fasts were recommended to be dealt with.

Through a combination of circumstances and conditions the bridge is being given a new lease of life and, except for the addition of a steel wire cable made in 1902-3, set above each bank of the original iron chains, the bridge appears essentially the same as when it was first constructed.

This book has attempted to bring together all recorded historical and current information collected from many sources; relevant to both the Bridge and its creator, Captain Sir Samuel Brown R.N.

Among the drawings reproduced are details from survey sketches made in the early months of 1974; before and during the first stage platform restoration. Likewise, photographs of the structure were taken before, during and after that restoration. The 'original' and subsequent drawings made of the Bridge by the Bridges Department of Northumberland County Council, are in the possession of that office, and reference to them and the privilege to reproduce them is acknowledged.

Other sources of information include the Northumberland County Council Record Office, the Scottish Record Office, Register House, The Maritime Museum, Berwick-upon-Tweed Library, the Berwick Advertiser and Herbert Morris Brown Lenox & Co. Ltd., the successors to Samuel Brown's original company, whose help and assistance is also acknowledged.

I am particularly grateful to the late Mrs. Helen Home Robertson of Paxton House and Wedderburn for allowing free access to her family texts and documents, and permission to reproduce many items. A special acknowledgement to Mr. Francis Cowe of Berwick, who, at the beginning of this investigation, made his own study notes available; and for his constructive advice. My gratitude to the late Mrs. E. Purvis of Horncliffe for permitting the reproduction of the bridge photographs and postcards taken sometime between 1910-20, and to the late Mr. and Mrs. Scott of Chain Bridge House for permitting the reproduction of old prints and photographs. Also my thanks to the late Tom Cockburn, the late Jim Turner and the late James Straughan, all of Horncliffe, for their reminiscences and use of old photographs.

My thanks are also due to Mr. Maurice Tester M.I.C.E. for his interest and help with structural calculations and to Mr. P.G.Lee C.P.A. for his assistance with patent records; also, the Royal Society of Arts for permitting Alexander Nasmyth's painting to be photographed and to the present owners of the painting, The Paxton Trust, for allowing its reproduction; and to Royal Pavilions, Brighton and Hove for allowing the reproduction of the only known existing portrait of Samuel Brown.

Notes on Sources – Chapters 1-9

Reference has been freely made to printed and published material and due acknowledgement is given to quoted text including:

Proceedings of the Institution of Civil Engineers, Vol. V, 1846.

Dictionary of Naval Biography, Vol III, 1776-1852.

John Marshall, *Royal Naval Biography,* Vol. VII, part 1, 1833.

S. Lewis, *A Topographical Dictionary of Wales,* 3rd Ed., 1844.

Charles Stewart Drewry, *A Memoir on Suspension Bridges,* 1832.

Historical Register of Remarkable Events, 1820.

Reference has also been freely made to printed and published material, and hitherto unpublished texts and papers as follows, for which due acknowledgement is given:

Sir John Rennie - Presidential Address, January 20,1846, Proceedings of the Institution of Civil Engineers, Vol.V.

Bishop, John George, *The Brighton Chain Pier, In Memorium,* 1896.

Rickman, John, *Life of Thomas Telford,* 1838.

Jakkula, A. A, *A History of Suspension Bridges in Biographical Form,* Bulletin of the Agricultural and Mechanical College of Texas, Vol.12.,No.7, July 1, 1941.

Hopkins, H. J., (1970), *A Span of Bridges.*

de Mare, Eric, (1954), *The Bridges of Britain.*

Drewry, Charles Stewart, (1832), *A Memoir on Suspension Bridges.*

Dictionary of Naval Biography, Vol.III, (1776-1852)

Marshall, John, (1833), *Royal Naval Biography Vol. VII,* part I.

Lewis, S., (1844), *A Topographical Dictionary of Wales* 3rd. Ed.,

Historical Register of Remarkable Events, (1820)

Barlow, Peter. F.R.S., (1845), *A Treatise of the Strength of Timber, Cast Iron, Malleable Iron, and other Materials.*

Pope, Thomas, (1811), New York, *A Treatise on Bridge Architecture.*

Tyneside Industries (1887)

Telford, Thomas, (March 1817), *Runcorn Bridge* - Referred to in the Report of the Select Committee. (July 1817), *Runcorn Bridge - Supplementary Report.*

Stevenson, Robert, F.R.S.E., The Edinburgh Philosophical Journal (1821), Vol.V, No. 10, Art.1, *Description of Bridges of Suspension.*

Erskine, Sir David, F.A.S.R.A., (1836), *Annuals & Antiques of Dryburgh and Other Places on the Tweed.*

Smith, John and Thomas, (1835), Paper read to the R.I.B.A. on Whinstone construction, including an account of Dryburgh Abbey Bridge.

Finley. James.(1810) The Portfolio Vol.III.No.6 'A Description of the Patent Chain Bridge' Fayette County, Pennsylvania.

Milne, David, (1891), Biographical Sketch of David Milne Home LLD, F.R.S.E., F.G.S.

Richardson, M.A., (1841), *The Local Historians Table Book of Remarkable Occurrences,* Historical Div.Vol.1.

Smiles, Samuel, LLD., (1859), *Self Help* with Illustrations of Conduct and Perseverance.

The Times (1820, July 20)

Berwick Advertiser (1819, April 3), (1819, July 31), (1819, August 7), (1819, March 20), (1820, May 13), (1820, July 22), (1820, August 5), (1821, June 30), (1820, July 29), (1883, March 16)

Country Life, July 6 1961, F. M. Cowe, 'A Pioneer Suspension Bridge of 1820'.

Statistical Account (1836), Ecleford, Roxburghshire.

Mechanics Magazine, (1847), Vol. XLVI.

Kerr, Robert, (1809), *General View of the Agriculture of the County of Berwick.*

Losh, James, (1811-1823), Diaries and Correspondence, Vol.I, Published Surtees Society.

Lauder, Sir Thomas Dick Bart, of Fountain Hall (1890), *Scottish Rivers*.

Rolt, L.T.C., (1958), *THOMAS TELFORD*.

Pigot's *NORTHUMBERLAND DIRECTORY,* (1834 p.580)
Report of the Stockton & Darlington Railway Committee (1833-1834), Minutes of Proceedings.

Edgar, Rev. John, Minister of the Parish of Hutton, *The Statistical Account of Berwickshire,* (1841).

Assistance from the following public and professional institutions is gratefully acknowledged:

Northumberland County Council Record Office
Glamorgan County Council Record Office
County of Cambridge Record Office
Greater London Council Record Office
Huntingdonshire County Council Record Office
City of Liverpool Record Office
Scottish Record Office
The Royal Scottish Museum
Edinburgh University Library
Science Museum Library
National Library of Scotland
Tyne & Wear County Council Archives Department
The British Library Science Reference
City of Newcastle Reference Library
The Maritime Museum
Montrose Public Library
Berwick-upon-Tweed Library
The Institution of Civil Engineers
The Royal Institute of British Architects
The Tate Gallery
Royal Pavilion and Museums, Brighton and Hove

My particular gratitude to the late Mr William L. A. McCreath of Sanderson McCreath & Edney, solicitors, Berwick upon Tweed, for the free access to minutes of meetings of the Tweed Bridges Trust. Also to Stephen K. Jones who, throughout the many years of my researches, added valuable information to the story through his contributions relating to the history of Brown Lenox and Co. Ltd. and his concluding chapter in this volume. My special thanks must also go to Mr Edward Cawthorn for his patience and time while helping me put this book together over the last twelve months.

Gordon Miller 2017

Records of the chain cable making activity of Brown Lenox & Co. Ltd., can be found at the Glamorgan Archives (DBL). Brown Lenox & Co. Ltd records were initially deposited by the then management in two batches each listed numerically. These have now been combined and re-arranged under subject headings, although the original numbering has been retained in the Glamorgan Archives catalogue. The records are arranged into: partnership; buildings and site properties; management and labour; as financial records; letters patent; papers relating to plant, technical issues and tests; miscellaneous correspondence; photographs and plans; general printed and miscellaneous material. In terms of his chain suspension bridge work Samuel Brown's correspondence and other papers have survived at the National Archives of Scotland. This was passed down from the law firm he used for a number of years and successive practices. Brown used the law practice of John Home (1758-1831), who was admitted as a Writer to the Signet (WS) in 1812. In Scotland, a WS is a senior solicitor who conducts cases in the Court of Session. Home was the eldest son of George Home, town Clerk of Leith, Edinburgh. He practiced at 12 Charlotte Street, Edinburgh, and this continued to be the office of successive firms. The Home family connection passed to John's son William Home (d.1846). When Home died, the building transferred to William and his then partner in the firm John Gibson, which traded as Gibson & Home in William's lifetime, and subsequently became the firm Strathern & Blair. William's son, John Home (d.1890), was admitted as a WS in 1866. The firm became Anderson Strathern LLP on 1st September 1992, the year J & F Anderson and Strathern & Blair merged. The National Library of Scotland hold these documents as *Papers of Sir Samuel Brown* (Strathern & Blair MSS).

Drewry, C. S., (1832), A Memoir on Suspension Bridges, Longman, London, 1832, reprinted by Cambridge University Press, 2014

Miller, Gordon, Union Chain Bridge: linking engineering, Proceedings of the Institution of Civil Engineers - Civil Engineering, Volume 159, Issue 2, 01 May 2006, pages 88–95.

Pope, Thomas, (1811), A Treatise on Bridge Architecture: In which the Superior Advantages of the Flying Pendent Lever Bridge are Fully Proved, printed for the author by A. Niven.

Skempton, Prof Sir Alec, ed., et al, (2002), The Biographical Dictionary of Civil Engineers in Great Britain and Ireland, Volume 1, Thomas Telford Publishing, London.

The Edinburgh Philosophical Journal Edinburgh, Vol.14, No.27, pp. 53-54, January 1826
an addition by the editor to the article *Account of a Bridge of Suspension Made of Hide Ropes in Chili* by Captain Basil Hall

Jones, Stephen K., (1981), A Link with the Past: The History of the Newbridge Works of Brown Lenox & Co, Glamorgan Historian, Vol. 12.

Kemp, E. L., (1977), Samuel Brown: Britain's pioneer suspension bridge builder, History of Technology.

Krankis, E., (1996), Constructing a Bridge: An Exploration of Engineering Culture, Design, and Research in Nineteenth-Century France and America, MIT Press, Cambridge, MA.

Stephen K. Jones 2017

List of Illustrations, Plans and Documents

All illustrations are by Gordon Miller or from his archive except where otherwise noted

Fig 7 - The bridge, showing the Scottish bank pier 1974

~ 1 ~
Historical Preamble

Samuel Brown's elegant 'Union Chain Bridge of Suspension' was completed in the last phase of the Georgian era, and the dawn of the great Victorian industrialisation of Britain, and remains today a graceful monument to the birth of modern bridge engineering.

In c1818, when Samuel Brown signed the bridge contract, there was a great change in the attitude of Government and people towards communications and the need for their improvement. Commercial and industrial requirements were being reasonably well satisfied by the combined improvements made by Smeaton and others to natural waterways now linked by a complex system of navigable canals. The building of Brindley's Bridgewater Canal in 1758 started the process that enabled seagoing ships to penetrate the interior of the country; but roads were another matter. Several Acts of Parliament had established Turnpike Road Trusts whose object was to build or improve roads. The Act enabled the Trusts to levy tolls for capital costs and maintenance, but very little progress was made initially.

The sea was still the primary means of business and private transport over any great distance. Linking seaport towns around the coastline had been developing over centuries through need and investment, but the climate was changing, and private investors were eager to share in the Government's proposed development of land routes. Sea transport was not, however, being ignored in the atmosphere of experiment and ambition when steam machinery was combined with ships as a means of propulsion which was to complement the road programme. John Fitch is said to be the first to propel a boat by steam power up the Delaware River in 1787, and his fellow Americans had several steamboats in service around their east coast well before the first truly commercial steamer was designed and built on the Clyde in 1812. But, one William Symington was close on the heels of John Fitch in 1788 with his own steam engine design which powered Patrick Miller's experimental steamboat demonstrated on Loch Dalwinton near Dumfries. This was followed in 1803, with the Charlotte Dundas which successfully towed two barges on the Forth of Clyde Canal.

Developments with both engine and hull design and manufacture were fast and furious, and some disastrous. In 1818, David Napier had 'caused the Rob Roy, of 90 tons burthen, to be built by Denny at Dumbarton'. This was one of the first vessels to be laid down with an iron hull and fitted with an engine of 30 H.P. driving paddle wheels, and was the first ship to establish regular seagoing communication between Greenock and Belfast. Steam locomotion had become a reality and dreams of steam locomotives for railroads were about to be realised, which may account for the failure of a scheme initiated by Marten Dalrymple of Fordel in 1809 for a Glasgow - Berwick railway to be built. Thomas Telford was appointed to report on the proposed venture essentially aimed at stimulating the economy between the east and west Border regions by the conveyance of coal and lime to the east and grain westwards. It was intended to be horse-drawn waggons on iron rails with inclined planes operated by fixed steam engines. Telford's sound economic senses weighed heavily of the canal system at the time but his heart and foresight inclined towards a nationwide system of Turnpike roads 'perfectly constructed'.

Improvements to Turnpike Roads generally followed the winding tracks of the centuries-old system, and no real interest existed to promote or solve the problem. Engineers considered road making to be 'beneath their consideration' and it was even thought 'singular, that Smeaton should have condescended to make a road across the valley of the Trent,' between Markham and Newark, in 1768 - (Sir John Rennie - Presidential Address to Institution of Civil Engineers, 1846). The emergence of Thomas Telford was to change this professional attitude, and arouse the interest of committees whose task it was to bring about such necessary change. Fortunately, these committees were often of men whose dreams of business expansion were thwarted only by lack of good transport to potential markets, and although they themselves lacked the means of answering the problem, they were receptive to ideas and practical imagination. Telford had studied 'architecture on scientific principles', and became Surveyor of the Public Works in Shropshire and eventually changed his interest to that of civil engineer, and between the years 1803-4 was appointed engineer for making roads and building bridges in the Highlands of Scotland. His output was prolific; he constructed roads with a sub-strata of large stones, built upon with successive layers of smaller stones that provided a fine smooth surface which, in turn, advanced the design of carriage wheels and related suspension. John L. Macadam returned to Britain in 1815 after a career of varied experience in America, and became surveyor for Bristol roads. This new position gave him scope to implement his ideas for road making, which differed from Telford's principles, by simply laying a 10"-11" bed of broken stones about 2" diameter, well consolidated and cambered in cross section to drainage ditches.

Greater faith in the ability to make good roads followed. The 'improved' long distance mail coach that had been introduced by Palmer in 1784 was then able to accomplish the journey between London and Edinburgh in three days and nights, and stage coaches rapidly developed as the new means of public transport. After the Napoleonic Wars, all attention was focused upon the fact that roads were an important national requirement, and the necessary expertise to carry out the work existed. This also meant bridges, but within the Turnpike system of initial provision and maintenance, there existed tight financial limits. The vast amount of bridges required to be provided precluded the continued construction of the monumental stone arched works, such as Smeaton's bridge over the Tweed at Coldstream (c1763) for although the solidity, and long life expectancy of this form of bridge was proven, the relative expense could not be justified for all new river crossings.

Cast iron entered the scene in 1779 when the iron founder Abraham Darby combined with the talents of Thomas Pritchard, and erected the first bridge in this material over the Severn at Coalbrookdale; a single arched span of 100 feet. Many more cast-iron bridge structures followed, of intricate highly-developed arch forms, in which Rennie, Telford and the lesser known Jessop were the major designers.

During the year 1808, Samuel Brown was engaged in producing ideas and calculations for suspension bridges and in 1813 designed and built a model of 105 feet span. The date of his model coincided with a revival of interest by engineers in the practical possibilities of suspension bridges, and the stimulus which was aroused by Brown's example may be taken as a starting point in development. Centuries-old use of the principle had sufficed simple needs, and lain dormant, until advancing economic and social pressures were able to relate with the products that the new iron industry, through ingenuity and scientific reason, was proving capable of manufacturing.

By September 1818, when Samuel Brown had presented his Union Bridge proposal to the Trustees, five bridges designed upon the suspension principle had been erected over the Tweed, or its tributaries, Gala and Ettrick. Although all were footbridges, they had attracted national interest, in particular the Smith Brothers' Dryburgh Abbey example, the first attempt at which had collapsed, and was rebuilt in April 1818 upon the catenarian principle. After conducting numerous experiments from 1814, Thomas Telford had put forward a scheme for bridging the Mersey at Runcorn upon the suspension principle, with cables made up with half- inch square wrought iron rods bunched together, 36 in number; about which he was to change his mind.

The nature of the main suspension cable was recognised as an essential element, and no satisfactory solution had been found within the limited field of technology and manufacture until Brown's model and cable experiments led to his obtaining the first of two important Patents – 'No. 4090, 1816 - Construction of a Bridge by the Formation and Uniting of its Component Parts'. This work opened-up possibilities, and suspension bridge techniques became a sensible reality for particular circumstances; viable and economic and, in a revolutionary way, epitomised the spirit of the age. Among the great wealth of 19th century suspension bridges, Union Bridge is comparatively unknown, and although the pioneer work of its creator has been acknowledged in both contemporary and subsequently published works, an appropriate credit for Brown's real contribution to the 'art' has been eclipsed by Telford's Menai suspension bridge. However, without Brown's design of bar- linked chains, which Telford adopted, the outcome of the Menai project and its solution may not have been so successful.

'Sam Brown', as he wished to be known, and as he signed his drawings and letters, established a reputation as a business man and engineer who was dedicated, dynamic and disciplined, all qualities which reflected his years in the Service. Brown served in the Royal Navy with some distinction between1795 and1812 with postings in the Newfoundland and North Sea Stations, and service in the French Wars. During his years of service he was obviously wrestling mentally with the problems of ships' standing rigging and cables. With ships' huge tonnage and windage areas above water line, ground tackle could not be relied upon, and the frequency of anchor cables parting was the cause of many taking ground, in consequence of which far too many were lost. Likewise, standing rigging frequently failed in a hard blow.

The best bower cables were then usually 25 inches in circumference and formed of 3,240 threads, which was an enormous bulk of material; expensive and relatively short-lived. Brown was convinced that wrought iron would provide an answer to the problem; it was not only stronger and more durable than hemp, but required much less storage space, though of course it was heavy and necessitated the reinforcement of hawse holes and riding gear. He started work on the subject in 1806 and within two years had designed and produced a type of iron chain for which he obtained the first of his many patents. In 1811 the Royal Navy adopted the use of Brown's chain for ground tackle, after a period of experimental use. Brown was so confident in the use and behaviour of iron that he equipped a vessel of 400 tons, the *"Penelope"*, with iron rigging, stays, cables, etc., in which he sailed on a voyage to Martinique and Guadaloupe. After four months, he returned to London in perfect order, having experienced every severity of condition to demonstrate the efficiency of iron in place of hemp.

Nelson's Trafalgar achievement was great news for the country but in its wake left many naval ratings in dire circumstances and ships paid off coinciding with Brown's need of a vessel to test his ideas. The *'Penelope'* was most likely to have been that noted by J.J. Golledge in his *Ships of the Royal Navy* as the 5th rate cutter built in 1798 at Barton, Liverpool and eventually wrecked in 1815 on the St Lawrence River. The experience and influence of Capt. Milne RN may have enabled Brown to secure the ship for his experiments, completed by 1803 and proving so successful that a committee of Naval officers investigating the outcome led to the anchor cable use.

Iron chains were first used in combination with hempen cable, mainly because of weight and the time and cost required converting ships. Iron quickly proved its worth, and for once the Navy was not slow in acknowledging its virtues.

Captain, afterwards Admiral, Sir David Milne, K.C.B. wrote to George Home of Wedderburn;

> 'H.M. Ship *Imperieux*, off Flushing, 30th September 1811
>
> My dear Sir, - I had the pleasure of receiving your letter of the 20th on the 27th.... We are here in a most tricky situation, watching the Scheldt fleet. We are laying at anchor out of sight of land, 9 leagues N.W. of Capel and Waldrern, a situation, in my opinion, extremely dangerous and not answering any good purpose. We cannot remain much longer. A British Fleet will do almost anything but they cannot do what is impossible.
>
> No anchor can hold the ship any time. Last Wednesday night it blew very hard from the S.W. Five ships of fifteen parted their cables, and if their other anchors had not brought them up, which I did not expect, nothing could have prevented their being wrecked, the sands laying halfway between us and the shore....
> In the Downs I saw some of the iron cables. The guardship there is moored with them. I think they will answer perfectly and be an immense saving, but great care must be taken that the iron is good.
>
> .... David Milne'

Sixteen months later David Milne wrote again to George Home;

'Portsmouth, 21st January, 1813

......I am happy to find the iron cables are again to be tried. The inventor of them was with me in London and wishes that I would try them in 'The *Venerable*' and report upon them. I am not sure if I shall do so as considerable alterations must be made in the ship and a great deal depends on working the iron properly. I dined with Mr. Rennie, the engineer, and asked his opinion of them. He says they will not stand well except when hammered by machinery and afterwards annealed, which the inventor has not done.   If this should answer it would be of very great consequence to the Navy, as they take up so little room, and a very great saving in expense....

.... David Milne'

During the time that David Milne was writing these letters Brown was enjoying commercial benefit from the manufacture of iron cables. Although Rennie was being critical about final treatment of the metal, and probably a little jealous about Brown's success as an engineer primarily in the trade of manufacturing, Brown would not have been regarded as being among the true professionals that were then currently emerging.

Hard work and business acumen had gained recognition but none of Samuel Brown's work would have developed if the Lancastrian, Henry Cort, had not invented a bulk method of manufacturing wrought-iron by the puddling and rolling process during the years 1783-4. From this date considerable improvements were being made in the manufacture of malleable cast iron, providing a tough, tenacious metal that could be wrought and rolled into bar iron, readily shaped, welded and bent cold, without fracture. A metal with relatively high tensile properties became available - it remained to be exploited, and Samuel Brown was not slow in realising its commercial value.

The Royal Navy wanted their cable to be consistent in strength and to have been subjected to an acceptable method of testing before being put to use. This was now a possible requirement since Joseph Bramah had developed a hydraulic press, and in 1810 the principle was first demonstrated for the tensile testing of materials. Need triggers off creative thought, and in 1816 Brown installed a testing apparatus to his own design at his Millwall works. Peter Barlow, who assessed the results of testing, was mathematician to the Royal Military Academy at Woolwich and had published *'An Essay on the Strength and Stress of Timber'* and *'A Treatise on the Strength of Materials'*, that included examples of Samuel Brown's work. The combined result of such practical experiments and tests provided the means of obtaining statistical data that was essential for Brown's progress and exploits into new fields.

Some experience, or knowledge, directed Brown's attention towards suspension bridges. He knew of the general interest that the subject was arousing, and was so advanced with chain manufacture and proving, that the proposed Runcorn Bridge project attracted a scheme from him. It was not until Samuel Smiles published *'Self Help'* in November 1859, with his romantic account of Brown's source of inspiration, that we have any clue as to possibilities;

> 'While Captain Brown was occupied in studying the construction of bridges, with the view of contriving one of a cheap description to be thrown across the Tweed, near which he lived, he was walking in his garden one dewy autumn morning, when he saw a tiny spider's net suspended across his path. The idea immediately occurred to him, that a bridge of iron ropes might be constructed in like manner, and the result was the invention of his suspension bridge.'

Although stated with some authority, the story is without foundation, and Smiles' opening to his chapter V *'Helps and Opportunities - Scientific Pursuits'*, is the key to a more probable reason:

> 'Accident does very little towards the production of any great result in life. Though sometimes what is called a 'happy hit' may be made by a bold venture, the common highway of steady industry and application is the only safe road to travel.'

'Bold Venture' was certainly an appropriate term, in an assessment of Brown's 'steady industry', for, although his proposal for Runcorn Bridge was, in essence, feasible, it was with extreme temerity that Brown could have believed in identifying all the theoretical, and practical problems that such an enterprise contained. The turn of the century had provided a material that answered the problem of tension in structures which was a happy release from the seemingly eternal yoke of having to deal with materials in compression only. The excitement thus engendered is therefore understandable and, in retrospect, the project did serve to pave the way for practical realisation within a very few years.

Brown may have seen the paper of the American James Finley, about the principles of stiffened deck suspension bridge design, (*The Port Folio*, Vol, III No 6 June 1810, James Finley Esq., of Fayette County, Pennsylvania). This paper had resulted from the experience of the eight bridges that Finley built, starting in 1801, with his:

> 'construction over Jacob's Creek' Union Town of 70 feet span, and 12 feet 6 inches wide, culminating with '...that at the Falls of Schuylkill, 306 feet span, aided by an intermediate pier; the passage eighteen feet wide'.

Finley's work was referred to by fellow American, Thomas Pope, in his publication; *'A Treatise on Bridge Architecture in which the Suspension Advantages of the Flying Pendent Lever Bridge are Fully Proved - New York. 1811'*. In reviewing the known historic examples of suspension bridges throughout the world, Pope made some *'Critical Remarks'* that accurately summed up the situation:

Fig 8 Pope's Flying Lever Bridge

'viz: the number of the chains, their inverted curve, the mode of fastening them in the ground, their horizontal platform, and the presumptive means of repairing, all prove similar.... It is an axiom that where a structure of any kind depends wholly on two parts, if any of those parts fail, and the other is not fully competent to support the whole, a downfall must ensue; hence we infer there can be no security in a bridge wholly dependent on two chains, for the following obvious reasons.

First, the sudden vibrating motion which is created by even an animal of small weight passing over these structures' is sure to produce a friction sufficient to destroy the same in a short period of time.

Second, as every piece of iron differs more or less from another in strength, by the superior soundness or fineness of its grain, so it is impossible to furnish a chain, the links of which shall be of equal strength throughout.

Third, if the former position was possible, yet, as the strength of each link so much depends upon the goodness of the workmanship in the tempering and forming of the same, it would be altogether erroneous to assert that every link in a chain would be made alike sound.

Fourth, could these two last objections be cancelled, there yet would remain another important truth behind, that must greatly conspire to prevent any sound calculation on the strength and durability of a bridge constructed of chains; namely, the inequality of strain or longitudinal pull on the different links composing each chain.'

Although Pope's four points of consideration seem obvious, the chain remained the questionable factor, which was to become Brown's important matter of concern and development. In 1816 he obtained Letters Patent for the improved manufacture of chain links, and in the following year a further patent for the improved manufacture and method of suspension bridge design, based upon the bar-link principle, which included a design span of 1000 feet.

It was somewhat ironical that, also in the year 1816, the Americans Josiah White and Erskine Hazare produced the first stranded wire rope, which was used in the replacement of Finley's Schuylkill River Bridge, and in 1817 Thomas Telford proposed cables of half inch square wrought iron bars for his Runcorn Bridge, but the potential was not realised for some decades, when high tensile steel wire became available. Telford's original idea of a number of slender wrought iron bars being bundled together, and bound parallel with collars was theoretically sound, but at the same time, wrought iron was not the material for such progressive thinking.

French engineers advanced wire rope suspension bridge techniques, rejecting bar-iron methods, but by the end of the century America had again taken over the lead using wire cables, and today the finest expression of its structural advance is in Britain with the Humber Bridge, having a span of 1410m to the design of Freeman, Fox and Partners. The general idea of suspension bridges was not new, for the principle had been used for centuries, and iron chains were known to have been used in very early times, as Pope thoughtfully gives praise;

'....the Bridge of Chuka is reckoned to be of more than mortal production. No less a being than the Dewta Tehuptehup could possibly have contrived so curious a piece of mechanism...'

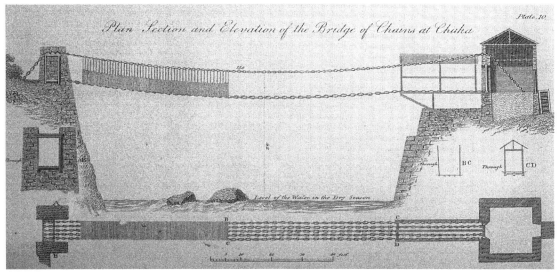

Fig 9 - Plan section and elevaton of the Bridge of Chains at Chuka

This was a chain bridge at Chuka-cha-zum which was also noted and mentioned in a letter by John Rennie to William Molle dated January 6 1818, in which he says;

'Turner in his travels through Bootan in India published about 17 years ago describes a chain bridge which he saw on the Tehiutchieu River a short distance above the castle of Chuka; it consists of five chains covered with string mat made of Bamboo over which horses pass, it has likewise two side chains to which the railings are fixed and is 110 feet span.' Pope's Treatise mentions Chuka as being in the East Indies, but does contain a line drawing which accurately relates to the description. Drewry's Historical Account of

Suspension Bridges 1832 also mentions the accounts of the 'Asiatic travellers', Turner and Major Rennel, and although quoting from their experiences of the 'Chouca-cha-zum' bridge gives the location as 'over the river Sampoo on the road to Lassa'. The differences in location of the bridge occurring in published references are of minor academic interest in relation to the importance of the date when Turner first saw the Chuks example, which was in 1783, while travelling to Tibet. The date of this bridge is not known.'

William Molle, whose name appeared very early in any records discovered relating to the bridge, was an unknown character, a name plainly important in the planning and achievement of the bridge, a signature on many papers but an unknown personality of no known address.

Then, in the summer of 2015, a Mr A.J. Molle arrived to see the bridge, holding a self-published book about his family which had taken him thirty years to complete.

Suddenly William Molle W.S., 1795-1840, became not simply a signature but a complex character who was probably the main instigator, financier and commissioning agent; the link between designing engineer, manufacturer, of ironwork, site location and finally the end users of this then unique structure. Though now lost, it is recorded that the foundation stone for the Union Bridge was laid by William Molle in 1819.

Molle was an extensive land owner and farm improver in the area, a partner in the law firms of Molle, Turnbull & Brown W.S. and Molle and Brown W.S., of Edinburgh, a Collector of Taxes (and owning stock in Brighton Pier). He inherited Netherbyres at Eyemouth from his mother's brother in 1813 but was declared bankrupt in 1831.

Nowhere is there any indication that the bankruptcy was in any way fraudulent or crooked. William was evidently both generous, honest (supporting two brothers, one in India, the other in New South Wales and even an old school friend in Duns) and an ambitious agricultural innovator. He lost financially because the expensive and extensive land improvements he achieved did not in fact increase the value of the land at that time. It is probable also that at least one outstanding loan for £5000 from George Home of Paxton had been used to finance the bridge. One of the main reasons quoted for building the bridge on its site was to cart lime and agricultural goods safely over the river. His law firm partner was probably a relation of Sam Brown and it was to Sam Brown that he sold Netherbyres, which probably helped clear some of his debts. But at the time of the grand opening of the bridge in 1820 there was no indication of what the future held. William Molle married Margaret Adams in 1795. They had at least four children. He died in 1840, though we do not know where. He may have been able to keep either Mains House in Chirnside or a property in Northumberland Street, Edinburgh, but at the time of the bankruptcy even his furniture had been sold. The bridge is surely a lasting memorial.

In Europe, vague records exist about a suspension chain footbridge across the Welland at Market Harborough, erected in 1721, but Winch suspension bridge over the River Tees near High Force,

Middleton in Tees, has become recognised as the first of the type. It was built in 1741, with a span of 59 ft and width of 2 ft- the platform connected directly on the chains, with underslung bracing chains and railings. It remained in existence until 1802, when it was replaced with a similar structure which stood until 1908, after which a 'true type' was erected and still exists, its name being changed to Wynch.

How it was that Brown gained the Union Bridge contract is not finitely established. It may have been through the failure of the Smiths' first Dryburgh Abbey Bridge, that attracted a visit from Liverpool merchants, and others, who were financially interested in the Runcorn Bridge project, or through an introduction by Admiral Sir David Milne.

Fig 10 - The Winch Bridge
Middleton-in-Teesdale

The design of the rebuilt Dryburgh Abbey Bridge has been attributed to Samuel Brown; a belief that probably stems from Sir John Rennie's Presidential Address to the Institution of Civil Engineers on January 20 1846 when, speaking on the subject of 'Suspension Bridges', he said, after mentioning Brown's 'Model' and 'Union Bridge' '...He subsequently built another, of smaller dimensions, across the Tweed, at Dryburgh...'. This may be true, but is not borne out by the subsequent published statements, of John and Thomas Smith, the bridge architects, and that of Sir David Erskine, about his father, who had financed both the first and second bridges. Both of these aspects will be dealt with in greater depth in the following chapter.

Brown undoubtedly enjoyed the confidence of Admiral Sir David Milne RN, a man of great character and influence, who had been impressed with his inventive and practical engineering ability. The Admiral's own early naval exploits had attracted the attention of his superiors and, after holding various commands, and distinguishing himself by making several captures, he was raised to the rank of Rear Admiral of the Blue in June 1814. As second-in-command to Lord Exmouth in the expedition against Algiers, he gained further distinction in the subsequent battle on August 27th 1816. During the expedition passage '...the Admiral and Captain Chetham trained their men in the use of guns which were fitted with sights according to an improved plan of the Admiral's.' He was dedicated to the technical advancement of the Royal Navy, and Brown's efforts had been quickly recognised by him as an important maritime development. Brown's work was also recognised by John Rennie who, in turn, also shared close mutual friendship with the Admiral.

Born at Musselburgh, the Admiral had a deep interest in the south-east of Scotland, and became a member of the Royal Society of Edinburgh; he contributed to agricultural improvement, and promoted plans for introducing steam navigation in co-operation with his friends, James Watt and

Rennie. With this perceptive attitude and awareness of Brown's qualities, it may well be that the Admiral brought him on to the scene by introduction to George Home of Wedderburn, who was involved with the *'New Turnpike Bill'* in 1790.

There is no evidence to support this view, other than the fact that the Admiral and George Home were very close friends, and in their respective correspondence the tides of war, politics and personal confidences formed the context of their frequent exchanges. Although of academic interest, Jean Milne Home, in writing about her Admiral grandfather and his wife Grace, made the point that they were very close friends of George Home, and his aunt Miss Jean Home. The bond between the Homes and Milnes was strengthened in 1832, when Admiral Sir David's son David married Jean Foreman Home of Paxton, whose father Mr William Foreman succeeded to the estates of Billie and Paxton on the death of his cousin Mr George Home in 1820. (Mr Foreman took on the name Home after succession). In the following year, Sir David bought the estate of Milne Graden, and in building the present house established his interest in the affairs of Berwickshire and the River Tweed.

Home confided to friends his dislike of the Bill '...there are too many roads in it...' '....upon the whole it may be good tho' nothing equal to a well conducted statute work'. Between 1790 and 1793 he was very involved in the general and detail aspects of the Bill, and in letters to close friends outlined his feelings about almost everything from farming to the state of the nation, and doubtless the matter of bridges in relation to roads emerged. Seventeen years after the Union Bridge was built, the Admiral's interest, and belief in bridging with iron chain suspension methods, was at last established. In 1837 both the Admiral and his son were members of the Berwickshire county committee, responsible for roads and bridges, when a proposal for a bridge at Norham was being discussed and a decision reached that the structure was to be iron suspension. At a subsequent sub-committee the decision was reversed in favour of a wooden bridge that was to cost £4370, instead of Samuel Brown's firm offer of £4950 for an iron chain suspension bridge. The Admiral and his son were incensed by this action, and resigned from the committee.

Apart from the strong possibility that Admiral Sir David Milne was primarily responsible for Brown's introduction to the Turnpike Trustees, it should be remembered that they had had sixteen years for contemplation from the time in 1802, when authority had been secured through Act of Parliament for a bridge at New Water Ford.   Other people may well have been influential in making the name of Samuel Brown known. Well before 1818, James Thomas Walker was in partnership with Brown Lenox & Co., and at the same time acting as a shipping and general agent at Leith, trading under the name of Walker Johnstone & Co.

Business links had also been successfully established with Hawks Crawshay & Sons of Gateshead and, with a glowing reputation for chain products, merit must have induced its own advertisement. Brown's interest in the north is also evidenced by the territorial extent given in the Patent Licence No. 4090 of 1816 *'Manufacture of Chains ...that they should and lawfully might make, use, exercise and rend within England, Wales and the Town of Berwick upon Tweed...'*

Business association through the Port of Leith may well have sown the seed about the scope of Brown's engineering services. Robert Stevenson was Engineer to the Northern Light House Board and patronised Samuel Brown & Co. with orders for Iron Chain Cable 'for the service of the Commissioners of the Northern Light Houses', a matter of which Admiral Sir David Milne would have undoubtedly been aware. By the time that construction of Union Bridge was well advanced Brown had established a close friendship with Stevenson in which a mutual respect existed concerning their respective talents. Stevenson had contemplated a design for a suspension bridge and wrote to Brown on March 9th 1820 '...On this subject I have been designing and once had thoughts of sending you a sketch to Estimate but upon trying it comparatively with stone I confined my attention to that material...' The quality of work evident at Union Bridge must therefore have impressed Stevenson and this, among other matters, developed their relationship.

At that time, there was an enormous gulf between the hard matters of practical engineering - then regarded as an 'art' - and pure science, which isolated itself in the realms of natural philosophy. Brown made use of information from testing apparatus and recognised the need to know the strength of materials. He avoided mathematical theory, and after advancing his ideas for Union Bridge, the design was submitted to, and scrutinised by John Leslie, Professor of Natural Philosophy (formerly Professor of Mathematics) at Edinburgh University. Stevenson and Jardine, and John Rennie, also examined and approved the proposal.

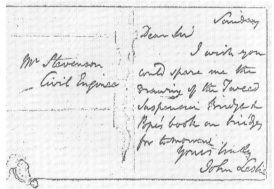

Fig 11 - Letter from John Leslie to Robert Stevenson

For academic standing Professor Leslie was an obvious choice, as was John Rennie, born at Phantasie, East Linton Lothian, who enjoyed both a national reputation as a 'celebrated' civil engineer and great local prestige, particularly following the completion of his fine five-arch stone bridge over the Tweed at Kelso, completed in 1804, all of which endeared him to the Trustees. James Jardine of Stevenson and Jardine also enjoyed a local reputation as a conservative and reliable engineer who, in 1837, designed and had constructed by J King, Builder, the elegant Hutton Mill Bridge over the River Whitadder, using the then fashionable stone pier and wrought iron inverted bowstring method.

Between 1811 and 1843 Samuel Brown produced many ideas and became involved in some great schemes, but chains and related matters remained the primary product. Although the circular section iron bar-link was Brown's singular obsession, the rectangular section bar-link was also his idea, subsequently adopted by Telford for his Menai Bridge. Brown did use rectangular section bar chains for his Wellington (1831) and Findhorn (1832) bridges but he remained faithful to circular section bar-links for other known works. There was little venture outside the scope of this specialised field, and his intensive involvement with ironwork manufacture denied him the

Fig 12 - Hutton Mill Bridge over the River Whiteadder, Berwickshire

SAMUEL BROWN AND UNION CHAIN BRIDGE

newly emerged professional standing enjoyed by his fellow engineers. Nevertheless, Brown was possessed of hard-won experience, determined, shrewd, honourable, and blessed with an eye and respect for beauty. He really cared about his commissions and wanted the results to be admired and enjoyed. A twinge of conceit existed in his make-up and this made him justifiably adventurous. He belonged to the fraternity of practical and intuitive engineers; advancing his methods by trial and error and not through scientific logic. This much was known about Brown at the time, and may be the reason why his Union Bridge was referred to respected 'mechanicians' for checking. His lack of academic knowledge probably accounts for the failure of his early twisted iron cables, the design principle of which was founded in confident belief rather than a fundamental understanding of mechanical and metallurgic behaviour.

His work was well known to both Rennie and Telford, and Professor Peter Barlow, who respected his skill, ingenuity and almost uncanny feeling for the properties and use of wrought iron. Although Telford adopted Brown's bar-link principles for Menai Bridge, it was William Hazeldine of Upton Forge, on the Shrewsbury Canal, who supplied the chain ironwork. A serious disagreement must have existed between Brown and Telford for this order to have been lost by Brown, but no records have been traced to explain the position, unless it was the outcome of the Runcorn encounter.

Although Brown appears to have lacked the mathematical logic of Telford, he certainly left nothing wanting in the extent and range of experiments carried out with iron bar, the test figures for which were accurately deduced and computated, but the strength of the material was only the beginning. The production development of wrought-iron bar, with punched eyes for bolts at the ends, connecting links and bearings for suspension bars, was Brown's key contribution and invention. This he had finally developed by 1816, and in 1817 patented his connecting link principle for application in suspension bridge design. From this time onward Brown devoted most of his time and energy to the manufacture of chains, and the design and construction of bridges and related works, including the design and construction of Brighton Chain Pier in 1823. This was probably the greatest of his engineering achievements, and in 1838 Queen Victoria honoured him with a knighthood.

The success of Union Bridge secured for Samuel Brown new business horizons; all related to his chain products, but none quite so splendid or lasting as the first adventure.

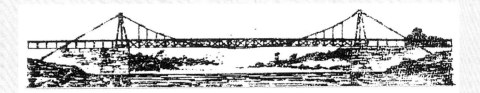

" . . . May I venture to glance at the grand, the majestic arch of solid stone, with any idea of contrast between it and our simple contrivance? Happy for me, utility, economy, and despatch, are the ruling passions of the day, and will always take preference of expense, idle elegance and show, until the minds of men become contaminated with variety of some worse passion . . ."

Fig 13 - From "The Port Folio - Vol. III No. 6, June 1810 - by Oliver Oldschool, Esq. - A description of the present Chain Bridge, invented by James Finley, of Fayette County, Pensylvania . . ."

Fig 14 - Captain Sir Samuel Brown RN
(Royal Pavilion and Museums, Brighton and Hove)

~ 2 ~
Samuel Brown

On November 10th 1825 John Rennie, later Sir John, the son of his better-known father of the same name, wrote to Samuel Brown '...about the expense of erecting Chain Bridges and as no person has had more experience than yourself in these matters I will thank you to inform me roughly and as soon as possible what would be the probable outside expense of the Iron work of a Bridge with one opening of 500 feet having a roadway about 24 feet wide to be capable of passing all ordinary carriages and to be constructed in a substantial manner...'

A bridge span of 500 feet was considerable and most likely referred to a possible Thames crossing in the region of the old Hungerford Market, as speculative ventures by people forming companies intent upon reaping benefits from improved links between the river bank areas were rife. The approach to Brown signified the continued esteem held by Rennie for his father's respected friend.

In this light of distinction it would be both interesting and appropriate to drift through Brown's childhood and formative years, with a view into the sparks which kindled his start in life, but nothing has been discovered. Considering the slender threads of his known family background it is reasonable to assume that the young Brown had some formal education which was absorbed with relish and combined with a natural talent for recognising the rights and wrongs of practical matters. It led to a shrewd and much-liked character.

Samuel Brown was born in London on January 10th 1774, the eldest son of Mr and Mrs William Brown.

His father came from Borland, Galloway, and his mother, Charlotte, the third daughter of the Rev. Robert Hogg of Roxburgh. He joined the Royal Navy in June 1795 as Able Seaman on board the *Assistance*, and rose through the ranks of Midshipman, Master's Mate and Acting Lieutenant on the Newfoundland and North Sea Stations until 1801. He was confirmed into the rank of Lieutenant in October 1801, and served as Third Officer on the frigate *Phoenix*, and was involved in the action which made the French frigate *Le Didon*, her prize, on August 10th 1805. Brown gained no promotion from this exploit until six years later, but the seeds of discontent about his future were implanted.

By 1805, Brown was actively engaged in experiments with his ideas for wrought iron chain, and spent months in two rooms of a house in Dove Court, Lombard Street, London developing and proving his invention. He had little money, but managed to employ blacksmiths who produced chains at premises in Narrow Street, Ratcliffe, also in the Borough near Waterloo Bridge. Lack of finance hindered the necessary development process, and in 1806 he formed a partnership with his cousin, Samuel Lenox, who was trading in Liverpool, which provided the necessary backing.

By 1813, Brown had established his business trading under the name of Samuel Brown and Company, and had secured outlets for all the chain products that could be manufactured within the capacity of his small works. Through the association of Samuel Lenox, Liverpool merchants had become important customers, and influential in the course of expansion that Brown needed and was earnestly seeking. In a letter of April 19th 1813 written from Dove Court to Samuel Lenox at Great Winchester Street, Brown was enthusing about his general state of affairs, and mentioned the 'lively interest' of one Mr. Clive, a Liverpool merchant, in the design of his iron cables. Brown was also pleased about Mr. Clive's offer of '...two or three thousand pounds if required, for the enlargement of the undertaking for which you observe that certain share should be submitted to his disposal...' The negotiations that had given rise to the offer had presumably taken place about January, following a proposition made by Brown about new premises, but owing to Mr. Clive's '...multiplicity of other important matters,' his anticipated involvement ended, though not his interest or connection.

The idea was temporarily shelved. At that time Brown had estimated his stock and machinery at £4,000, and now in April, his interest in new premises was regenerated, particularly as a result of increased business. During the early spring months, Brown had been successful in negotiating for '...an establishment (on the Banks of the Thames immediately opposite the Dock Yard, and within reach of the West India and London Docks...)' He had plans for 'erecting works to the

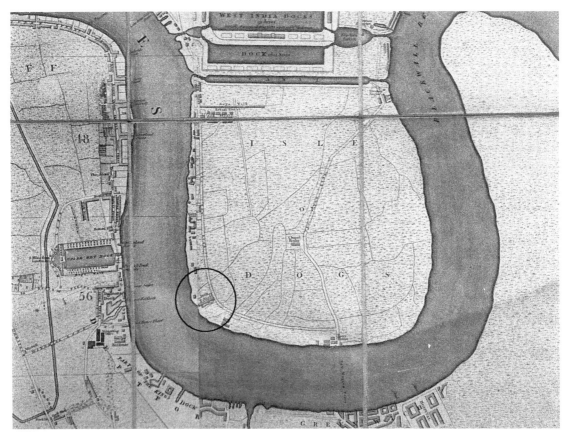

Fig 15 - Detail: Map of the River Thames showing Millwall Works, Isle of Dogs

amount of £5,000', and hoped that he would be in possession at the beginning of October '… capable of constructing with the greatest chain or cable in a day, or on an average 35 ton a week…' With such a new works he forecast 'trebling of production within six months, and wrote that with the new 'Mode of Construction', in relation to his '...perseverence in the precautionary method of proving, this will suspend the use of hempen cable entirely...'. Brown was thus full of confidence, and continued to describe his 'establishment'.

'...My situation which I have taken is capable of containing 80 forges with various offices and jobbing shop. It fronts the river, and on the other side has a front of 120 feet on the new road made behind Mill Road. These are capable of making 50 ton of cable a week and the whole including a small steam engine will require about £8000 to complete, the greatest part of this I can furnish of my own resources, and if Mr. Clive for himself or his friend concedes a fourth of this manufactory as an equivalent for his interest and assertion of £3000 to be expended in the erection alluded you are at liberty to mention to him my reading to make it the basis of an arrangement. Again if he is of opinion that it would not be prudent to go so largely into this business at one Port, I would willingly establish a manufactory at Liverpool or perhaps in a central situation in the country to whatever extent Mr. Clive may think prudent, and I will instruct a respectable foreman or managing man in the whole process of constructing and proving the cable; there can be no possibility of error for he should have patterns of the cable shewing stages of construction from the cutting of the bolt to its formation into chain every different-sized cable contains so many lengths united by shackles, every length contains so many links and every size is to be proved to bear a strain equal to the rope for which it is to be applied, a correct table calculated or rather determined by actual experiment should be his guide. If this plan is in general to give of his wishes I would devote myself to its formation in the first instance and participate with the party in a half share. I think a plan of the kind would require about £200 to get going and might be increased according to the encouragement it might receive. These are the outlines of my ideas, they can be subject to various modifications which may be considered necessary. I beg leave to add that I remain with great regard.'

By late Autumn of 1813 Samuel Brown & Co had secured their new works on the Isle of Dogs, Millwall, London, in the completely rural atmosphere of the East End of London. This was an enterprising choice of site at the south west heel of the Isle, on land between the 'New Road' (later to become West Ferry Road) and the river bank. Brown Lenox's 'Iron Cable Manufactory' was one of the first industrial buildings to appear

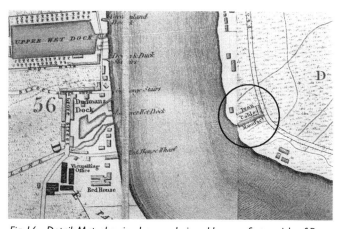

Fig 16 - Detail: Map showing Iron or chain cable manufactory, Isle of Dogs

SAMUEL BROWN AND UNION CHAIN BRIDGE

Fig 17 - Detail: Map showing Chain cable manufactory, Isle of Dogs

among the green meadows, immediately opposite the Royal Dock Yard at Deptford on the south Thames bank, from where a great source of business was to derive. 'New Waggon Ferry' was established over the river, only a matter of yards from the factory, (see 'Cary' survey c 1815, LCC Ref:FJ421, which is the earliest plan record of the works, and 'R Horwood' survey for the Phoenix Fire Office c 1819). During the four years that separate these two surveys, it will be seen that some development changes to the works had been made, which, no doubt, resulted from the outcome of increased business following Brown's Patent No. 4090 in 1816 *'Chain Manufactured by a new Process; and Apparatus and Improvements in Performing and Executing the Same'*. Within a few years, the whole Isle of Dogs area was to become overwhelmed with industrial and commercial enterprises, mostly related to the sea and ships.

The Isle of Dogs lies south of Poplar village, and is contained within a loop formed by the River Thames between the Reaches of Blackwall and Limehouse. Formerly known as Stepney Marshes the area had been grazing meadows since the reign of Edward II when it was drained and embanked by Freedmen and Bondsmen of the Bishop of London. For hundreds of years the river banks along this area, between Thames and Lea, had been associated with shipbuilding, and the building of wooden vessels was continued well into the new industrial age, even after 1839 when iron hull ship construction was started at the Bow Creek yard of Mare & Company. Transformation of the Isle of Dogs was first considered in 1796, when the beginning of the Napoleonic Wars intensified demands on the Thames by both naval and commercial interests. Commerce could no longer accept the scale of theft losses which resulted when cargoes of ships moored in mid-Thames were unloaded by hog or lighter to traders' quays. Docks with adjacent warehouses provided a solution to the problem and this inaugurated a new epoch. West India Docks, at the north end of the Isle of Dogs, were completed in 1804 to the design of the engineer Ralph Walker. Rennie became involved with the overall project and conceived the design for warehouses that completely answered the needs of commerce. The buildings were grand and functional and although vast by comparison with domestic standards, they strongly reflected the decorative vernacular style of larger town housing.

Brown's naval career continued, with appointment, in August 1806, to the *Imperieuse*, followed by short periods, December 1806, and November 1809, to the *Flore* and *Ulysses*. Fortunately for Brown, these periods at sea were spent in the Channel, which allowed him to maintain active control over his new interest. He became very committed and, to demonstrate the value of his work at his own expense, fitted out the small vessel '*Penelope*' with all the standing rigging and ground tackle of chain. This experience secured his first award of Letters Patent of Invention on February 4th, 1808 for 'Rigging of Ships or Vessels'. He sailed this vessel to the West Indies and back in 1808, and proved to his own satisfaction the superiority of iron chain cable over hempen rope. Brown presented to the Navy Board the results of his experiment, and they appointed a Committee of Officers to investigate and report on the matter. The outcome was favourable, and in consequence, four ships were fitted with chain cables for further experiments which proved the claims made, and in 1811 chain cable ground tackle was adopted into the Service. In the same year, on August 1st, Brown was advanced to the rank of Commander.

Demands for chains increased, extending to all general marine use, and because further promotion in the Navy was not forthcoming, in May 1812, Brown accepted the rank of Retired Captain, which made him free to prosecute his business interests with extreme vigour. Brown's first chains were of the twisted link type, in the belief that the twist would provide 'built-in' mechanical elasticity. Contemporary accounts criticised his academic knowledge:

> 'This error arose from a prejudice natural to persons who are not thorough mechanicians, or who overlook those mathematical dicta which ought to guide every mechanical arrangement - an idea that a certain portion of elasticity should be given to the chain...'

That this derangement of particles, and consequent diminution of strength, does take place in twisted links, is plain from what happens in proving the chains composed of such links;

> '...a cable for a ship of 400 tons will stretch, during this operation, in a whole cable, nearly thirty feet! and will recover about ten, when the strain is taken off.'

He had recognised the properties of elasticity in hempen cable, saying:

> 'There cannot ever be any certain advantage deduced from the portion of elasticity which cordage is known to possess; for the force which caused its extension may be extended for a considerable time after the cable has been stretched to its utmost limits - of course, under a further strain it must break.'

These early failings were eventually overcome, but not until Brown had introduced a process of factory testing by means of a proving machine. Records of Brown Lenox & Co., claim that 'Brown and Rennie built the first proving machine', and some sources refer to their being assisted with the design by James Thomas Walker who, as works manager, would have most likely become involved. Peter Barlow was more specific in his work 'A Treatise on the Strength of Materials...' which stated:

> '...The first application of Malleable iron which rendered the knowledge of breaking strains indispensable, was the invention of iron cables by Captain Brown, and he accordingly was the first person who constructed a machine capable of making experiments on a sufficiently large scale to be depended upon; this was made to work by wheelwork and a well-balanced system of levers, but subsequent experiments have generally employed the hydrostatic press...'

Peter Barlow considered results from Brown's machine to under-rate strength, while results from Bramah's hydrostatic press tended to be over-optimistic. As is natural in business, Brown's success had attracted competition from other iron workers, and one, William Brunton of Commercial Row, London, was using a hydrostatic press for testing. Peter Barlow was aware of their respective test results variations, and in consequence designed an apparatus that combined the merits of both. The relative accuracy of Brown's experiments was to be confirmed by Barlow; '...his results certainly agree best with subsequent experiments made by myself on the machine in His Majesty's Dockyard, Woolwich'

Brown had carried out experiments on the 'strength of chain, made of varying descriptions of re-manufactured Foreign and English iron...', and likewise, Messrs. Brunton, had carried out similar tests, which Barlow quotes in his 'Treatise' and summed up as follows;

> 'In the preceding experiments the mean of Messrs. Brunton's and Brown's experiments gives 27 tons, but from these experiments I consider that we ought not to assume the strength of good medium iron at more than 25 tons per square inch. It will be seen by subsequent experiments that the elasticity is destroyed with about 10 tons, and that iron ought not to be strained beyond its elastic power...'

Barlow was therefore sounding a cautionary note, which echoed the discovery of the English mathematician, Robert Hooke, in 1676, about the Law of relationship between ' load' and 'extension'. Thomas Young had not yet produced his findings of 'physical constant' (Young's Modulus), obtained from the stress-strain ratio, but all the experimenters in wrought iron bar, had recognised the conditions during test loading, that had clearly suggested the limit of practical design stresses, before the elastic limit was reached.

The firm of Samuel Brown & Company prospered, and the full output of their Millwall works, including manufacturers working under licence, such as Crawford Logan & Co. of Liverpool, was inadequate to satisfy demand. Expansion was a necessity for both marine chain making and related chainwork, and suitable premises in a well-serviced location were being sought after. In 1813 Brown had mentioned the idea of establishing a chainworks in every principal port, which was an ambition never achieved, but in about the year 1816 Samuel Brown & Company leased premises (including a disused nail factory and blast furnace) from the Ynysyngharad Estate of Lord Llanover at Newbridge (Pontypridd) for the purpose of manufacturing chainwork. A move from London to Newbridge may have seemed startling but it was backed by some sound reasoning, for although Cardiff was the nearest port to Newbridge, and was not, at that time, a port of any consequence, the Glamorganshire Canal Company was actively engaged in seeking improvements to the Cardiff sealock for enlarged wharfage facilities, which had started in 1814.

The idea about Newbridge may have stemmed from Brown's business relationship with the Gateshead firm of Hawks Crawshay & Sons whose London agency supplied Cyfarthfa iron to Samuel Brown & Co. The Cyfarthfa Works at Merthyr were then producing 12,000 tons of bar iron annually, and it was little more than ten miles from Newbridge; coal was also readily available from the Rhondda Valley, and all interconnected by canal transport, with the lowest toll charges in the country. The sealock connection at Cardiff was undoubtedly a cause of delay, but at that time such troubles would have been acceptable problems. Water was a primary asset of the Newbridge works; a branch off the main canal served two canal basins with one at high level for raw materials and one at low level for dispatch, with the difference in water level providing motive power for machines and blast for the furnaces. In the beginning, full use was made of the existing buildings and forges.

Apart from the possible influence of Hawks Crawshay & Sons, the Newbridge situation may well have resulted from the local knowledge of Philip Thomas, one of Brown's smith foremen, who was also involved with the development of chain cable design which led to his joint Patent with Brown in 1816. Philip Thomas eventually became the first manager of the Newbridge works, and played an enormous part in the development of Brown's company until his death in 1840, and although his life

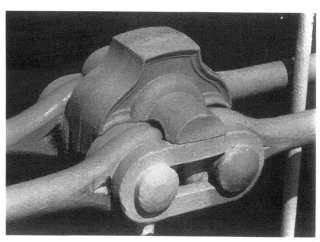

Fig 18 - Brown's patented bar link couplings and saddle

and work is another story, Brown's recognition of his qualities may have been revealed through the establishment in the 1800's of an iron-trade business by his father in London, in which Philip Thomas worked and managed a workforce of about one hundred men. Philip Thomas is described in the Liverpool Directories for 1816, as an 'iron cable manufacturer', at 3 Stanhope Street. At some time Thomas had probably worked with Logan and Company; also cable manufacturers, at 26 Stanhope Street. At this same address, the merchant John Crawford Logan had his counting house, and between 1805 and 1814, he was connected with the merchants, Logan, Lenox & Company, who also manufactured chain cable and anchors.

Brown's flair for invention in the field of ironwork was obviously attractive to his cousin Samuel Lenox, and the Stanhope Street connection was a sound introduction into the necessary business, and practical matters which were of direct concern to his interests. From the hard aspect of manufacture, Brown's association with Hawks, Crawshay & Sons undoubtedly provided him with an insight into the business of ironworking on a relatively large scale. This firm had been established in 1748 by Mr. William Hawks, and became primarily involved in the large-scale manufacture of general ironmongery. In 1790, Hawks installed a 12 horse-power Boulton and Watt steam engine, which coincided with a Government contract for the supply of iron, and at about that time he invented a machine for turning the links for mooring chains. Partnership with George and Edmund Crawshay produced a rapid development in their engineering interests and ability, and at the turn of the century, Messrs Hawks, Crawshay & Sons had built and equipped a new foundry at Gateshead.

Chain manufacture was to become one of the firm's principal products, and although a Patent for chain-making granted to Philip White in 1634 is recognised as being the earliest recorded, the next, in 1804, was to William Hawks. In 1812 William Hawks installed a chain-testing machine into his works, but no details about the apparatus have been discovered. Brown was not slow to realise the great need for better chain products, or that their constant improvement was a necessary part of increasing output. Until 1816 chain links had been; '...almost universally welded in the crown...' with their hand forging and welding requiring '...four heats to turn them into the form of links....' with unpredictable results. During the period of his working association with Brown, Phillip Thomas had been making useful practical suggestions for improving manufacturing techniques, and this had led to their collaboration in the invention of a machine for shaping links with scarfed side joints. The whole cycle made in a series of mechanical operations with one furnace heating. Connecting links and welding scarfs completed the sequence, which gave a quality-controlled product that was no longer totally reliant upon manual skills. The method was granted Letters Patent No 4090 in 1816.

Brown sought every possible use for his firm's iron and ironwork, and having established his manufacturing industry, was able to offer both design and finished product, coupled with the major role of contractor. He must have been disappointed by the failure of his iron chain rigging experiment to impress the Admiralty, but at the same time would have realised that the existing standing rigging performed perfectly well, and did not fail with the catastrophic results that followed ground tackle parting. However, relatively long iron bars connected by eye links were elements of construction that had been proved to work under extreme conditions of strain, and to what practical use they might be put was obviously Brown's searching question.

His earliest exploits into the 'art' of suspension bridge techniques were made in 1808 at a time when he was fully absorbed with the problems of ships' rigging and ground tackle. He recorded; '...About that period I made drawings and calculations of the strength of bridges of suspension...' but it was not until the year 1813 '...when I constructed a bridge of straight bars for this purpose on my own premises; the span and extent of this bridge is one hundred and five feet, and although the whole of the ironwork weighs only thirty-seven hundred weight, it has supported loaded carts and carriages of various descriptions.'

This early experimental work was started, two and three years, respectively, before the published accounts of James Finley and Thomas Pope. The bar and chain testing was a company matter; but it was Brown's own drive, privately and entirely at his own expense to avoid a conflict of business interests with his cousin, which launched him into bridge experiment. Brown's model suspension bridge, and his submission of a design proposal for the projected bridge at Runcorn, had alerted Thomas Telford to the existence and relatively advanced experimental work made by Brown. Liverpool merchants and other business interests were anxious for improved communications. Drewry:

'...a plan was brought forward by a Mr. Dumbell, of Warrington, for making a direct road from Runcorn, in Cheshire, across the Mersey to Liverpool. This scheme included a bridge in lieu of the ferry across Runcorn-gap, an idea was thrown out of stretching across the river a web of metallic rings...'

This was in 1814, by which time commercial pressure, material technology and engineering science were beginning to create a climate for action. Runcorn Bridge presented an enormous engineering challenge arousing Brown's interest, imagination and business acumen. The initial challenge was launched by 'Gentlemen of Landed property in both Counties... also many eminent Merchants of Liverpool...' which attracted a considerable number of 'Plan and Estimates of Proposed Bridges', from 'Engineers and Artists' among which was a proposal from Samuel Brown, based upon his strength test and model bridge experiments.

Consideration of the proposals was recognised as being beyond the capabilities of the interested parties, and a Select Committee was appointed from the General Committee to examine and report upon all the detail and wider issues. On January 27th 1817, the Select Committee met and decided to consult Thomas Telford about the whole matter. In February, 1817, the Select Committee and its Secretary met Telford in London and revealed all the schemes that had been received for the bridge. Through past experience, Telford was very familiar with the River Mersey and its problems, particularly the mercantile pressures against piers for any bridge that would obstruct the channel. With this in mind Telford had also included in the submissions the design for a suspension bridge that included a model 50 feet in length made in 1814.

Telford's model was therefore designed and constructed in the year following Brown's, and with the same Runcorn objectives in mind. In his evaluation of the various proposals, made to the Select Committee on March 13th 1817, Telford-discounted all submissions, other than Brown's, with these words:

> '...it will be evident that any plan formed upon a principle different from that of suspension, is, in my opinion, quite inapplicable. In regard to all those which fall under this description, it therefore seems unnecessary to enter into any investigation of their comparative merits; and as the same observations apply to those on the suspending principle which are constructed with chains, it follows, that of all the plans submitted to me by Mr. Fitchett, it is that produced by CAPTAIN BROWN only which corresponds to the principle adopted by me in 1814: that is to say, Suspension by malleable Charcoal Iron, preserved as nearly as practicable in straight lines, and having a degree of flexibility to avoid cross strains. His perpendicular Suspenders, Cross Ties, and diagonal Braces, correspond precisely with mine. His main suspending Lines of the upper Curve, instead of being composed of a number of flexible Rods, as in mine, consist each of one Rod or Bar of malleable Iron united by Forelocks. From four of these it was proposed that the whole structure should be suspended, and according to this CAPTAIN BROWN had constructed a Model 100 Feet in length at his Patent Chain Cable Manufactory, opposite Deptford. Your solicitor and I examined this Model and drove a Hackney Coach over it. We afterwards had a full

conference with CAPTAIN BROWN in London, in the course of which he very distinctly explained his ideas, and they in general very nearly corresponded with my own. I then communicated to him the whole of my Operations in 1814, which have already been detailed in this Report and shewed him the Drawing I had then made. These communications first disclosed to him the true situation in which a Bridge was required, and convinced him of the propriety of having one great opening of 1000 Feet, and one of 500 Feet on each side. He was also convinced of the propriety of having at least Eight Rods or Bars in the great Suspending Line of the upper Curve, (I prefer having still more), and likewise instead of throwing the whole bearing upon them, as he had formerly proposed, that a great advantage may be derived by forming the Roadway, as in my Plan, in a curve of one fiftieth part of the Chord line; thereby gaining additional strength, instead of leaving it merely a dead weight. His Roadway is very ingeniously contrived of timber, in shape of the cover of a Ship's Hatchway, which, though certainly not so durable, is much lighter and cheaper than that which I had composed; and as his may be so contrived, as to be in future, if necessary, replaced by mine, I think it had better in the first instance be adopted, with perhaps a few Inches of mine upon the top of the Timber. I pointed out to CAPTAIN BROWN the manner in which his Roadway should be supported, tied, and braced.'

John Rennie also enjoyed the experience of Brown's model bridge, which he referred to in his evidence before the Committee of the House of Commons about the Menai Bridge (April 1819) and by way of transmitting a confidence in the revolutionary idea '...perceived very little vibration... having had a carriage driven over it several times...' Although, in general principle, the respective proposals of Telford and Brown were similar, their respective ideas about the form, and nature, of the main cables was entirely different. To a very great extent, Brown had already proven the strength and reliability of his iron-bar linked chains and was fully confident about its use for suspension cables. On the other hand, Telford was pursuing a more theoretical approach, which by its very nature alienated chains. This is surprising since Telford had obtained a copy of Pope's *Treatise on Bridge Architecture*, and in support of his Runcorn proposal to the Select Committee, recognised the American achievement; '...It is well known that chain bridges have long been employed with success over very considerable openings...' He continued to question the validity of chains:

'...But on considering the matter maturely, it occurred to me, that on the suspension principle, chains are not the most perfect means to be employed, but that the metal should be kept, as far as practicable, in straight lines, and also have few joinings. In order to proceed with due caution upon this principle, I made during the Summer of 1814 above 200 Experiments upon malleable iron, of from one twentieth to one and half inch diameter and on lengths varying from 31 to 900 Feet.'

Telford then continued to describe the experiments and conclusions reached:

'The Results were, that a Bar of Good Malleable Charcoal Iron, one Inch square, will suspend 27 Tons, and that an Iron Wire one tenth of an Inch diameter (100 feet of which weighs 3lb. 3oz.) will suspend 700 lbs., and that the latter with a Curvature or versed sine of one fiftieth of the Chord line, will besides its own weight suspend one tenth part of the weight suspended perpendicularly, when disposed at one fourth, one half, and three fourths of its length; and that with a Curvature of one twentieth of the chord line it will suspend one third of the aforesaid perpendicular weight, when disposed in a similar manner.'

Telford was thus convinced that the 'great suspending cables' should be composed of 'small iron rods', bundled together. His design for the 16 main cables, each of which was to be formed with 36 half inch square iron bars, welded together in their length; bundled together and secured by straps every 5 feet, to provide a flexible cable. In his Runcorn Bridge 'Supplementary Report', Telford acknowledged the significance of the extension in length of bar-iron under test loading:

'By my experiments, it was ascertained that, with a curvature of 1/20 of the length, malleable iron besides its own weight sustained 1/3 of what broke it perpendicularly: as Inch bar would therefore bear 1/3 of 15 tons, without deranging its parts, but in order to be considerably within its power, I have only assumed that 1 Inch square of Section shall be loaded with 4 Tons...'

Brown was also aware of the symptoms, evident under test, before bar failure. Of the numerous tests that he carried out at 'Mill Wall, Poplar, 28th May 1817'- *'Experiments on different Descriptions of Iron'*, it was 'Bar No. 7' that he found 'A highly interesting one. A bolt of Welsh iron denominated No. 3; 12 feet 6 inches long, 2 inches diameter, required a strain of 82 tons 15cwt, to tear it asunder. When subject to a strain of 68 tons, it stretched 3 inches, and reduced to 115/16ths inch in diameter. When the strain was increased to 74 tons 15 cwt., it had stretched 6 inches, and was reduced 1/8th of an inch gradually in the diameter. With 82 tons it stretched 14 inches. With 82 tons 15cwt the bolt broke about 5 feet from the end, the levers being exactly balanced. It had stretched during the whole process 18½ inches and measured at the place of rupture 15/8th inch in diameter. These, and earlier tests, provided Brown with the basis of design for his Specification under Patent No. 4137 July 10th 1817.

The Runcorn project was abandoned, but the knowledge gained was not forgotten. Brown lost no time in securing his advantage, and as an almost natural outcome of the experimental years, and practical involvement, his *'Specifications for the Construction of Bridges'* was granted 'Royal Letters Patent - No. 4137. July 10th 1817', which he fully described as; *'...my Invention or Improvement in the Constructions of a Bridge, by the Formation and Uniting of its Component Parts, in a Manner not Hitherto Practised...'*

A copy of this Specification is reproduced in chapter 3, and the following is given as a brief explanation of the essential contents. The substance of the Specification relates to techniques for uniting ends of bars, by the use of:

'...side plates and bolts, coupling boxes, welding, or other suitable methods, so that these bars, bolts, or rods so joined become in effect one active length or piece, the whole extent or length of the bridge and support their proper proportion of the tension in the direct line of the curve which they assume or partake of, and these constitute my main lines or means of suspension'

Fig 19 - Extract from pages 72 & 73 of 'Alphabetical Index of Patentees of Invention' 1617 – 1852 Patentee 'Brown, Samuel' until Progressive No. 8994 when his name is recorded 'Brown, Samuel, Sir'. (Brown, Samuel Junr.) appears against No. 12,431, but as Samuel Brown is recorded to have died childless, the Jnr appendage cannot be explained.

No	Date		Subject Matter of Patent
3107	1808	4th Feb	"Rigging of Ships or Vessels"
3888	1815	28th Feb	"Rudder, and apparatus connected therewith
4090	1816	19th Dec	"Chain manufactured by a new process; and apparatus and improvements in performing and executing the same
4137	1817	10th July	"Construction of a bridge by the formation and uniting of its co component parts"
5126	1825	15th Mar	"Apparatus for giving motion to vessels employed in inland navigation"
5929	1830	24th Apr	"Making bolts and chains"
6045	1830	6th Dec	"Drawing up ships and vessels from the water on to the land; moving ships, vessels and other bodies on land, from one place to another"
8994	1841	19th June	"Drawing carriages or other machines along inclined planes, railways and other roads, and drawing or propelling vessels in canals, rivers and other navigable waters."
9680	1843	27th Mar	"Construction of breakwaters; constructing and erecting lighthouses and beacons, fixed and floating; apparatus connected therewith; anchors for mooring the same, applicable also to ships"
10,790	1845	29th July	"Formation of embankments for canals, docks or sea-walls; propulsion of locomotive-engines and other carriages or bodies on canals and other inland waters, and on rail and other roads; Propelling vessels on the ocean and navigable rivers."
11,295	1846	14th July	"Railways and railway carriages; construction and arming of ships or vessels"
11,887	1847	7th Oct	"Propelling and steering vessels; mariners' compass"

Before describing his jointing methods, Brown made '...observations on the principle and effects of bridges of suspension which have been in use prior to this Invention...' He summarily dismissed the idea of '...metal chains formed of links, wires, or by other methods', and described '...A bridge of wires - the most objectionable...' and in more derisive terms; '...intended for the convenience of foot passengers'. His reasoning is nevertheless understandable, for, as explained; '...The immense surface exposed to the action of the atmosphere would infallibly cause rapid decay, and the common preventatives of corrosion could not be made generally beneficial...'

As linseed oil and lead-based paint were the only means of protecting iron from corrosion, the life of any such treatment was being acknowledged, so here was Brown's practical common sense being displayed. Brown was more cautious about making scientific explanations, and in stating his case in favour of catenary chains made of 'straight bolts' says: '...It will not be necessary to enter into any theoretical reasoning on the subject.' His point being that information gained from testing bars was adequate, which would have been satisfactory if the bars, bolts etc. were the only matter of consideration in the proposed bridge design.

Experiments carried out recognised the work of Mr. Barlow through his publication, *'An Essay on the Strength and Stress of Timber'*, in which Welsh iron No. 3, or cable iron was used. Brown quoted three results; the descriptions are simplified as follows:

Description		Extension	Breaking Force
1.	2" dia. Round bar 12' 6" long of 132 lbs wt.	18½"	82¾ tons
2.	1" x 3" Rectangular bar 12' 0" long of 124 lbs wt.	13"	72¼ tons
3.	Chains of 1½" dia iron 12' 6" length of 241 lbs wt.	23"	79 tons

The significance being that multi-link chain must be almost double the weight of bar to attain relatively equal strength. No information is given about strength of connections or the loading relative to yield points. The Specification includes a design proposal for a suspension bridge of one thousand feet span, using the various components described: 'It consists of eight principal double lines of suspension...and forms lower lines of bars for the support of the roadway...'

Brown explains that as a means of '...counteracting the effect of undulatary motion ... during the violent storms and gusts of wind to which these bridges may be exposed...' that the roadway supporting chains be arranged in an upward curve, having a versed sine of twenty feet in one thousand feet length. Quite obviously, this suggestion was overlooking the principle of stiffened level deck put forward by James Finley in 1810, but it did possess the advantage of weight reduction, and would have effectively shed water. An astonishing feature of the design is the shallow catenary curve '...the greatest point of deflection... being forty feet below their respective points of suspension...' This would create high strain in the chains, and to avoid long back chains to produce equal angles at the pier bearings they are shown arranged over a massive curved bank of masonry. Over the whole length of masonry the chains are described as being enclosed in '... iron cases or trunks...of sufficient strength to resist the internal pressure of the iron bars, bolts etc...'.

Brown conceded in the explanation; '...In some cases, also, when the points of suspension are naturally much elevated, or when they can be conveniently heightened, a more relaxed curve may be used...' He must have appreciated the reduced strain that a '...more relaxed curve...' would exert in chains, but obviously preferred an increase in chain size and strength to building relatively high towers of masonry, the expense of which was an important consideration in favour of suspension bridges.

The proposed back chain arrangement would produce intense friction and pressure, but this was most likely wanted, as the combined effect would be to minimise strain at any given point. Although the idea is not completely clear from the drawing, it can be assumed that the two roadway arches, shown in the pier face, carried through the masonry mass in the form of tunnels.

Both Finley and Brown quoted very similar figures for the strength of their bar-iron; their average respective quotes being '...60,000 lbs per inch bar, when the sinking or curve is nearly one sixth of the span', diminishing to '...a sinking of one thirtieth, it will bear only 15,000. Thus we see the effect of greater or lesser curve...' Brown claimed a figure of some 53,000lbs. per square inch '...to tear it asunder'. His proposal for a one thousand foot span included a chain sinking of one twenty fifth of span, and from the information contained in the specification and drawing, the total dead weight of structure between towers amounts to 530 tons.

Recommendations for the catenary bars are two inches thick and six inches deep, and 'about fourteen feet long...' with those supporting the platform of similar section, but half the length. Perpendicular suspension bars are arranged to hang alternately from the twin sets of catenary chain joints, which engage with the respective platform chain joints. '...The Platform roadway I construct of wood' and this was to provide for two carriageways, each twelve feet in width, having a central footpath of six feet.   Its construction is described as being made up from pairs of three inch x twelve inch planks, chocked three inches apart with timber blocks, secured together and fixed by cleats to the supporting chains. These deck transoms, or beams, are shown spaced an approximate equal distance apart, two between each set of suspension bars and covered with a single layer of three-inch thickness planking.

Recognising that '...durability is an object of great importance in all Public works...' Brown explains that his design, through '...simplicity of the construction...' provides '...an opportunity of applying the usual preservatives against decay...' He continues, and explains a method in which '...bars may be removed and new ones introduced into their places, by which means the structure may be maintained for ever'. The dead weight of 530 tons produces a tension at the lowest point of 1656 tonf, and a maximum tension adjacent to piers of 1,677 tonf, and this in turn produces a stress due to dead weight alone of some 8.73 tonf/in2 that approximates to a quarter greater intensity than for Union Bridge. Assuming a yield stress of 12.5 tonf/in2 the stresses at yield in suspension chain would be produced by a total superload of 228.8 tonf, which allows a superload of about 17 lbs/ft2 over the total 30 ft. width roadway, or 510 lbs/ft run of bridge to produce yield in the chain bars. Although these conditions appear adequate, they make no allowance for wind loading and increased stresses that would inevitably be produced. However, the bar-link principle and related method of connection was basically sound.

There may be significance in the few months between Brown and Telford's discussions about the Runcorn project, and Brown's successful application concerning his Patent No 4137. Big business was at stake, and by revealing his bar-link device, Brown had exposed many years of work, and most likely felt threatened. In exchange, Telford had been convincing about the advantage to be gained with a 1,000 foot span suspension bridge, coupled with the '...propriety of having at least Eight Rods or Bars in the great Suspending line of the upper Curve;' also the idea of '...forming the Roadway, as in my Plan, in a Curve of one fiftieth part of the Chord Line...' In fact, both men had gained, and probably out of fright, Brown quickly gathered everything together, took Telford's observations to heart, and produced the 1000 foot span bridge scheme, which he very soon patented. Whatever political innuendo may be read into the known facts, the result of the Brown and Telford encounter was to further suspension bridge design, and accelerate the great works coming into being.

Having confidently ventured so far with the theoretical development of a rectangular section bar, and linking method, together with a design proposal for a one thousand foot suspension bridge, why did Brown then employ round bar eye links in his Union Bridge? Flat section bar would have given greater scope, but probably because his company was geared to producing vast quantities of the basic round bar for chains, exploitation of the common element was a prudent and economic decision, which also avoided the expense of a change in production tooling. The decision to use round bar cables in Union Bridge posed the problem of their connection in relation to suspension rods. This was admirably overcome with imagination and skill in the design of a cast iron saddle that straddled the twin bar linked joints. This same type device in combination with round bar was also used in the design of Brighton Chain Pier. The cast iron saddle joint was a sophisticated design idea, which must have been the outcome of considerable development work, that for some reason Brown chose not to register. He probably realised that the future of chain cable for use in suspension bridges would revolve around the form of his flat eyebar link, and that it was unlikely that others would copy.

During the time that Brown, Telford and others were engaged with the grander projects of communication, others were quietly solving the lesser problems of footbridges. All were suspension bridges across the Tweed, or its tributaries. According to Robert Stevenson in his; *'Description of Bridges of Suspension', Vol. V., No. 10 1821*; '...the first wire suspended bridge in Great Britain was a footbridge...of slender iron wires; conceived by 'Mr. Richard Lees, an extensive woolen cloth manufacturer at Galashiels, whose works are situated on both sides of Gala-Water'. The bridge was erected in November 1816; '...its extent is 111 feet, and it cost £40'. Another wire suspended footbridge was constructed in the summer of 1817, which spanned the Tweed on the march between the Kailzie and the Kings Meadow estate by Sir John Hay, Bart., between 1795 and the 1850's; '...It was ...a little below Peebles...is 110 feet long, and four feet in breadth, and is ornamented with a handsome lodge or cottage'. Stevenson fully describes the general and detail construction which, in the main, comprised pairs of hollow cast iron columns from which suspending wires radiated diagonally at varying angles to support the platform. It was designed by John Stevenson Brown, a partner in the firm of its builders Messrs. Redpath and Brown of Edinburgh (no relation of Samuel Brown). Little is known about Thirlstane Wire-Bridge; which was erected over the Ettrick, at Thirlstane Castle by the Hon. Captain Napier. It was of some 125 feet span, and is worthy of mention as being the third, in a type line, that was recorded by Drewry as 'similar' to that at Kings Meadow.

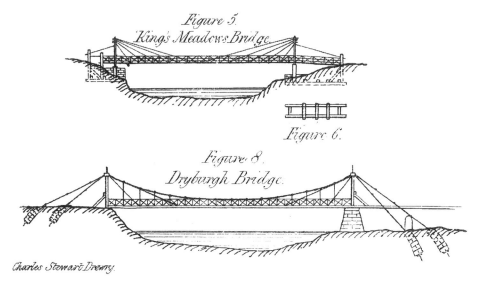

Fig 20 - Drawings of King's Meadows Bridge and Dryburgh Bridge (Charles Stewart Drewry)

The two Dryburgh Abbey bridges are important, in that they respectively represent the fourth and fifth examples of Suspension Bridges built before Union Bridge. The second, or replacement bridge was constructed upon the catenarian principle, and because its design identifies with Brown's principles, it has been attributed to him. However, there are two descriptive accounts that both relate to the first and second bridges. The first account is by John and Thomas Smith, architects, of Darnick near Melrose, contained in a paper on Whinstone Construction, dated November 2 1835, and which was communicated to the Royal Institute of British Architects by J. Hamilton of Edinburgh:

"Suspension Bridges

We erected the first chainbridge that was done in Britain of bars linked together forming a chain and of which we have sent with this the original Plan. There was a small wire bridge done at Galashiels before ours but the span was short.

Ours was erected in the summer of 1817, over the River Tweed at Dryburgh in Roxburghshire and was blown down in a great storm in 1818.

The span as executed was 261 feet between the points of suspension. The longest suspending chains were 1 inch in diameter and they diminished as they shortened to half an inch. The links were about 10 feet long and were joined in this manner; the one eye welded and the other fixed down at the point with a collar. This we afterwards found not to be a good plan as the point of the hook drew through the collar and then broke off, under a great strain. The bridge was beaten to pieces between the supports but they with the back stays stood firm. We restored it in the summer of 1818 in its present form and it has stood very well ever since.

It was only meant as a footbridge at first but horses go along it quite well. The main suspending chains are 4 in number 2 on each side $1^3/_8$ in. diameter in links about 10 feet long with welded eyes and coupling links thus. They are hung on the catenarian Plan and have perpendicular suspenders at each short link as most of them are now done. The chains were all made by our own Blacksmiths as well as the rest of the work, but we had the means of proving them. We did the first bridge by estimate for about £560 and we restored it for £240.

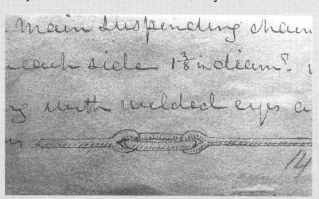

Fig 21 - Detail: Extract from Thos Smith's Paper on whinstone construction

The undulating, or perpendicular motion we found even more inconvenient upon our bridge than the lateral motion, but it was greatly stiffened by a small wooden rail slightly trussed, (Margin note 'along each side of the roadway') We think a strong trussed wooden railing, for the above reason, better than an iron one for chain bridges."

The suspending wires of the first Dryburgh bridge were arranged diagonally, in the form of those at Galashiels, Kingsmeadow, and Thirlstane. It had a footway, 4 feet in width; was started on April 13, 1817, and openedon August 1, 1817. Stevenson's account recorded John Smith's observations, at the time of its completion, '...it had a gentle vibratory motion, which was sensibly felt in passing along it; the most material defect in its construction arising from the loose state of the radiating or diagonal chains, which in proportion to their lengths, formed segments of catenarian curves, of different radii. The motion of these chains we found so subject to acceleration, that three or four persons, who were very improperly amusing themselves, by trying the extent of this motion, produced such an agitation in all its parts, that one of the longest of the radiating chains broke near the point of its suspension. Examination of the chains, following the collapse of the bridge, revealed that although one or two of the welded eye-ends had failed, there was uniform failure of those with open eye ends...' a mode of construction that had been recommended to Messrs. Smith, by an experienced blacksmith.

Even with its short initial life, the value of the bridge, in comparison with the ferry, was established, and the Earl of Buchan directed that it should be reconstructed. Very soon after the bridge collapse had become generally known '...several Gentlemen of Liverpool, interested in the proposed Runcorn bridge project, made a journey to Scotland, for the express purpose of inquiring into the circumstance of the misfortune....'. Whether or not Brown was among their number is not known, but at such time any member of the 'Select Committee' that may have been present would have been acquainted with the catenarian design principles disclosed by the schemes of both Brown and Telford. Without doubt, the Liverpool group would have met the Smith Brothers and most likely the Earl of Buchan, and it seems almost unlikely that the general principles of the Runcorn suspension ideas would not have been mentioned. Whatever may have taken place, the reconstructed design included catenarian chains with vertical suspension rods, while retaining a number of the former radiating chains or wires. The four new main chains, arranged in pairs, bore no relation to Brown's eye-bar link methods being simply bars with all welded eyes, coupled with a single welded link from which the suspension rods were attached with '...a kind of cross head...'.

The second account about Dryburgh is from *'Annals and Antiquities of Dryburgh and other Places on the Tweed* - Second Edition: by Sir David Erskine of Dryburgh Abbey, 1836'. On the subject of 'The Chain Bridge', Erskine described it as '...one of the most useful things erected by David S. Erskine, Earl of Buchan.' The general content of his account merely repeats Stevenson's description, but also emphasises the structural value of the '...strong trussed wooden rail, which also answers the purpose of a parapet, the good effects of which were strongly exemplified while the bridge was building; a high wind having occurred before the side rails were erected, one end of the platform was lifted up above the level of the road-way, and the undulating motion produced on the occasion, is described as resembling a wave of the sea, an effect which prevailed the whole extent of the bridge, and went off with a jerking motion at the farther end. But after the side rails were attached this vertical motion was checked, and is now found to be highly reduced.'

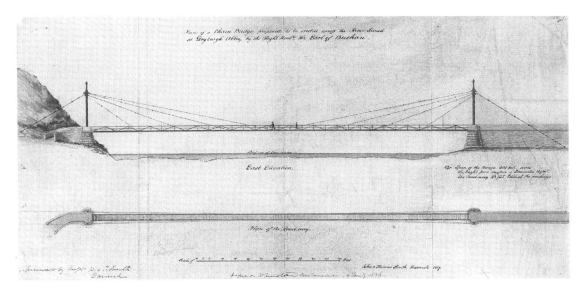

Fig 22 - Plan of proposed chain bridge across the River Tweed at Dryburgh Abbey

Erskine's final comment leaves no doubt about the credit for design, '..and the enterprise which marks the design and execution of it confers honour on the Messrs Smith.' The available evidence does suggest that J and T Smith were solely responsible for the design of the bridges. They may have been influenced by remarks from the Runcorn visitors, and, if so, it was flattering to Brown that they should have followed the trend he was setting.

Steam powered vessels had become commercially very successful, particularly along the north east Scottish coast, and facilities for landing at all states of tides was an important matter. In many cases the existing stone piers accommodated the need, but at Newhaven owners of steam vessels operating in the Firth of Forth could make no satisfactory arrangements with the proprietors of the Stone Pier. The outcome was a proposal by an agent of the London and Edinburgh Steam Navigation Company to erect a new pier. This was acted upon by various 'speculators' in association with 'several gentlemen forming the Trinity Pier Company' who appointed Samuel Brown to carry out the work. This provided Brown with a novel opportunity of demonstrating yet another application for chain suspension techniques, and in March 1821 pile driving for the pier clusters began.

Brown described the work, after its completion, in a paper that was published in the Edinburgh Philosophical Journal. No. XI which was subsequently quoted by Drewry, from which the following account is abstracted.

The overall length of the pier was 700 feet, divided into three main suspended bays of 209 feet span, with a 4 feet width deck, and 14 feet deflection. The pier head, supported by 46 piles was 60 feet wide by 50 feet long, all securely tied with horizontal beams and diagonal members, and with raking shores. Intermediate pier clusters were 'merely sufficient to form a secure framing for the cast iron standards, over which the main chains or suspending bars are supported'. A single stone pillar, 6 feet square and 20 feet high, formed the landing pier over which the cables passed, and at an angle of 45° were secured into the clay by cast iron plates. At the pier head, the cables were carried over the cast iron standards, and secured into 'a rider, which is locked to the piles, and these riders are backed by spur shores to resist the drag of the bridge'. There were two main chains, of iron eye-bolts about 10 feet long, which diminished in diameter from 1⅝" near the points of suspension to 1¼" at the centre of span, and the typical Brown links and bolt pins were made to be proportionate in strength . The platform construction was made in exactly the same principle as for Union Bridge, and the suspension rods were simply carried up between the pairs of link couplings and held by a wedged cross key. Parapets at each side of the platform comprised wrought iron horizontal rails secured to the suspension rods and with intermediate balusters some 4 feet high. The cast-iron main standards comprised pairs of triangular frames, each cast in one piece of T shape section, arranged transversely across the platform and tied together by diagonal braces to form a rectangular pyramid. The main chains and bracing bars terminated in a form of saddle or socket at the head of the standards which were secured by nuts. Some time after the initial construction, radiating stays were added to restrain the platform vibration. They comprised 1" diameter eye-bolts, 13 feet long, coupled with links and bolt pins, arranged in pairs above and below the platform.

Fig 23 - Trinity Chain Pier, Newhaven, Edinburgh; painting unattributed

Fig 24 - Chain Pier, Brighton; painting, John Constable (Tate Gallery)

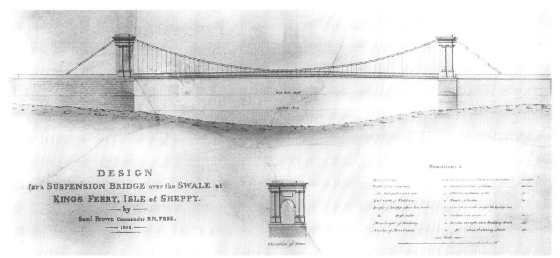

Fig 25 - Detail: design for a Suspension Bridge at King's Ferry, Isle of Sheppey; engraving

Apart from Robert Stevenson, Brown also enjoyed the friendship of 'Mr. Rennie' to whom he had supplied plans for a suspension bridge over the River Swale, Isle of Sheppey. Brown greatly admired both Rennie and Telford, and on October 15 1821 wrote to Robert Stevenson from his Billeter Square address about the death of Rennie and the various works with which he was involved:

'I was yesterday favored with yours by which it would appear that you were not at that time acquainted with the death of Mr. Rennie otherwise I think you would have adverted to it altho the information you require seemed to glance at that event too. I think it would be too much for any one man however eminent to succeed to Mr. Rennie's extensive and important operation. Mr. Telford is considered as one of the principal Government Engineers and had the Caledonian Canal and the Menai Bridge which may be considered a work of government and other concerns of great magnitude, things he cannot in conscience I think or in justice either to the completion of Mr. Rennie's works undertake the whole and a timely application from you might be successful on some of this in which I should sincerely rejoice. The principal works which Mr. Rennie had the management of unfinished are the following; the works at Sheerness. At present under a most important crisis but which it was presumed Mr. Rennie had conquered. The Management of the West India (Docks not quite sure of the East India). The London Docks at present unfinished but going on with the opening at the Hermitage cut. The Breakwater at Plymouth a new cut or canal at Lyn some considerable work in Lincolnshire the Pier at Scarbro. The Dock, and Rum and Tobacco Warehouses of Dublin where he was a great deal occupied . - a Bridge of Suspension over the Swale Isle of Sheppey was contemplated - plans of which I furnished him with etc etc etc. These are all that I know of at Present the London Bridge would of course have been his. I have a great mind especially - if I could get my plans approved by some Eminent Engineer to propose a Bridge of Suspension over London Bridge. It is one of the principle recommendations of this sort of Bridge when you know what the bars will bear in a given curve and span, which I do, and which I have the means of proving them to do, That you can make it as strong as you please. If 20 main suspending chains are not sufficient. I can employ 40 and if that is not considered enough I can up a hundred, and get them all to bear alike in fact I can set them up, or tune them if you like the phrase Please as accurately as Miss Stevenson can tune her harp. I could erect the Bridge of Suspension over the present one without any interruption, indeed if it was considered an advantage, the public might have both one over the other.

My mind has been entirely occupied in bringing to a close a copartnership of 7 years standing which may plead some excuse for not attending to my worthy friend and old Shipmate's letter about the bridge Kalzie over the Tweed, but I will set about it immediately and send down a plan as soon as my Dftsman has finished the plan of a Pier for Brighton which will be done next week, do write to Napier or see him and tell him this with my reasons for not being more punctual, and when you see Lord Melville get him to go down with you to the Pier and tell him what I intend to do for Brighton, the Pier is to be a rather or should I say I propose it to be carryed into water deep enough for the yacht to lay alongside at any time of tide. If Napier has seen Mr. Telford I shod like to know what passed with best regards to Mrs Stevenson Miss S and the family believe me to be my dear Sir Yours most sincerely

Sam Brown'

The letter is also revealing about Brown's thoughts and dreams of activity and future involvement. Of particular interest is his reference '...about the bridge Kalzie over the Tweed...' which in fact means the Kings Meadow Bridge that has already been mentioned. The 'old Shipmate' comment may refer to Sir John Hay who had '..considerable connections overseas' and most likely knew Brown sufficiently well to consult him about the bridge.

Brown's keen sense of humour about everyday matters is clearly evident in the letter, also his abounding confidence; and introduces the scheme for Brighton Pier.

As a creation, Union Bridge was Brown's first triumph, but it was a touch of genius that brought Brighton Chain Pier into existence in 1823, after less than twelve months' work. Brighton was in the final stages of its transformation from a small fishing village into a fashionable and lavish architectural town. This transformation had followed the Royal Patronage of George IV, then Prince of Wales.

Passenger traffic between England and France had grown beyond all realisation, and there was a desperate need for landing facilities that would dispense with the tiresome pulling boats between shore and ship. Towards the end of 1821, firm ideas for the formation of a pier company were initiated, and land was given for the project by Messrs T.R. Kemp and C.S. Dickins, which overcame legal problems concerning the otherwise necessary authority to levy tolls. In 1822 a Parliamentary Act was applied for which would enable the work to be undertaken.

The success of Trinity Pier had spread far and wide, and the experience was to prove invaluable to Brown in carrying out the new challenge. A Report of the Pier Committee had 'nominated' consultation with Samuel Brown, and by way of stimulating public confidence, a Report from the Directors of the Trinity Pier Company was obtained which carried all the necessary recommendations as to Brown's ability and good standing. Brown was duly appointed; the Pavilion was almost complete, and an air of grandeur, affluence and prosperity dominated the scene. Brown pitched all his skill and energy in this new venture. He committed £17,000 to the undertaking, 'at his individual risk', in respect of a £27,000 joint stock declared by the Brighton Pier Company to be raised in £100 shares. Work on the actual pier started in October 1822, following the commencement of the preliminary approach works, and the first cluster of pier piles was completed on December 20. The pilework proved to be more difficult than Brown had contemplated, and friendly advice about the problems was forthcoming from Stevenson in a letter of June 20 1822:

'The accompanying letter from Mr Lime is the result of a conversation I had with Mr Lime at Leith which I take the opportunity of sending you under the favor of Capt Wemyss Frank. In whatever way you may ultimately resolve ending the work at Brighton – I am decidedly of the opinion that the Piles should penetrate the soil to a considerable depth.
In pile driving the great object is to get a solid basement for the extremity of the Pile. That the ground on which the point rests may be beyond the wash of the sea. I called to say this much to you on the day I left London – but missed you. The observation proceeds from one made by your friend from Brighton whom I met with – about the blowing of the chalk. But I put no value on the lateral or side matters – it is of no use – the object is to get the point to rest upon a firm basis – which is not likely to be disturbed by the pressure of the superincumbent matter – or the wash of the sea. No contrivance will answer this so effectually as going down into the soil. I had a circular from Mr. Molle - wrote him a note - I have had the honour of a call from him. I am leaving town for a few days.'

Severe weather conditions prevailed throughout the months of construction, with considerable loss of constructional equipment, but nothing daunted Brown and by the end of March 1823, the 'shears' for driving the fourth and last cluster of piles was positioned; in April all the chains had been assembled, and by July they were suspended. The platform decking was completed during August, and in September a sale of waste materials was held.

The opening ceremonial was even more grand than that of Union Bridge and had been delayed from October 15 to November 25, in the hope that either George IV, the Duke of Clarence or the Duke of York would be present, but sadly for Brown and the Directors, a royal occasion was not to be.However, some 250 persons of 'rank and respectability' gathered to enjoy the spectacle and entertainment, and throughout crowded the Esplanade.

After the feasting, dozens of loyal and appropriate toasts were given and warmly received. "The health of Captain Brown" was proposed in the most flattering terms by Mr Thos. Read Kemp, M.P.   The 'gallant' Captain, in acknowledging the honour, said - "Gentlemen, I am sensible that it is incumbent on me to say a few words on this gratifying and interesting occasion, and I shall therefore have to rely much on your liberality while I am speaking on a subject in which I am so particularly interested. I commenced my operations about this time last year, and had to encounter many difficulties during the winter, but these obstacles afford the best proof of the strength and stability of the Pier, now that it is completed, and the crowds of spectators assembled on this occasion must have put it to a much more severe test than it can ever be subject to."
The gaiety spread into the night with displays of fireworks on the Pier, and Brown entertained a hundred guests at a grand ball and supper at his house in Marine Parade.

Brighton's gratitude was expressed in 1824 when, through public subscriptions, the Pier Commisssioners and townspeople presented Brown with a 'massive and exceedingly handsome silver vase, surmounted by a figure of Britannia - and encirculed by chain cables resembling those introduced into Naval service....'. A commemorative medal was also struck and sold in bronze at 10s. and in silver at £1.11.6d. Bruce's *Brighton* (1831) and Drewry (1832) briefly described the structure, with the inevitable minor variations as to dimensions.   However, the following is an abridged account. The structure comprised four main suspended bays, that extended 1014 feet out to sea from the face of the esplanade wall, with an overall length of 1136 feet.The chord spans of 255 feet had a deflection of 18 feet, and the pier head, in the form of a T, was 80 feet by 40 feet, and decked with Purbeck granite 12 inches thick that overlaid 150 piles, laced with diagonal piles, walings and braces. The intermediate pile clusters each contained 20 piles, which were also laced with diagonal piles and cross braces. The suspension towers were of cast iron, in the form of two pyramidal towers 25 feet high, spaced 10 feet apart, and united by an arch at the pier head; made up from plates riveted together.

The main chains were formed from round iron eye-bolts, 2 inches diameter, and 10 feet long, that were connected by coupling links and bolt pins. So far Brown's details followed those of Union Bridge, and although the cast iron saddle that supported the suspension rod engagement was also similar, the suspended rod attachment was now designed to provide for freer movement. The 'T' head of the suspension rod engaged into a rectangular cavity cast in the cap with a slot opening that allowed the 'T' head to be inserted and rotated and finally seated transversely within the cap. Four chains each side, arranged as twin coupled banks in two tiers supported the platform with 1 inch diameter suspension rods at 5 feet centres. The chains connected with the saddles over the suspension towers, and at the land end were carried over a masonry pier and into the cliff face through tunnels, which terminated in brick chambers, and finally secured with heavy cast iron plates which acted as anchors some 50 feet back from the cliff face. At the pier head, chains were fastened by plates and bolts to walings fixed to the diagonal pile clumps.

Fig 26 - Chain Pier, Brighton after the storm of December 4th 1896
(from 'The Brighton Chain Pier; In Memoriam' by J. G. Bishop 1896)

Also in 1823, three years after the completion of Union Bridge, and the completion of Brighton Chain Pier, Brown had produced a scheme for a 'Bridge of Suspension at Montrose', a project that developed through the circumstances of the extreme scouring action of the river South Esk, that was seriously undermining the existing timber bridge pile supports.

George Buchanan, Civil Engineer, was appointed by the Commissioners of the Montrose Bridge to 'Report on the present state of the Wooden Bridge at Montrose and the Practicability of Erecting a Suspended Bridge of Iron in its stead', and this he did on February 15 1823. His opening statement skillfully dismissed the use of timber for bridge building, and continued to introduce iron as a material and the merits of suspension bridges as a concept. '...A wooden bridge, therefore, of more approved construction would be the only expedient, were it not that the material of Iron already applied with success to the purposes of bridge-building, presents new resources in this, as in every other branch of practical mechanics into which it has been introduced'. Buchanan did not underestimate the problems by commenting 'The general construction of such bridges will be seen by the annexed drawing; but, as their nature is not generally understood, I may remark, that the suspended arch is, in most respects, the reverse of the common arch.' In the relatively short time that Union Bridge had been in existence Buchanan, like others, had learned from its prototype. He specified a versed sine of 60 ft for a span between pillars of 420 ft., with iron plated and bolted individual pillars, an iron bar framework stiffened platform and main chains compounded from 1 ½ inch diameter bars into coupled units of 36 each side. He was disturbed by the shallow curve of Union Bridge chains, and explained the virtues to be otherwise gained: '...owing to the deepness of the curve, this load (970 tons) will produce no undue strain upon the arch; it will first stretch the chains as if they had been hung perpendicularly, and the weight suspended by their extremities. In the middle of the arch, indeed, the strain on the chains will scarcely be so much as this. This advantage is owing entirely to the height of the towers; for had these been so low as those of the Tweed Bridge compared with its span, the weight of the roadway would have produced on the chains, owing to the flatness of the arch, a strain almost double that of their natural weight'.

Buchanan based his design on the assumption that 'Good English iron will bear .... at least 8 tons of strain upon every square inch.......as it takes from 20 to 30 tons to tear it asunder....'.

In his Report and Specification Buchanan recognised design problems with clear description and understanding, but he owed the knowledge to Samuel Brown who, in turn, had not allowed pioneer success to cloud thoughts about his own design proposal for Montrose Bridge.Brown sent his 'plans and Estimates' to the Commissioners from Brighton on July 8 1823. These comprised a single drawing showing the general form and principal details, with a Specification under the cover of a letter giving an estimate of costs. This proposal was eventually accepted and the bridge was completed in December 1829 following a construction period of one year.

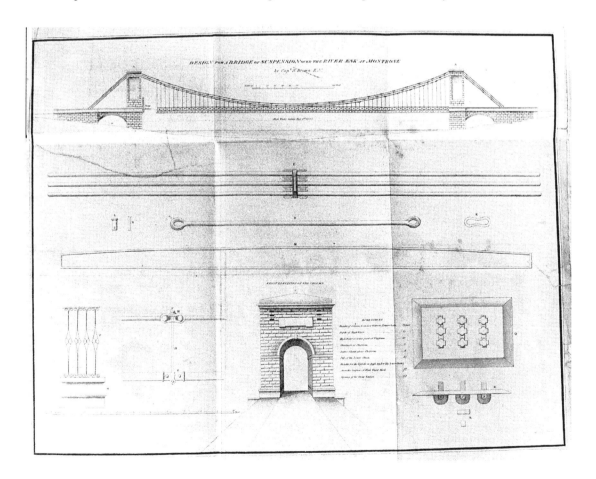

Fig 27 - Design for a Bridge of Suspension over the River South Esk at Montrose

BRIGHTON, 8th July, 1823

SIR,

I have been prevented from sending the Plans and Estimates for the Bridge of Suspension at Montrose before this time, by the illness of Mr Gardener, who had all my papers and documents for making plans and estimates.

When I attended the meeting of the Commissioners in May last, the impression on my mind was, that the most eligible and cheapest plan would be the erection of a column for the south abuttment in the opening of the preset drawbridge; but on entering into the calculation, I found that forming a coffer-dam, to enable the work to go on, under the water level, and the additional masonry, would be more expensive than erecting the columnwhere the present breast-work stands, and allow of a draw-bridge at the end, as it now exists; and which will not in any way affect the stability of the bridge. I am willing, however, to erect it either on the last-mentioned plan, and construct the draw-bridge with the requisite machinery; or on the former, which is in the possession of the Commissioners; - the piers in both cases to be of stone; - the plan herewith sent to cost L12,500; the other* alluded to, L13,500. The specification of the above, in regard to the construction of the bridge, will do for either; and I would be willing – indeed I would prefer, that the work should be done agreeably to plan and specification, under the inspection of the Commissioners' own Surveyor. Begging reference to the plan and specification,

I remain, SIR,

Your most obedient humble servant,

(Signed) SAM. BROWN

The other plan here referred to was abandoned, as not embracing the draw-bridge, which was considered indispensable.

SPECIFICATION

OF

A BRIDGE OF SUSPENSION OVER THE RIVER SOUTH ESK

AT

MONTROSE

BRIGHTON 6th July 1823

THE columns **A, B, C** to be founded on piles, if necessary; the south column on the same place as the present breast-work. which, if found perfectly secure, is to for part of the pier. The north pier to be founded immediately behind and adjoining the north-west breast-work, - the foundation of which is to remain as high as low-water-mark.

The columns to be of the form and dimensions shown by the scale; and all the outside courses to be laid in what is termed headers and stretchers, in good ashler work; the interior to be of good rubble work, properly grouted with the best lime mortar; the stone to be of the same quality or equal to that in the present bridge. The headers and stretchers not to be less than 3 feet 6 inches in length, 2 feet in breadth, and 14 inches in thickness.

The outside courses to be rusticated, if the Commissioners prefer that to plain dressed frontings; if the latter, an abatement to be made of the difference of the expense.

In the pediments of the columns, there are to be cast iron saddles fixed for the support of the principal chains; and which principal chains , and the rest of the components of the bridge, are described as follows:

The bridge is to be 28 feet wide between the railing, and 418 feet in length, or thereabout; there are to be three rows of principal suspending chains over each other; each row to consist of 3 chains parallel.

D is a view of one of the bolts of the above chai; 2¼ inches in diameter, and 15 feet long – or 20 feet long if I prefer that length.

E shews one of the rows united parallel to each other with side plates and bolts.

F is a side view of the above, shewing the perpendicular bolt **G** passing between the chain and resting by the saddle **H**, which bears on all three principal chains; the above bolt to be ¾ inch diameter, the length will depend on the position in the bridge.

I is a side view of the lower bars, which extend the whole length of the bridge; the beams rest on these bars; they are 4 inches deep and 1 inch thick; the bolts will be 1¾ inches in diameter; the points are to be hooped tight; or otherwise properly secured.

K is a view of one of the side coupling links, 1¾ in diameter (square iron)

L is a bolt for uniting the main bolts, as shewn by the letter **H**; it is to be 4 inches , and sufficiently long to admit of a forelock, key, and washer, to draw the joint up tight.

M is a side view of one of the main beams of cast iron; it is to be 10 inches deep at the ends where it rests on the longitudinal bars, and rise with a regular curve to the centre, where it is to be 15 inches deep; it is to be I inch thick throughout between the flangs, and 28 feet six inches long. These beams are to be held transversely on the lower longitudinal bar, and to be 5 feet asunder from centre to centre.

N is a section of the above.

O is a side view of a cast iron stringer or clamp, which is to be bolted or otherwise properly secured to the sides of the bridge; it is to cover in all the ends of the beams, and acts as a stiffening plate to the whole bridge. It is to be 22 inches deep and 1 inch thick, besides the extra thickness of the cornice, which is either to be cast in the solid, or brought on by means of screws, as found most proper.

P is a view of an iron railing on each side of the bridge. The pattern for this may be at the choice of the Commissioners. It is included in the estimate.

Q is one of the iron plates which is to be laid under ground, of sufficient depth to resist the drag of the back-stay chains, which pass through the plates, and are secured by means of bolt, as shewn in the section.

E,f,G is a section and side view of one of these back-stay bolts; they are to be 5 inches deep and 5½ thick, and sufficiently long to have a good bearing on the back of the plate. The plate will be 6 feet by 8, and about 4 inches thick in its general section.

The plates which are to form the covering or road of the bridge need not be shown by a drawing; they will be cast in suitable lengths for bolting or screwing down on the beams. Their thickness will be decided by some experiments which I am about to make.

The foregoing are Specification of the principal parts of the work. There are a variety of minor objects, which could not possibly be comprehended in a specification, but which may all be embraced under the general head of – the whole being completed in a workmanlike manner!

SAM. BROWN

Fig 29 - Specification of A Bridge of Suspension over the River South Esk at Montrose

Both the Specification and Brown's letter, together with a photographic reproduction of the drawing, are illustrated. As will be seen, the general design is similar to that of Union Bridge employing circular section bar chains '...2½ inches in diameter, and 15 feet long - or 20 feet, if I prefer that length...' arranged in 3 rows over each other, each row consisting of 3 chains. Masonry towers contained cast iron saddles, which were presumably to be of roller bearing type, as the angles, that the main chains and back chains make with the tower differed.

Fig 30 - Montrose Bridge

Couplings between chain bars with links and suspension rods are also typical, except for the shape of actual saddle bearing which the engraver of the drawing did not seem to have understood. The lower bar supported by the suspension rods, being one inch thick and four inches deep, is where the typical Brown design ends, for the platform and deck are designed in iron.

Principal main beams, or transoms, are spaced at 5 feet centres, seated on the support bar, and cambered to provide a centre carriageway crown. No details about the iron plates proposed for the roadway are given, and it must be assumed that the fascia 'stringer or clamp' provided a locking and securing device for the ends of beams and supporting bar; which was also the only platform stiffening element. A feature of the design was the Commissioners' insistence upon a passageway for shipping which the 'draw bridge' provided. The bridge survived until 1929 when it was replaced with a new structure.

Brown's achievements had spread far and wide, and in no small way it was due to his own personal zeal and reliability in seeing a project through, but pressure of commitments was causing him some concern. His company was enjoying the benefit from the supply of ironwork for various schemes, which was reinforced by increasing markets for chain cable. All this profitable production allowed for the preparation of proposals and estimates, and the workload was becoming a burden that required professional assistance. His letter to Stevenson (November 6 1824) (opposite) gives a very clear picture of his activities, particularly the mention about the possibility of prefabricated bridge ironwork being exported to India. The letter also confirms the contract '...to erect a Bridge of Suspension over the Thames at Hammersmith..'. This was for W. Tierney Clark's design which was commenced in 1824 and completed in 1827.

'My Dear Sir

I was only favored with your letter the other day having been travelling in France and on my arrival in this country was directed by the Navy Board to proceed to Deal and sound probe and survey the shore there for the purpose of erecting a Pier and Breakwater between the Piles. They are satisfied of the great utility of the plan and are to be governed in their determination by the probable efficacy of fitting the piles with iron nails now under consideration to prevent the ravages of the works which are known to exist.

I mentioned on a former occasion the experiment you made by the serpentine application of strips of copper but they had lately ascertained that at Sheerness that not even coppering the Piles entirely would prevent the destruction of the timber by the worms, as they stripped some piles that had been previously coppered and found them totally destroyed. It is somewhat singular that at Brighton when the ground is the same as at Deal there is no worms.

With regard to the erection of Bridges of Suspension in India. The Directors are aware of the Utility of Bridges and in fact a New Office is created and a Director of Bridges of Suspension is appointed. I sent my plans a long time ago to the Board of Directors and got a usual sort of reply from them stating that they had directed the plans to be deposited in their Library. I should be most happy to have the object promoted by your friend in India and will supply the Iron work at 40/per cwt. this price may appear high but it is less than I receive from government for my proved and warranted chain cables. It should however be considered in the light of a work completed not merely at the price of detatched wrought Iron work all the component parts of the Bridge will be put together and proved ready for erection and no mistake can occur. I will make this a matter of business with you which need not break friendship notwithstanding the old adage (there is no friendship in trade) and allow you a commission of 5% on any order you may procure from that quarter. Do you know of any clever active and operative man with good address and well educated and connected and good Draftsman that could take an oar with me in the same bark I forsee more work than I shall be able to execute myself., write me on this point as soon as convenient I have contracted to erect a Bridge of Suspension over the Thames at Hammersmith and I think it likely to get one to build at Kingston I shall try the great Bridge over the Thames at Iron gate again this session. Believe me to be Dear Sir

Yours truly Sam Brown '
Billetter Sq Lon.6 Nov 24 '

Brown's optimism about a bridge for Kingston came to nothing. In July 1825 Mr Edward Lapidge was appointed Surveyor to the Commissioners for the bridge for the purpose of valuing property in the path of a new bridge, and subsequently secured the design commission for a masonry arched structure. The new bridge was a little way upstream of the old wooden bridge whose dilapidated state had been of great concern since 1812. The curious part is that the deposited plan entered on November 30 1824 for the 1825 Parliamentary Session named Lapidge the architect, in which Telford was being consulted about the design by Lapidge. Brown was, apparently, quite unaware of the Lapidge enterprise. A proposal for a suspension bridge over the Thames from 'Little Tower Hill to Horslydown' was a dramatic scheme put forward by Samuel Brown in association with James Walker, Civil Engineer FRSE, on March 22nd 1824. Had it been carried out it would have been Brown's most important work for it was a grand and sound design, but it was not to be. The intent arose from the sheer pressure on London Bridge and the need to provide a river crossing directly related to the commercial expansion of London Docks within Bermondsey, from which south bank point roads radiated into Kent and Surrey.

Brown and Walker's *'Plan, Prospectus and Report of the Proposed St Catherine's Bridge of Suspension'* outlined the economic and other advantages of the suspension bridge principles, touching upon historical background and Samuel Brown's own accredited experience.

James Walker was at that time Chief Engineer to the London Commercial Dock and had attained both public and professional respect. In 1835 he became the second President of the Institution of Civil Engineers in the wake of Thomas Telford, its founding President. The Professional team was strengthened with Walker's engagement of the young Charles Blacker Vignoles, whose skill as a draughtsman gained him the task of making the final drawings for the bridge. Vignoles' diary entry for February 23rd 1824 records that he '... waited with Captain Brown on the Duke of Wellington, to present the plan for his approval...'

After that involvement, Vignoles was engaged by Tierney Clark for a similar purpose on his Hammersmith Bridge scheme, which was built using Brown's flat-eye bar link system, and opened in 1827. Twenty years later, Vignoles was appointed engineer for bridging the Dnieper at Kiev; a monumental project which required Tsar Nicholas I to be convinced that a wrought iron bar suspension chains design was superior to that of wire cables; having taken the important decision to use Captain Brown's system of suspension by chains made up of flat wrought iron bars bolted together. With his son and new assistant William Coulthard, Vignoles carefully surveyed Clark's Hammersmith and Shoreham Bridges and also visited the Montrose bridge which, at that date, would have been Brown's reconstructed bridge. The contract was secured, formidable obstacles overcome, and with all the ironwork made in England, the bridge was opened in 1851.

PROSPECTUS,

AND

Report,

Of the proposed

ST. CATHERINE'S BRIDGE

OF SUSPENSION,

DESIGNED BY

CAPTAIN SAMUEL BROWN, R. N.

AND

JAMES WALKER, Esq. CIVIL ENGINEER, F.R.S.E.

Printed by J. Darling, 31, Leadenhall Street.

ST. CATHERINE'S BRIDGE OF SUSPENSION,

DESIGNED BY

CAPTAIN SAMUEL BROWN, R. N.

AND

JAMES WALKER, ESQ. CIVIL ENGINEER, F. R. S. E.

Prospectus.

As the situation of the Bridge, with its dimensions and plan of construction, are fully stated in the annexed Report, very few preliminary observations will be necessary in laying before the Public, a Prospectus of the proposed undertaking. It seems to be generally admitted, by persons of the first scientific and mechanical abilities, and by the intelligent observer in every class of the community, that it will open a new field for the advancement of the best interests of the country.

England has taken the lead in this, as well as in all the most important improvements in the arts, which have so materially benefited mankind: and the advantages which she cannot fail to derive from this new era in the construction of bridges, will rapidly spread to every quarter of the globe. They will, in the first place, create an immense increase in the consumption of iron, which is one of the principal staple articles of the kingdom, give rise to a new branch of manufacture, and open an extensive channel for the employment of British capital at home. They will promote the improvement of agriculture, establish an intercourse and traffic with districts at present separated by impassable rivers, and thereby facilitate the conveyance and interchange of every article of internal commerce. But in no manner, or in no situation, can their utility be so completely exemplified, as by the erection of the Bridge now proposed; because, while it interposes no impediment to the navigation, it forms a direct communication, (the ascent being only one foot in twenty) with the most populous parts of the metropolis on both sides of the river, east of London Bridge; it shortens the distance from the Minories to the Green Man turnpike, on the great Kent Road, a mile and a half; and from the Minories to the Lower Deptford Road, nearly two miles.

On looking at the map of the eastern parts of London, and the populous suburbs, where the principal roads of the adjoining counties concentrate, it must be evident that it will form by far the nearest and most preferable line of communication with the eastern parts of Middlesex, and the whole of Essex, the south-east parts of Surrey and Sussex, and the whole of Kent, and even with the more distant counties within that parallel; and there is a population, forming a part of the metropolis, of at least three hundred thousand persons, on both sides, independently of the towns and villages embraced within the line of St. Catherine's Bridge. There can be no question that four-fifths of the merchandize from any of the Docks into the Borough of Southwark, or into the counties of Surrey or Kent, would pass over this Bridge. . . . .

The statements which have been already published of the transit of carriages all descriptions, of horses, cattle, and foot passengers, over London Bridge, ren the calculation of the revenue of the proposed Bridge very simple. An acco was taken in July 1811, with a view to forming some data for the produce of Southwark Bridge, and it appeared that there were—

	Number.	Rate.	Amount.		
Foot passengers	89,640	1d.	£373	10	0
Waggons	769	1s.	38	19	0
Carts and Drays	2,924	8d.	97	9	4
Coaches	1,240	1s.	62	0	0
Gigs and Taxed Carts	485	6d.	12	2	6
Horses	764	3d.	9	11	0
Per Day			£593	11	10
Per Year			£216,660	19	2

The population and traffic of the metropolis and suburbs have very much in creased since that time, and continue to increase; therefore, in computing th revenue of the St. Catherine's Bridge, it will be perfectly safe, and perhaps greatl under-rated, to take one-fifth of the above amount as the datum; in which case i would yield, after paying every expence of keeping it up, and for annual disburse ments, a return of upwards of ten per cent., as hereafter shewn. These calculation are made without reference to the proposed Tunnel below the London Docks which, when completed, according to the expectations of the projectors, will, ne doubt, reduce the revenue of St. Catherine's Bridge. Let it be supposed, that the Tunnel will carry off £10,000 per annum from the revenue of the Bridge; or even if it should produce the income calculated in the Prospectus, still there woulc be a return of upwards of seven and a half per cent. to the proprietors of the St Catherine's Bridge, after defraying all expences of maintaining the Bridge, collecting the tolls, and reserving two per cent. for repairs.

The Bridge will be executed upon the principle and plan of construction of a patent granted to Captain SAMUEL BROWN, Royal Navy, bearing date the 10th of July 1816.

The estimates have been made by JAMES WALKER, Esq. Civil Engineer, F. R. S. E., and the calculations formed with the greatest care and accuracy. They are comprised under the following heads :—

Expence of purchasing property, and indemnifying the owners or occupiers of land, will not exceed	£30,000
Coffer Dams and Piers in the River	132,000
Land Piers	55,000
Abutments	40,000
Approach	11,000
Ironwork	96,000
Platform	14,000
Law Expences, Surveys, and Expences of obtaining the Act of Parliament	2,000
Superintendance of Engineers and Contingencies	12,000
Total Amount	£392,000

One of the principal features in the above estimate is the small expence of the approaches, compared with those of the Waterloo and Southwark Bridges. The capital to be invested is here brought within a limit that could not fail, even in a situation less favourable for a bridge, to yield a good return of interest to the proprietors.

Annual receipts, charges, and disbursements, may be classed under the following heads :—

Estimated gross amount of the revenue			£43,000	0	0
Two per cent. on the gross amount, to be reserved for repairing and maintaining the Bridge	£860	0	0		
Cleaning and painting	300	0	0		
Lighting and watching	250	0	0		
Four toll-keepers	320	0	0		
Bridge-master, with power to regulate the order of carriages	100	0	0		
Secretary, clerk, and office	450	0	0		
			2,280	0	0
Net proceeds			£40,720	0	0

It is proposed to raise the sum necessary by subscription, in transferable shares, of £100 each.

The proprietors will be formed into a joint stock company, under the authority of an act, now in progress through Parliament. It will be provided for in the act, that no proprietor will be liable for more than the amount of the stock he holds in the concern.

The affairs of the company to be managed by   directors, who will select out of their own body a chairman and deputy chairman.

The subscription will be paid by instalments, which will be called for when necessary, due notice being given.

A deposit of £5 per cent. on each share, to be paid into the bank of Messrs.   , on or before the   day of   next.

At the expiration of six months, from the opening of the Bridge, a dividend will be declared to the proprietors, and paid half yearly afterwards.

As the Act of Parliament will give the company ample powers for the good government of their affairs, it will not here be necessary to advert to points which will, in due time, come under the consideration of the directors.

The probable time of executing and completing the Bridge, will be about eighteen months from the date of the contract.

Information on all subjects relating to the St. Catherine's Bridge, may be had at

March 22, 1824.

The towers will be constructed either of granite or some other stone of equally good quality, and the best rubble-work in the interior, plans and specifications of which will be in due time given in.

The Bridges will be supported by 64 principal bars or bolts of suspension, $2\frac{1}{2}$ inches diameter, as shewn in the designs.

The bolts will be 20 feet long, joined by side plates and pins of proportional strength. They will be extended, from their respective points, over the towers, in four rows, over each other, one foot apart, each row to consist of four lines of bolts, parallel with each other. Those principal lines of suspension may now be denominated chains, although differing from the *common* form and *usual acceptation* of the word. The joints being exactly opposite to each other, the saddles which support the perpendicular bolts rest on them, and bear equally on all. The principal suspenders are so arranged, that the beams are alternately supported by a different row of chains, so that an equal strain is produced; as, for instance, the first joint from the towers is 5 feet long, and supports the first beam; the second joint is 10 feet long, and supports the second; the third is 15 feet long, which supports the third; and the fourth is 20 feet long, and supports the fourth beam. The others are all 20 feet long. Having thus set off with different lengths, this alternate system extends over the whole, and the perpendicular bolts are all 5 feet apart, corresponding with the distance of the beams.

The foregoing plan renders the united strength of the principal suspenders certain; and we may now proceed to apply a calculation of strength, from the known principles of the catenarian curve, and the strength of iron, as found by so many accurate experiments.

It may here be briefly noticed, that as the strain is somewhat greater at the points of suspension, the main bolts might be, in a small degree, gradually diminished to the centre; and in erecting the Trinity Pier in the Frith of Forth, I adopted this rule; but the expence and trouble attending it exceeds any advantage to be derived from a closer approach to mechanical precision.

The least force that will break a $2\frac{1}{2}$-inch bolt, when strained vertically, or supported uniformly in a horizontal direction, is 142 tons, and the least force that will stretch it, under similar circumstances, is five-ninths of the above, or 79; but when extended in the catenarian curve, whose versed sine is one-fourteenth of its chord, three-sevenths of the 142, or about 61 tons, equally divided, will produce the same degree of tension, or the breaking strain; and the same rule will obtain as to the stretching point, viz. five-ninths of 61 tons, or 34 tons, will produce the same effect on the curve; but no force less than this will cause any change.

Then the least force that would break down the whole of the main suspending chains in any one span, is 3904 tons, and the least force that would strain them to stretching is 2170 tons.

The weight of the Bridge, the main suspending chains, and every thing within the points of suspension, will be 750 tons.

The centre division of any span of the Bridge would contain 20 waggons, with 8 horses, which, taken at 12 tons, including the weight of the horses, is 240 tons; a promiscuous collection of carts and waggons would perhaps be nearly the same; there could not be room for many other vehicles, but allowing 60 tons for horses and droves of cattle, say 300 tons. The side paths are to be solely appropriated for foot passengers, and it is just possible to place (allowing 2 feet in breadth, and 15 inches in width for each) 3648 persons on both sides, which, at 11 stone, is 250 tons. The total weight which it is possible to load on the area of any one division is therefore 550 tons; so that, in this extreme case, there would be 2604 tons less weight than would break down the main chain, and 870 tons less than the weight that would stretch them.

This calculation of a single span applies to the others; if the whole area were filled, it would contain 14,592 people, or 1003 tons, and there would be a burden of 1200 tons in waggons and carriages; those, together with the weight of the Bridge, make the whole strain 5200 tons: but then we have the strength of all the main chains in the respective spans, viz. 15,616 tons, to support this, or 10,416 less than would break down the Bridge, and 3480 less than would stretch them.

This I consider to be a surplus of strength, that will be deemed quite sufficient even with the most cautious mind; but in a bridge of suspension, we are not at all limited to strength, more than in any other structure. I can increase either the number of the chains, or the diameter of the bolts; a due regard to economy, and mechanical proportion, however, should always prevail, and guide us in rejecting whatever is not absolutely useful and necessary.

The towers will not be effected by any strain or drag from the main suspending chains, being only subject to vertical pressure. The area, or base of the last iron framings, on which the principal chains rest, will be about 500 feet, and computing the cohesion of the masonry under them, which is the weakest substance, it would require, at the moderate calculation of $1\frac{1}{2}$ ton to a cubic inch, upwards of 100,000 tons to crush one of the towers.

With respect to the probable durability of the Bridge, I do consider that, with the exception of the timber, it may be deemed an imperishable structure.

If it was to be totally neglected, the time would arrive, but that at a very remote date, when oxidation would waste the bolts, and a diminution of strength in the ratio of its loss of weight would ensue; but even in this case (which is so improbable to occur, that it seems like courting an objection to notice it), we have the fact before us, that every part of the Bridge can be taken out, and renewed in detail, without either endangering its strength, or disturbing the passage.

The ironwork will, in the first place, receive several coats of the anticorosion paint, which will be cleaned off, and renewed every year; and there is no part of the work that will not be accessible; even the chains under ground will be extended within covered ways, or barrel arches, like the Brighton Pier, and there can be no question, that, with common attention, the whole may be kept in a state of constant preservation; indeed, were it considered necessary or desirable, all the principal chains might be covered close round with thin sheet lead, which would not only be impervious to water, but the joint, or seam, which would be *under* the chains, might be soldered, and prevent the action of the atmosphere altogether.

The platform, or road of the Bridge, being defended with plates of iron, will not be subject to wear; but it will require occasionally partial repairs, owing to the decay of the timber, which in about 40 years may amount to a total renewal; yet this need not at any time stop the passage of the Bridge: a beam can be taken out, and another introduced, by wedging up the planks from below; the planks being longitudinal, may be lifted and replaced, without much trouble or inconvenience at any time.

The cheapness of the material, and the simplicity of the construction, are strong recommendations for its adoption. It is quite practicable, and consistent with the design, to build the road entirely of cast iron, with wrought iron plates rivetted across, to afford a sure foothold for the horses; but in that case, the main suspending chains would require to be stronger, to support the additional weight, and the expence would be so much greater, that the difference of interest would not render it desirable in an economical point of view.

The space occupied by the columns in the river on each side, will not be greater than the length and breadth of two small sloops or brigs; speaking as a seaman, I should say, that they would rather be an advantage, than a hinderance, because the spread of the yards of two vessels would be more likely to impede the passage of other vessels, than the towers will be.

It is necessary to state most unequivocally, that no hinderance whatever will be created, either in the river or the adjoining streets, during the erection of the Bridge. When the towers are finished, chains of sufficient strength to carry a temporary gangway will be stretched across, which can be hove up in half an hour; the principal bolts will be hoisted up to the temporary Bridge, and the whole put together aloft.

REPORT

ON THE

PROPOSED PLAN OF ERECTING A PATENT WROUGHT IRON BRIDGE OF SUSPENSION,

OVER THE THAMES, NEAR IRON GATE AND HORSLYDOWN,

BY

CAPTAIN SAMUEL BROWN, ROYAL NAVY.

THERE is not in this, or in any other country, such an extent of fertile and valuable districts, with such a numerous population, separated by an unfordable and navigable river, without any means of communication, except by boats, as the counties on both sides of the Thames, on the eastern parts of the metropolis.

Nothing can more clearly manifest the paramount importance of the commercial and maritime interests of Great Britain, which will not admit of the least impediment or injury to the navigation, even to attain such immense public and local advantages, as must result from the erection of a Bridge, at the spot proposed in the present design.

I need not therefore have recourse to argument, in order to prove, that if such advantages can be obtained, without prejudice to the great desideratum, a free passage to sea-going ships and vessels, as heretofore, it would be a highly important acquisition to the city of London, and to the country at large.

My object is now to show, that the measure is not only in itself practicable, but that it is a task of much less difficulty than its apparent extent and magnitude would seem to indicate.

It will not at all lessen the importance of the present proposal, if it be admitted that bridges of suspension have long existed in other countries, and it cannot be pretended by any man, that a new principle has been discovered. The properties of the catenarian curve are obvious in the Indian bridge of suspension, formed of ropes or bamboo canes, and in those constructed of common chain, as well as in a variety of objects which must be familiar to every person of common observation. But those simple contrivances, which have been noticed by some writers, have no more resemblance in their construction to the bridges or piers of suspension which have been erected in Great Britain, than the rude bridges of remote ages, which consisted of logs supported on props, are to be compared to the architecture of modern times.

The first Bridge of Suspension that we hear of in this country, is the one thrown across the river Tees, in the county of Durham, the span of which does not, I think, exceed 80 feet. It is formed of two common chains, stretched over the river, from abrupt banks, with battens laid across, and boarded, the gangway partaking of the curve of the chains.

Such an arrangement is evidently a bad one, inasmuch as we must ascend to the points of suspension, then descend, and rise according to the curve of the chain, which, in that which I have usually adopted, would be a pull of one foot in seven. This is hardly practicable, and my earliest attention was employed to remedy the evil. In 1814 I erected a bridge, with the road or platform perfectly horizontal, on my premises at Mill Wall, where it still remains. This is effected by introducing perpendicular rods through the joints of the main suspending bars, and adjusting their length to the curve above, so that they form a series of straps for the reception of a row of bars on each side, placed edgewise, and extending the whole length of the bridge, parallel to the entrance. The beams being laid across these bars, the platform or road becomes quite horizontal; or an ascent may be given from the sides to the middle, in the same plane as with the roads leading to the bridge. The span is 105 feet, and the iron work only weighs 38 cwt. It was inspected by the late Mr. Rennie and Mr. Telford, who drove their carriages over it; and it has been considered by men eminent for their skill in mechanics, as a remarkable combination of strength and lightness.

The advance to improvement in this new era of bridge building, may be traced to the invention of iron cables, which necessarily introduced the powerful proving machine. A knowledge of the strength of bolts and bar iron of large dimensions, was thereby obtained, which formerly was deduced from trivial experiments, leading to most erroneous calculation; and as the importance of this new branch of naval equipment developed itself, the principal iron manufacturers of England vied with each other in its improvement; and British iron is now brought to a state of perfection, that will, for general purposes, entirely supersede the use of foreign. There is also a uniformity in the strength of the improved British iron, beyond that of any other country; so that by adopting straight bolts or bars, united end to end in the direction of their length, by coupling plates and pins of proportionate strength, instead of chains, we have an increase of strength with less weight; the risk of bad workmanship is almost entirely obviated; and the subsequent proof to which every part of the work is subjected, reduces the calculation of its strength to a certainty.

The consideration of the plans at present submitted, will be much assisted by an examination of the model of the bridge which was erected about four years ago over the river Tweed, near Berwick. It is called the Union Bridge, from one of the towers standing in England, and the other in Scotland. Although it consists of but one span, the principle and plan of construction are precisely the same. The foundations of the towers were laid on the 19th of July 1819, and it was completed and opened to the public on the 19th of July 1820, by a procession of two rows of loaded carts and carriages, after which there were admitted about two thousand people. It has been in constant use for waggons and loaded carriages, and all the usual traffic of the country, without any regard to weight or number, the same as any bridge of arches. The span is 437 feet, only 133 feet less than the present design, the width 18 feet, which admits of two carriages passing in opposite directions, and a narrow path on each side, protected by cast iron brackets, for foot passengers.

The road is constructed of beams, 5 feet asunder, laid across the lower bars, covered with 3-inch planks, and the carriage-road in the centre is defended by cross bars of wrought iron, which afford a firm foothold for the horses. The bridge is supported by perpendicular bolts, resting on saddles, on 12 main lines of suspension, which consist of eye-bolts, 15 feet long, and 2 inches diameter, united as before mentioned. They pass over the towers, and rest on cast-iron saddles, built into the masonry, and are extended on an angle of about 35 degrees, the extremities bolted behind strong cast-iron plates, fixed about 40 feet under the road. The back stay bars on the English side are secured in the solid rock.

I have ascertained the degree of tension which is created under every deflexion of the catenarian curve, by numerous experiments.

The versed sine of the main suspending bolts of the Union Bridge is, as near as may be, one-fourteenth of its chord; in this position the bolts will only bear about three-sevenths the weight which would be required to tear them asunder in a vertical position, or when uniformly supported and stretched horizontally.

I have found that a 2-inch bolt, 12 feet long, and 2 inches diameter, was torn asunder horizontally by my machine, which is on the lever principle, like the weigh-bridges in the Royal Dock Yards, with a strain of 82 tons; it began to stretch with 47 tons, and lengthened, during the experiment, 2 feet 9 inches, and was reduced, at the point of rupture, to $1\frac{5}{8}$ inch diameter.

But, according to the power indicated by the hydraulic engine, used for the same purpose by Mr. Brunton, of the Commercial Road, it requires a strain from 95 to 100, sometimes 103, to break a bolt of the same dimensions and quality.

Mr. Barlow, Mathematical Professor of the Royal Military Academy at Woolwich, has published, in his treatise on the strength and stress of materials, an account of experiments on my proving machine, made in presence of himself, as well as others made by Mr. Brunton, and he ascribes the difference to the peculiar nature of the action of the two engines—Mr. Brunton's overrating, while mine registers less than its full power; and he considers 27 tons as the measure of strength of an inch square.

Taking the mean results, therefore, of the above trials, 91 tons are the measure of strength, corresponding nearly with Mr. Barlow's datum; therefore, as three-sevenths of the weight which will tear a 2-inch bolt in the position before mentioned, will produce the same strain when equally divided on a catenarian curve, whose versed sine is one-fourteenth of its chord, 39 tons is the least weight that would break down one of the main lines of suspension of the Union Bridge, and 468 to break down the whole, and the area of the bridge could not contain half that weight in any shape.

It is also to be observed, that even admitting the possibility of the bolts in a bridge of suspension being overstrained, or strained to stretching, it is very evident, from the wonderful ductility remarked in the experiments before mentioned, that the very effect of their lengthening reduces the strain, because, as the curve becomes relaxed, the tension is diminished. It is quite different from a sustaining power, whose inertia is continually exerted.

It is interesting and important to note the changes that the iron undergoes in proving bolts or bars. It seems perfectly rigid and unaffected by any force less than five-ninths of its measure of strength, when a change is indicated by small exfoliations, or scales, from its surface. This is the consequence of the bolt stretching, and necessarily lessening in diameter, and a certain proof of its yielding is the phenomenon of its becoming sensibly warm: the heat increases in the ratio of the strain, and when the rupture takes place, which is generally near the middle, it is almost too hot to hold.

It cannot but afford additional satisfaction, in the consideration of this subject, to know that, in the evidence given before the House of Commons respecting the Menai Bridge, which is now constructing under the direction of Mr. Telford, the most eminent men, both engineers and mathematicians, were not only unanimous in their opinion of the practicability of that measure, but also that both theory and experiment confirmed the possibility of extending it far beyond the limits of the present design.

Having made these preliminary observations, I shall proceed with a brief explanation of the plan itself, the eligibility of the situation, and the facility of forming approaches contiguous to the great roads and principal streets on both sides.

The designs are projected by James Walker, Esq. F. R. S. E. Civil Engineer, and myself.

There are 3 spans of 600 feet each, and 2 side spans, supported by the back stay bars, of 300 feet each. The total extent of the Suspended Bridge, including the width of the towers, is 2400 feet.

The embanked approaches, which form an integral part of the plan, are, together, 900 feet, the whole extent being 3300 feet, or little more than half a mile.

The road on the North side takes its rise on Little Tower-Hill, near the bottom of the Minories; that on the South side near Dock-Head, in Bermondsey, which forms a central point to the streets leading to the great Kent and Surrey Roads.

The rise, from its commencement on each side, is formed by an easy acclivity of 1 foot perpendicular in 20 feet horizontal.

The carriage-road of the Bridge will be 21 feet wide, the footpaths on each side 8 feet wide.

The Bridges will be constructed of strong beams of Baltic timber, covered with 3-inch plank. The centre, or carriage-road, will be defended with wrought iron bars of different thicknesses laid across, forming ribs, which will afford a secure foothold for horses.

The height of the Bridge, as shewn in the design, above high water mark, is 70 feet in the front of the towers, rising gradually to 75 feet in the centre. The height will allow ships of 200 tons to pass under without striking their top-gallant masts, and ships of 300 or 400 tons to pass with main-top-gallant masts down.

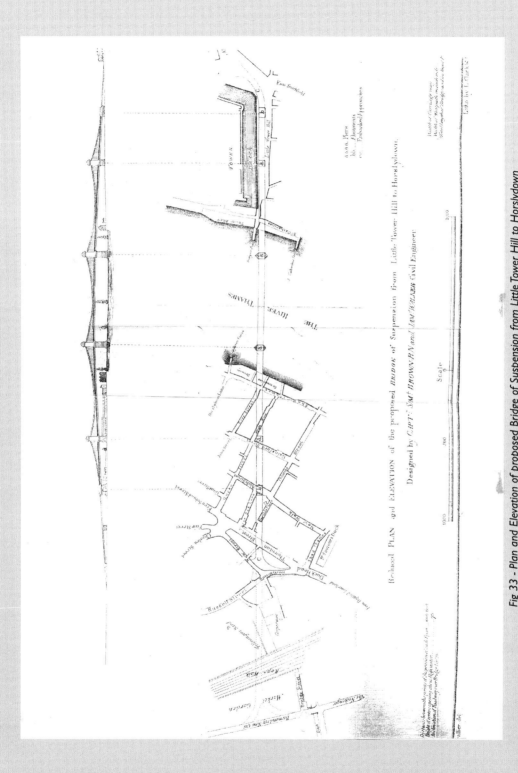

Fig 33 - Plan and Elevation of proposed Bridge of Suspension from Little Tower Hill to Horslydown

Prospectus and Report of the Proposed St Cathrine's Bridge
Littletown - Bermondsey

(Estimates of expenditure and income were prepared
by James Walker and given in the prospectus)

Expence of purchasing property, and indemnify
the owners or occupiers of land, will not exceed £30,000

Coffer Dams and Piers in thee River 132.00

Land Piers 55,000

Abutments 40,000

Approach 11,000

Ironwork 96,000

Platform 14,000

Law Expenses, Surveys and Expences of obtaining
the Act of Parliament 2,000

Superintendence of Engineers and Contingencies 12,000

Total Amount   **£392,000**

Annual receipts, charges, and disbursements may be classed under the
following heads:-

Estimated gross amount of the revenue **£43,000**

Two per cent. on the gross amount, to be
reserved for repairing and maintaining the Bridge £860
Cleaning and painting 300
Lighting and watching 250
Four tollkeepers 320
Bridge master, with power to regulate the order of carriages 100
Secretary, clerk, and office 450
Total amount **£2,280**

Net Proceeds **£40,720**

It was proposed to raise the sum necessary by subscription in transferable shares, of £100 each. Following 'Preliminary Observations' made in the Report, the authors paid respect to 'Menai Bridge, which is now constucting under the direction of Mr Telford' - which was by way of reinforcing the theory and practacability of the scheme described in the Report.

The design was explained thus:

'There are 3 spans of 600 feet each and 2 side spans, supported by the back-stay bars, of 300 feet each. The total extent of the Suspended Bridge, including the width of the towers, is 2400 feet. The embanked approaches, which form an integral part of the plan, are, together, 900 feet, the whole extent being 3300 feet, or little more than half a mile.

The road on the North side takes its rise on Little Tower Hill, near the bottom of the Minories; that on the South side near Dock-Head, in Bermondsey, which forms a central point to the streets leading to the great Kent and Surrey Roads.

The rise, from its commencement on each side, is formed by an easy acclivity of 1 foot perpendicular in 20 feet horizontal.

The carriage-road of the Bridge will be 21 feet wide, the footpaths on each side 8 feet wide.

The Bridges will be constructed of strong beams of Baltic timber, covered with 3-inch plank. The centre, or carriage-road, will be defended with wrought iron bars of different thicknesses laid across, forming ribs, which will afford a secure foot-hold for horses.

The height of the Bridge, as shewn in the design, above high water mark, is 70 feet in the front of the towers, rising gradually to 75 feet in the centre. The height will allow ships of 200 tons to pass under without striking their top-gallant masts, and ships of 300 or 400 tons to pass with main-top-gallant masts down.

The towers will be constructed either of granite or some other stone of equally good quality, and the best rubble-work in the interior, plans and specifications of which will be in due time given. The Bridges will be supported by 64 principal bars or bolts of suspension, 22 inches diameter, as shewn in the designs.

The bolts will be 20 feet long, joined by side plates and pins of proportional strength. They will be extended, from their respective points, over the towers, in four rows, over each other, one foot apart, each row to consist of four lines of bolts, parallel with each other. Those principal lines of suspension may now be denominated chains, although differing from the common form and usual acceptation of the word. The joints being exactly opposite to each other, the saddles which support the perpendicular bolts rest on them, and bear equally on all. The principal suspenders are so arranged, that the beams are alternately supported by a different row of chains, so that an equal strain is produced; as, for instance, the first joint from the towers is 5 feet long, and supports the first beam; the second joint is 10 feet long. and supports the second; the third is 15 feet long, which supports the third; and the fourth is 20 feet long, and supports the fourth beam. The others are all 20 feet long. Having thus set off with different lengths, this alternative system extends over the whole, and the perpendicular bolts are all 5 feet apart, corresponding with the distance of the beams.'

The Report continued to explain the strength of the 2½ inch diameter bolts, in terms of strain, up to their Elastic Limit for the proposed versed sine of one-fourteenth of its chord, arriving at a figure of 34 tons: stating that '..no force less than this will cause any change..'. Then, by way of summary, the figure of 2170 tons (it should be 2176) is given as the least force that would strain the whole of the main suspending chains in any one span.

Computations for the weight of the Bridge and anticipated live loads are also given: ' The weight of the Bridge, the main suspending chains and everything within the points of suspension will be 750 tons. The centre division of any span of the Bridge would contain..', which are listed as follows:

20 waggons with horses amounting to 240 tons; 60 tons for horses and cattle, and allowing for 3648 persons at 11 stone a. figure of 250 tons is given. The combined bridge and live loads acting upon the main chains therefore amounted to 1300 tons, that is, for one division; and the point is made '.. that, in this extreme case, there would be 870 tons, less than the weight that would stretch them..'. The effects of loads over the whole area of the bridge are given in comparative figurative terms, and the anticipated bridge life-span and maintenance that the structure will require is also dealt with, and concludes '.. that no hindrance whatever will be created, either in the river or the adjoining streets, during the erection of the Bridge..'.

Had the scheme succeeded it would have been tremendous for both Samuel Brown and London, but, also in 1824, the St.Katharine's Dock Company was formed with the aim of constructing new docks on the 27 acre area bounded by Little Tower Hill, East Smithfield, Nightingale Lane and the Thames, with Thomas Telford appointed Engineer and Philip Hardwick, Architect. Their great project was completed on October 25th 1828 and, in its wake, swept away the mediaeval chapel of St. Katharine's, and may have been the reason for the abandonment of the suspension bridge idea, which meant raised approaches along the length of Little Tower Hill.

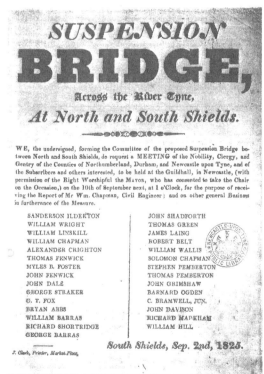

Over fifty years then passed before the problem of cross-Thames traffic became acutely serious, when petitions from many public organisations were presented, urging either the widening of London Bridge or the building of a new bridge. A census taken over two days during August 1882 produced figures of 22,242 vehicles and 110,525 pedestrians. In his bridge Prospectus, Samuel Brown quoted figures taken in July 1811 as being 6,182 Waggons, carts and Drays, Coaches, Gigs and Horses, and 89,640 Foot passengers. The commercial situation was therefore tense, which resulted in Horace Jones' Tower Bridge which opened on June 30 1894 on the exact site that Samuel Brown had chosen.

Fig 34 - Suspension Bridge Across the River Tyne ; Notice of Meeting Sept 2nd 1825

Although Union Bridge was an 'experiment' that received far-ranging professional acclaim, it was the success and publicity of Brighton Chain Pier from which Brown gained many prospective commissions. To the aware merchant and trader the suspension bridge offered an economic means of bridging rivers that lay in steep-banked approaches without hindrance to the normal passage of shipping, and such a case was the River Tyne. A proposal to link North and South Shields with a suspension bridge over the river was put forward by the 'Nobility, Clergy, Gentry, and Landed Proprietors of the Counties of Northumberland and Durham, and of the Inhabitants of the Towns of North and South Shields....' and was considered at a meeting on February 23rd 1825. Brown had prepared a very comprehensive Report for the purpose of the meeting, concluding that '...the total expense of erecting the Bridge, will be £85,700; and the time of completing it within Two Years.' The meeting resolved to proceed with the undertaking, and the public notices that followed stirred some critical adversaries and supporters into being with challenging correspondence through the columns of the local newspapers. The critical campaign was aimed at undermining the public confidence in Brown, and raged for some months before the project, for unaccountable reasons, dissolved into oblivion. The arguments did, however, provide the first ground for open public discussion about the merits of suspension bridge design, which is sufficient reason for the following digest of the published correspondence.

Brown opened his Report to the Committee on September 2nd 1825 with a brief account of suspension bridges which touched upon ancient history. He included mention of the visits made by the late Mr. Rennie, and Mr. Telford to his Millwall experimental bridge, and also described some features of Union Bridge, and the outcome of experiments upon malleable iron bar that had been carried out by himself and Professor Peter Barlow. In further support of the creditability of his Tyne Bridge proposal, Brown cited Telford's successful evidence given before the House of Commons respecting the Menai Bridge, which he apparently included to convey that both '..Theory and Experiment confirmed the possibility of extending it far beyond the limits of the

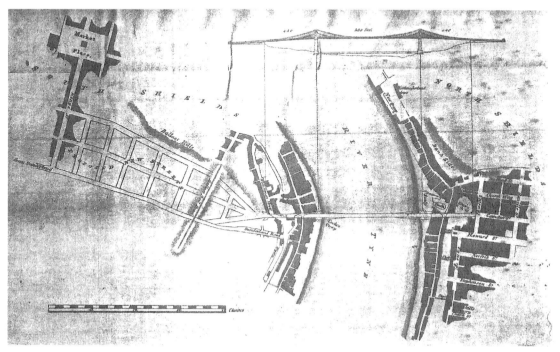

Fig 35 - Map showing proposed location of Tyne Bridge

present design.' By seizing upon Telford's professional stature and his own proven competence, Brown left nothing to chance in communicating his skill, and particularly his integrity, to the Committee.

The Report described a Bridge to consist of two 780 foot spans, including the width of a central tower which was eventually changed to the more conventional arrangement of two towers with a central span of 800 feet with side spans of 300 feet each in consequence of recommendations made by Mr. W. Chapman Civil Engineer. "...40 principal bars or Bilts of Suspension 2½ inches diameter" were to support the platform with suspension rods spaced 5 feet apart, connected with saddles to form alternative tiers of chains on the principle of Union Bridge, and with the same versed sine of 1/14 of its chord. Brown gave figures to support his claim of adequate strength, and described his device whereby links could be taken out for replacement "should occasion arise", although he did make the point "with respect to the probability durability of the Bridge, I do consider, that with the exception of the timber, it may be deemed an imperishable structure".

The cost was put at £85,700, with a completion date of two years. The Report of the Committee was presented to a Public Meeting on Saturday September 10th 1825, following the Report of Mr. William Chapman, who had been commissioned to survey and report upon the whole undertaking. On matters of principle Chapman agreed with Brown's project ideas, but, "...determined on the propriety of altering the sites of the pillars as at first projected...timber, it may be deemed an imperishable 800 structure". For an additional security to the bridge against pendulous vibration, he recommended the adoption of bars as side braces emanating from a column on each pier, or supported by cast iron framing from the piers. The matter did not rest with Chapman's appraisal of the design, and the anxiety of the Committee, which was to be expected, led to Thomas Telford being consulted "as to the propriety of carrying the proposed construction of a chain bridge into effect...".

An independent critic, who was no doubt commissioned by opponents to the project, entered into the scene of activity in the guise of '*Investigator*' and received publication of lengthy letters in the *Tyne Mercury*, which started on September 27th 1825. *Investigator's* line of attack was his belief that, in comparison with Brown's Union Bridge, and Telford's Menai Straits Bridge which had not been completed, the proposed Shields Bridge was very much under strength. *Investigator* argued that the Menai Bridge was "incomparably stronger than the projected bridge

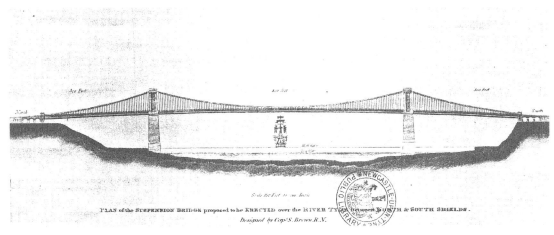

Fig 36 - Engraving: Proposed Tyne Bridge

over the Tyne". He made the point "...that an inverted arch of 580 feet span and exhibiting a cross section of 330 inches (referring to the Menai span and total chain cross sectional area) would be stronger than a similar arch of 900 feet span, exhibiting a cross section of only 196 inches" (referring to the Shields proposal). Although these respective figures were not exact they were relatively proportionate, and did pose the question as to who was right. Another matter of concern to *Investigator* was the "...effect of the wind upon the bridge..." A difference of opinion existed about the wind force that the bridge might possibly experience. A figure of 21lbs per square foot was quoted by a *Tyne Mercury* correspondent as being a maximum likely amount, but *Investigator* quoted "35 lbs on the square foot" that had been recorded by Dr. Lind's portable wind gauge (Phil. Trans, for 1775), and Smeaton's estimate of 49lbs per square foot. He also mentioned experiments made by Dr. Hutton, which dispelled the idea that the cumulative effect of wind pressure over a bridge was in exact proportion to the surface exposed, "...the force of the wind is much more than in the simple ratio of the surfaces, with the same velocity, and this increase of the ratio is the more, as the velocity is the more". *Investigator* went further in his critical assessment by questioning the merit of Telford's Runcorn Bridge proposal, and the fact that his Menai Bridge reflected considerable - design and relative strength improvement, his point being that Brown's Shields proposal corresponded almost identically with Telford's Runcorn proposal insofar that their respective spans to cross sectional area of chains were similar. He was therefore advancing the idea that, while Telford had changed his mind in the course of time, Brown had not; but *Investigator* was not to know that Brown and Telford had come together over the Runcorn scheme and exchanged ideas. The continuing line of attack was summed up by *Investigator* in the statement "...The projectors of the bridge over the Tyne seem, however, with respect to its strength, to have most sagaciously adopted the first and imperfect ideas of Mr. Telford, and to have totally disregarded the principles by which he was afterwards governed in the actual construction of a bridge over the Menai straits". For all this, Telford was discreet in his response to the Committee's inquiry of him, and made no adverse comment upon the project, and confined himself to correcting figures that had been quoted about his own schemes, stating that "...In the Menai Bridge there is no reason to apprehend any inconvenience from either horizontal vibration or vertical undulation". He was wise enough to avoid being drawn into any deep controversy, but in Brown's favour he did not condemn the Shields scheme, and in any event was overwhelmed with professional pressures and not enjoying the best of health.

Brown reacted to the mounting published criticism in a letter dated December 17th 1825 from his Edinburgh address to Thomas Wilson, secretary of the Committee of Management which, if nothing else, displayed the essence of his stalwart character in response to an attack upon his ability. He took exception to the frivolous manner in which *Investigator* had dealt with Telford's letter concerning figures, and almost as an outburst exclaimed "..And, what of all this? Does it materially affect my conclusion that the bridge over the Menai Straits is incomparably stronger than the projected bridge over the Tyne.." Brown's confidence was not to be undermined by the probing critics, and he simply answered the case of comparative strength analysis by saying '..my object has been, to combine a sufficiency of strength with due regard to economy; and I trust it will be found that both these objects are embraced in the design'. Brown continued by describing the behaviour of the chains when subject to the designed loading, and the effects of excess loading up to the yield point, and expressed complete satisfaction with his theory. On the question of wind pressure he dismissed the very idea that such forces would be capable of bending the platform sideways, and saw no need of either guys or sub-braces. His views were firm, and he continued '...*Investigator* evidently labours under the persuasion, that the bridge is suspended

A Pitman's

Humourous Description of the Projected

CHAIN BRIDGE,
AT SHIELDS.

Now, Geordy, my lad—sit as mute as a tead,
An' aw'll tell ye 'bout the Chain Brigg its gaun to be mead;
Aw'll begin at the first, an' gaun on till aw cum
To the end o' my story, an' then aw'll be deun.
Some folks tell a plain simple story at times,
But aw'm nothing like them—aw tell a' things iv rhymes.
Smash, Geordy, sit quiet—keep in thaw greet toes,
An' aw'll gaun as straight forrat as waggoners goes.
Wey, ye see, the folks thought, i' gaun ower the water,
'Stead o' crossing wi' boats, it a Brigg wad be better,
So the gentlemen gather'd a greet congregation,
The seame as folks de at the heed o' the nation;
Then they brought some things forrat, an' sme they put back,
So they sattl'd a Brigg sud be built iv a crack.
'Twasent lang efter this, aw gat had iv a paper,
It tell'd the size it should be as nice as a taper.
How! says aw to mysell, but they hevent been lang,
Dash! a fellow like me may stite meak up a sang,
Or some sic like thing—just to meak a bit fun:
So its ne suner said then its cleverly dune.
Folks thought me a genius when first aw was born—
But what is aw deing?—aw mun tell ye the form
O' this said Iron Brigg it aw's talking about,
When aw pull up my breeches, an' blaw out my snout.
Huge abutments o' steane, aw think they are call'd—
When aw com to that word aw was very near pall'd,
On each side o' the river yen o' thor things is mead,
To fit intiv a hole they howk out wiv a spead.
Fre' the tops o' thor pillars to the edge o' the banks,
Very strang iron chains mead o' wrought iron links,
Hingin ower the house tops o' beath sides o' the river;
Thor chains is continued fre' pillar to pillar.

Continued over ...

Fre' the big'uns is hung some inferior in length,
To the boddom of which a foundation of strength
Is fixt, wrought wi' iron an' cover'd wi' steane,
Then surmounted wi' railing—its dune skin an' beane.
Now, Geordy, what de ye think of it, my lad?—
Wey, speak—what's the maiter—or ye tean very bad?
Or its extonishment that has sew'd up yer mouth?
But aw divent much wonder—so aw'll tell the real truth.
Aw wonder wor owners disent see into it,
An' meak a Chain Brigg for to gaun down wor pit.
A! man, but its cliver—its use 'ill be greet;
For to what lad o' Shields wad the thought not be sweet,
To cross ower the water without danger or fear,
As aw've mony a time dune i' gaun ower the Wear.
When we cross ower the water i' boats we're in danger,
But the hazard is warse tiv a man its a stranger.
While this hang'd ugly sailing o' packets survives,
We're in very greet danger o' lossing wur lives;
But its ne use to tell the unnumber'd disasters
Which happen to 'prentices, workmen, and masters,
On crossing the Tyne i' them sma' sculler boats,
Or ony thing else on the water that floats.
It ony rate, the Chain Brigg is a far safer plan,
And would seave mony lives—contradict it whe can!
Besides, ye naw Geordy, its easier an' better,
For the canny folks it leves on the banks o' the water,
To walk straight afore them 'stead o' gaun down the street,
And when they're iv a hurry, running down a' they meet;
Forbye being kept meast an hour in suspense
By cairts, that sometimes meak a plague of a fence,
Then the folks is a' stopt—suppose they be iv a hurry.
Now ye blithe lads o' Shields, let it be a' your glory,
To get this Chain Brigg rear'd on high in the air,
Then we'll ne'er hae to soom amang steam boats ne mair:
Smash their greet clumsy wheels, aw like nane o' their wark,
They once coupt me owerboard an' aw was wet to the sark;
But catch me gaun ony mair near them again—
If aw de, say aw divent belang Collingwood Main!!!

POLLOCK, PRINTER, NORTH SHIELDS.

as free as air without any connection with the masonry, and that it must oscillate to and fro, like a pendulum, with every gust of wind. If the platform was to be unconnected with the towers at both ends, it would certainly be liable to be driven on one side by the effects of a hurricane, out of the horizontal position in which it is suspended, and the surface would consequently be, as it were, turned obliquely to the wind; but the thing is quite impossible; for, while the ends of the bridge are secured in the masonry, there can be no pendulous motion. We cannot consider the platform of the Bridge in any other shape than as an immense plane, 40 feet wide, braced by one hundred and seventy- five transverse cast-iron beams and various diagonal trusses in the structure, with an edge only three feet deep. No hurricane that ever blew would bend it edgeways...'.

While it is easy to ridicule the substance of the argument, from both points of view, it is interesting to remember that no serious scientific investigation into an understanding about the effects of wind conditions and turbulent air pockets, such that caused the failure of the American Tacoma

Narrows suspension bridge in 1940, was undertaken, until after that disaster. During the 1930's suspension bridge engineers had come to accept the proportion of 1/30 span for the road width, and a relative depth for platform stiffening of 1/50 - 1/90 span. These proportions, however, had been derived from experience rather than from scientific investigation, and in the case of the Tacoma Bridge the relative proportions had increased to 1/72 and 1/350 respectively. For the Shields Bridge, Brown had adopted the respective proportions of 1/20 and 1/266, but it must be remembered that at that time very little comparative experience existed and the evidence provided by wind tunnels was a century or more away.

Brown continued with his letter to Thomas Wilson, making '...a few observations respecting the undulatory motion. On this subject, Mr. Telford says, that "...the Menai Bridge is not yet completed; but, from what has been observed, there is no reason to apprehend any inconvenience from the horizontal vibrations or the vertical undulations...".'.

The question as to whether the wind blew stronger on the east or west coast of Britain was a point of argument. Brown cited the examples of his Trinity Chain Pier being subject to easterly gales, and the extreme exposure of Union Bridge which received '..sudden gusts of wind..', neither of which indicated the need for '...braces or any other contrivance..' Brighton Chain Pier was also quoted, and the 'raging fury' to which it had been subjected, although admitting that '...the undulation was tremendous... no change whatever had been made in the deflection of the chains..' By openly revealing the tremendous undulation, Brown was demonstrating the strength of the structure under adverse conditions in which the sea '..broke over all the towers..', and the pier survived.

Convincing practical evidence was therefore being offered to the Committee, but it was not yet the end of the matter. Henry Atkinson, a local schoolmaster who was well versed in mathematics, entered into the controversy with a letter that took *Investigator* to task: 'To the Editor of the *Newcastle Chronicle* (Feb. 4th 1826)
"His weapon is misrepresentation, and, armed with that alone, he wages hopeless strife."

Investigator's letter of Jan 14th 1826

'Sir, - It is at all times an unpleasant task to have to expose the errors and misrepresentations of any person; but when that person has assumed the disguise of a fictitious signature, there are additional circumstances which render it still more irksome..'.

Atkinson took great exception to the anonymous attack upon Brown, and although he credited *Investigator* '..to be a person of some talents,... he has some wit, and seems to imagines that he possesses a great deal more... he affects to treat his opponents with contempt and sarcasm; talks about his own "modesty", and the "absurdity and folly" of a gentleman to whom the country is much indebted, and who is as high above him as the heavens are above the earth; and this he calls a style "appropriate to scientific controversy."

After examining the figures quoted by *Investigator*, Atkinson found their accuracy was wanting, but although '...very trifling, ...By these means he has brought out 1358 tons, as the strain of the chains at the points of suspension, instead of 1327.4 tons.' He also reviewed the then current knowledge concerning strength and proving of bar-iron, in relation to available theory. 'Now as the cross section of the 40 chains in the proposed Bridge at Shields contain an area of 250 circular inches, it follows that they might occasionally be exposed to a strain of 12.066 x 250 = 3016.5 tons with perfect safety for a short time, and without injuring them in the slightest degree; consequently, according to *Investigator's* own mode of calculation, he ought to have found that 3016.5 – 1358 ÷ 1.7 = 975 tons, "would be the greatest weight it would be safe to intrust upon the bridge", so long as its strength shall not be impaired or the chains should not be destroyed by wear, etc. he ought to have found that the chains would still safely bear a strain of 241.2 tons; hence, according to his method of computation, 2413.2 – 1358 ÷ 1.7 = 620.7 tons of passing weight would still be safely borne by the bridge which is certainly much more than will ever be on it at any one time. And as the lowest estimate I can find of the permanent load which iron will safely bear, viz, that of Mr. Tredgold, is 17,800lb. to the square inch, the 40 chains will therefore bear a permanent strain of 1560 tons, which is 202 tons more than even *Investigator* says they will ever have to bear. It is therefore plain, that the Bridge is so strong, that, to use Mr. Buchanan's words, the 'breaking of the chains is a contingency which cannot take place by any possible concurrence of accidents". What then, Mr. Editor, are we to think of *Investigator's* expedient of designedly misrepresenting Mr. Buchanan's opinion, and by that means bringing out 124 tons, as "...the greatest weight it would be safe to intrust upon the bridge."

In order to establish the figure of 8 tons per square inch as the safe working load for bar-iron, Atkinson continued with references to experiments that had been made by various eminent engineers and academic authorities.

He ridiculed the suggested wind forces of 49 lbs per square foot by pointing out that '...most women expose a surface of between 5 and 6 feet to the wind ...' which would produce a '...force of between 17½ and 21 stones; a force so much above their weight, that many of them would inevitably be whirled into the air like the leaves in autumn.' The heat of the argument remained intensive with *Investigator* launching into a pernicious attack upon Brown through the columns of the *Tyne Mercury* on January 17 1826. "I think there be six Richmonds in the field- Five" "But Modesty prevents me completing my quotation. Well, then to my new opponent, Capt. Samuel Brown, R.N: - His weapon is misrepresentation, and armed with that alone, he wages hopeless strife." No attempt to establish the true facts about the proposed bridge dimensions or agree the limit of safe loading for bar-iron was being made. Observations and opinions expressed by eminent engineers were being scorned in order to create confusion and mistrust, yet, in the shallows of the analysis *Investigator* was justified in taxing Brown's remark that "...we cannot contemplate the sudden destruction of a bridge of suspension under any circumstances, because admitting the possibility of its being loaded so as to cause some extension of the suspending bars, they would cease to yield the moment the deflection and the strain became equiponderent; it would bear to be loaded down to the water-edge, without being suddenly broken down".

The altercation conducted in the columns of the *Newcastle Chronicle* and *Tyne Mercury* was concluded in a final attack by *Investigator* (*Tyne Mercury* February 14th 1826) upon the competence of his adversaries. In the battle of words the real object of concern had been lost with *Investigator* assuming a conscious superiority in his final paragraph. "...I shall conclude by giving my doughty opponent a piece of advice which I hope may be of service to him, and this is surely a most courteous return for all the abuse he has lavished upon me (reference to 'correspondent' *Newcastle Chronicle* Feb 4th 1826.) Let him for the future stick to his proper vocation, and avoid the field of controversy. His arguments are often very ingenious, but unfortunately, when properly applied, they generally make against himself. It is said that pigs are excellent swimmers, only that they cut their own throats in the process. If our champion should ever again think of entering the field, let him remember the pigs, and stay at home."

'...Owing to the agitated state of the country.' application to Parliament by the Committee of Management for the necessary enabling Act during the 1826 Session was abandoned. T.W.Beaumont M.P. was strongly in favour of the project, and doubled his share subscription, but just as the bridge project idea had aroused fervent protagonists, and generated into near reality, so it was that for diverse and not technical reasons it was forgotten.

Opponents of the Bridge may well have been encouraged by an awakening letter addressed to the *Newcastle Courant* by the Duke of Newcastle (December 17th 1825), that was obliquely aimed at drawing the attention of the City of Newcastle to yet another threat upon the River Tyne, which provided '..a principal part of their revenuc.'. The Duke cited the 'great man' of refuse from lead mining and lime kilns that was being dumped in the river causing '... mischief to the navigator ...' and pointed out that if the projected rail road between Carlisle and Newcastle should be realized, that the commercial benefits that may be derived were dependent upon the river being deep and clear.

General fear as to the possible consequences of a Shields Bridge by some commercial interests had probably provided the opposition, and Brown must have been bitterly disappointed about the harassment upon his reputation, as much as the abandonment of the project. He doubtless gathered some consolation from the fact that had the bridge been really wanted the 'trifling' differences in figures and methods of computation that became the subject of argument were well within his capacity to resolve.

For the purpose of building a suspension bridge over the River Esk Colonel James Wilson of Sneaton Castle brought Samuel Brown to Yorkshire. The bridge was to be '...close to the high side of Ruswarp Flour Mill...' some 2¼ miles by road and up river from Whitby bridge. Reference to the bridge is made in the Whitby Repository for 1825, as being built by James Wilson to provide a direct road between his home Sneaton Castle, and the estate at Sneaton to overcome the problem of Ruswarp ford.

Brown designed and supplied the iron-work for the bridge which was transported from his London works by Robert Holmes in his Ship 'Ruby'. An Agreement for '...doing the timberworks at Ruswarp Bridge...' between James Wilson and 'Mrs William Clegram of New Shoreham in the County of Sussex' exists, and describes the work that was to be done, '..for and on the part of Samuel Brown Esquire a Commander in the Royal Navy now resident in Golden Square London...' dated January 3rd 1825. The document is of interest for the information it contains and also as the only discovered example of a contract between Samuel Brown, client, and one of his sub-contract agents. Brown was to be paid £160 '...over and above the original Sum of...' £280 '..for building the said Bridge on consideration that said Samuel Brown, do complete the said Bridge including all materials Labour Etc, etc, in manner following that is to say:

> To find, fix and properly fasten the Bridge way Beams, to be twenty one in number twelve
> Inches in depth and five inches in thickness cut from Memel Timber, without sap,
> To find, fix and properly fasten the Deck of the Bridge to be one hundred and four feet in

length, fifteen feet in width more or less as may be found necessary and three inches in thickness the deals to be cut from the best American Red pine without sap.

To find, and properly fix and fasten the Iron sides, to be 7/8 of an Inch in thickness and deep enough to cover the bottom of the Suspending Rod. Gib etc. to have a three Inch wooden Moulding along each side, as shewn in the Drawing No. 4.

To find, fix and properly fasten a Cast Iron fence on each side of the said Bridge as shewn in the Drawing No. 3 - and to hang the Gates (which are to be found by Mr. Wilson.

To cut a door way in one of the standards, for the purpose of hanging the small Gate to for the foot path.'

As the Agreement was '..for completing the Bridge over the Esk..' it is evident that the primary structure existed at the close of the year 1824, and that during the summer and autumn months of that year it must have been designed, manufactured and erected.

A delightful wood engraving (E.S. 4 1/16" x 6 15/16" within a marginal border - I. Bird, delt. W.Cave, Sculpt.) illustrates the essential character of the Bridge. It can be seen that the catenary chains pass over individual towers, the shape of which suggests that they were made of cast iron; little else is accurately distinguishable.The view is upstream from the Bridge, with Ruswarp Mill on the West left river bank.

On Sunday July 13th 1828 the River Esk rose in full spate and destroyed the bridge. The flood water enveloped the platform by some two or three feet, and in recording the event the *Whitby Panorama* for August 1828 mentioned the point that '..some old persons predicted when it was built, that a flood might come of sufficient height to reach it...' Like the Tweed, the Esk was a turbulent river that was well known for its flooding characteristics, but on that particular occasion it '...was swoln

Fig 38 - Engraving: Suspension Bridge over the River Esk to the Lordship of Sneaton; W Cave

to a greater height than it had attained for many years, ...At the Bridge, the waters not only rushed through the arch in a mighty current, but overflowed the banks on each side; the south bank presenting the appearance of a broad river flowing over the low ground towards Waterloo Place; while another torrent, on the Ruswarp side, rushed along the road in front of the Mill, to the opening of Mrs. Earnshaw's garden, where for several hours there was no passage. As the waters rose, the pressure on the bridge became more and more violent, especially as the hay and brush wood, brought down by the stream, in some degree choked up the small space between the surface of the water, and the under part of the bridge; and at length the fury of the torrent became irresistible, the strong iron chain at the south-west angle, where the force of the flood was particularly felt, was torn asunder, in consequence of which the platform at that corner sunk into the water, and the opposite side rising up, a larger surface became exposed to the impetus of the torrent, while one chain only was left to resist it: hence, in a few minutes, that also gave way, and the platform, being disengaged at the south end, swung round to the Ruswarp side, where it remained suspended by the chains at the north end. The latter, though violently strained, did not break, but were torn down from the pillars on which they rested; one of the latter with the iron gate attached, was thrown over into the water, along with the parapet wall; while the upper part of the other pillar, and of the iron gate which it bore, was violently broken off. One of the pillars at the opposite end was also thrown down, and some damage was done to the toll-collector's lodge, the inmates of which were for a time in the most perilous condition.'

In view of the fact that the site of Union Bridge was changed to give a judiciously clear distance between the platform and the possible high flood water level, it may seem unlike the meticulous mind of Brown not to have applied the lesson to Ruswarp. The circumstances were, however, extreme, and in all probability the proposed bridge level was discussed in relation to flood levels and decisions taken, albeit they were wrong.

In any event there is no record that Brown was held to be liable for the loss, for Ruswarp was only one of many, including '..The handsome county bridge at East Row..' that were swept away on that July Sunday.

James Wilson ordered '..the immediate restoration of a fabric so useful and so ornamental..', with much of the original ironwork used in conjunction with new iron supplied by a local ironworker, George Chapman.

The river finally won, when during the great flood of October 28th 1880 the bridge was swept away and not replaced.

1825 was a busy year for Brown with many inquiries about costs of bridges for a variety of situations, all either north of the river Tweed, or near its source in the Lowther Hills. These approaches may have resulted from the influence of Brown's marriage to Mary Hume in 1822; daughter of John Hume W.S. an Edinburgh lawyer through whose office a considerable amount of correspondence then flowed for his son-in-law.

The general process was for one of Brown's foremen to survey possible sites, propose a scheme, and, after acceptance, to supply the necessary metalwork which local tradesmen would erect, including the associated piers of masonry and timber deckwork.

The simplicity of acquiring a suspension bridge by a 'mail-order' system provided a cheap, effective and speedy solution to otherwise expensive answers. It was therefore novel and attractive. Once the span, deck width, loading and other site conditions were known, the proposed scheme was put on paper, and while the piers and anchorages were being built the metalwork was pre-fabricated and despatched to its destination by means of canal barge, ship and cart.

On April 2nd 1825, Brown wrote to John Hume in reply to questions from a Mr Crichton '., as to a bridge over the Nith Dumphries - I may say in general terms that the Bridge for 2 carriages to pass at once would cost about £4000 and for one row of carriages £3200..'

In this letter Brown also mentioned that he had contracted to build a bridge over the Tyne -'., of somewhat larger dimensions mentioned in Mr Crichton's letter for £4500. The road or platform 20 feet wide, the carriageway suspended with wrought iron plates - the beams and platform timber ..'. This may have been for a crossing of Tyne Water at East Linton on the route of the Great North Road through the Lothians, very near to Phantassie, the birthplace of John Rennie. There is no evidence that the bridges were ever built.

Sometime before September 1825, the Duke of Buccleuch's chamberlain sent Samuel Brown, through Mr John Hume, a description of the River Annan for a proposed chain bridge between Lockerbie and Lochinalon. In consequence, Brown's foreman James Slight set off and wrote him two letters on September 16th and 17th 1825, reporting upon his survey of likely sites for bridges over the Annan and Dryfe in the Borders area of Annandale. It was with the object of forming a direct line of communication between Lockerbie and Lockinalon. Mr Slight received local instructions from a Mr Douglas '...to make such a survey with levels, borings of the river and the points laid down as would enable you to give them a plan of the River between the two lines of Road, with a Report as to your opinion of the most adviseable site for a bridge, keeping in view that the River is very liable to change its bed, and at the same time Plans of Bridges for both lines with estimates of their separate expense independant of Road making except the Roadway of the Bridges and approaches. From this data and from what they themselves know of the expense of forming the roads the Trustees will determine upon the line to be followed..'. Mr Slight pointed out that making a new road line would enable crossing the Annan with a 300 foot span bridge, but that a road line higher up the river at the junction between the Annan and Dryfe would mean two bridges: '... The Annan upon this line may be crossed with one of about 100 feet, on this line the roads are already made. The ground in all cases is gravel through which I bored to the depth of 25 feet without meeting any change but I have reason to expect firm clay at a little lower ...'. There ended the Annan and Dryfe story.

While speculations for bridge contracts north of the Border were still in a state of flux, the contract for a bridge at Welney Norfolk was secured and under way by September 1825.

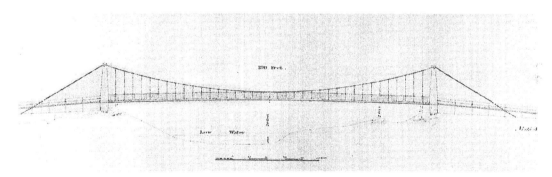

Fig 39 - Engraving:View of a Bridge of Suspension at Welney, Norfolk

The Rev William Gale Townley of Beaupre Hall, Outwell, Norfolk obtained a Lease and covenants from the Bedford Level Corporation to build a suspension bridge over the Hundred Feet River. In a letter of September 20th 1825 to Samuel Brown he mentioned leaving instructions for Mr Lenox, who had arrived in London from Wales, to inform him in '... which state the Iron for the Welney Bridge is..', and expressed the hope that Brown had '., arranged everything with Mr Thomas for its being ready by the time fixed as well as for its conveyance to the spot .. I know not whether you have contracted for the joists and timber of the Bridge with Mr Swansborough, this however I shall know on my arrival at home...'.

Gale Townley had, evidently, been to Paxton House by the Tweed, for, in reference to the toll gates for Welney, said '....I should wish the iron gate to be very stout and the spikes of such a nature as to prevent anyone climbing over – the Gate at Paxton would afford little opposition to an agile Fen man, indeed a Highland Bullock would make very light of it..'. Townley wrote again to Brown on the 26th, letting him know that after a meeting on site with Mr Swansborough the contractor, he believed that '.. in less than three weeks everything will be ready for the Bridge..'.

Townley was getting very anxious about the bridge completion date, and wrote to ask about the possibility of finishing the work in 3 months. '... Do they hurry the Iron People in South Wales..', and in a concluding quip '.. I find the flooring of the Menai Bridge is to be supported on a light Iron Frame work - at Liverpool they talk much of the Bridge over the Mersey, you must do this for them, I think you will not be seven years in completing it..'.

Productive capacity of the Newbridge works was at its limits with the manufacture of ironwork for Tierney Clark's Hammersmith Bridge, when Brown asked Philip Thomas if he could have a pair of Iron Gates made for Mr Townley's Bridge, which met with a firm no, '.. unless we stop the Hammersmith Bridge.'. Thomas was exasperated and continued in his letter of September 28th 1825 to say '.. nor have we men fit for such a purpose excepting those so employed, the persons at Cardiff that made the lamp iron for you has left the place and no one there but Bill the Iron Founder to make them if indeed he can do so but if made by him would last your men that if done in London..'.

In disapproving of a single 14 foot gate Thomas concluded the matter, '. I think it will be your better plan to have them gates made in London.', and in reference to Welney, '…the Wrought Iron work for this Bridge will be finished in a few days ... I am anxious to get on with the Hammersmith Bridge work what will be long enough in hand without being interrupted by other work and what we are not properly prepared for. I will ship the Townley wrot Iron work to London by the first opportunity..', and that was that.

Townley's anxiety about the iron work was a little premature, as work on site was in its early stages, about which Mr Swansborough reported to Brown in Edinburgh from Wisbech on October 6th 1825.

> '..I am sorry I have not been able to answer your letter sooner - I have not yet sunk the pits for the fastenings of the chains, but a letter of the 24th of August from your Mr Slight directs that the centre of the Plate should be at a horizontal distance of 51 feet from the respective Pillars, and 22 ft.6 in under the level of the Roadway or surface of the Masonry - this will give to the Back stay Chains an Angle of about 40° with the horizontal instead of 30° which I think you at first proposed - and I conceive you may have made this alteration with the view of bettering the approach on the South Side - but as I think this is still attended with some difficulties, I have drawn a plan of that side, that you have them all before you, you will observe that by passing round the Chains on this side, the Road will be driven a considerable distance from the back slope of the Bank, and instead of one defence (by Rails or Wale) to the side, it will require two besides taking double the quantity or Earth, as the Ground a t a distance from the foot of the Bank is very low and swampy - The Corporation Toll Gate at the back of the Public House, is also so near, that the descent to it will be very steep - I have thought it incumbent upon me to apprize you of these matters, and shall be ready to adopt your directions with regard to them - The Piers on the South Side are nearly level with the top of the Bank and those on the North side will be as high

by Tuesday next - I expect the Stone for the upper part, from Yorkshire (where it has been wrought ready for setting) in a few days - and trust by the time of the arrival of the Iron Work we shall be ready for the fixing - The Piling has been a most heavy job but ensures us a good Foundation - You will excuse my asking again whether the size of the brickwork for the moorings 5ft. 0 long 4.0 deep and 2 feet thick is correct - and whether I need build them before the Iron Plates arrive - I shall be glad of a little money.'

In response, Brown had not completely appreciated Swansborough's dilemma, and a further explanation of the problem was sent on October 20th:

'Either I do not understand your sketch for the South Approach, or you have in endeavouring to give greater headway under the Chains forgetting the obstacle that one of your Walls (the West-side) would present to Carriages coming from Ely - As I am sure you will excuse me if I am in error - I shall be free to offer my reasons against the Plan - and first, as I have stated, is its obstruction to the approach at the West Angle of the Bridge - secondly - I apprehend the Brickwork of those Abutments would not stand without they were carried up from the solid ground - What objection would there be to continue the back stay Chains at the Angle you have given in your Sketch to the upper part - down to the ground.

The Moorings would then be within the Garden - and as it appears to me would best answer the purpose and at much the least expense - as the same height for carriages would be preserved without the incumbrance of the Walls - and would keep the Road where it will be most easily made and maintained - at the foot of the Bank - but by reference to the Plan I sent you last, you will see there is still some little difficulty to

Fig 40 - Engraving: Bridge of Suspension erected at Welney, Norfolk; J H West

overcome at the opposite side - I mean the South East Angle; on account of the Toll Gate behind the Public House which is so near the Bridge that I am afraid it would be a very steep Ascent from that side - and I see no way of surmounting this difficulty but turning the Road from this Gate round the Foot of the Chains into the Road from Ely at the South West Angle or what would be much better - by bringing the Gate from its present situation to the Front of the House, and I can see no objection to this last measure, but that it would require the consent of the Bedford Level Corporation - If you do not greatly prefer the Road passing between the Chains (which I admit is the best way of approach, but in this case, would require a much longer quantity of Earth to construct the Road - and 2 defences to the sides instead of 1) I think the lengthening of the Back-Stays as I have suggested would answer the purpose - I shall be happy to give any further explanations if necessary.

I hope you will not forget my application for some money - and I shall be glad to have your decision respecting the South Side as soon as possible - I want to get on with Earth - Work.'.

This was followed on November 4th with further explanation and a section showing the effect of the proposed extended length of Back Chain to permit headroom of 15 feet between it and the raised road levels, which was adopted in the final design together with the inclusion of a retaining wall for the raised road approach.

'Absence from home has prevented my replying to your last letter before now - which I much regret, as I fear it will delay the business - On the other side I have drawn a Section of the South Approach, by which you will see the back Stay Chains will require to be 90 feet long from the centre of the Pillar to the surface of the Ground - how far they should be underneath I leave to you. I still think it will be the best mode to approach the Bridge from the West under the Chains and if you think 15 feet height enough, it may be done as I have drawn it - I think it will be an advantage to have the Chains enter the Ground off the Public highway, as they will be more secure from mischief - I don't seem to have made myself clearly understood in my last - I certainly did not mean to say (if I did) that " it would require more embankment and 2 Rails instead of one if the Road passed under the Chains " -but if it passed round them - As I think the Corporation will rebuild the Public House when the Bridge is complete, perhaps it does not much signify about the approach from the East - but if the House remains as it is - it would be difficult to go under the Chains on that side on account of the steepness of the Road caused by the proximity of the Toll Gate at the back of the House, see my plan, and indeed by the House itself - as the Door on that side will not admit of the Slope of the Road being extended beyond the Toll Gate to the Eastward and it was with the view of avoiding this difficulty that I proposed to bring the Road in Front of the House - However if that is objected to by the Corporation (which Mr Townley thinks would not) I now think it might be managed by descending from our eastern approach some distance before we arrive at the Chains, and thus pass under them upon the level of the present Road - A -
I hope you will understand me - and a reference to my former plan of the South Side will I think make this clear - I should be glad to have your final directions upon these points, as I much wish to proceed with the South approach - the North one cannot I conceive be done before the Bridge is in a more forward state.

The Piers are up to where the Stone courses begin, and I expect the Stone daily as it has been shipped some time - I hope you will forward the Iron Work - Enclosed have sent a Bill for your acceptance, which you will please to return. '.

The last, discovered, letter from Mr Swansborough of November 17th 1825 concludes the matter, and the whole correspondence well illustrates the problems which Brown's method of selling bridges attracted:

'Your Bill came duly to hand - By referring to my last letter you will find that I suggested that the back Stays on the South Side might be continued underground at the same Angle as above, which I then thought would readily get rid of the Stone Blocks (yes) but on looking again at my dimensions I find that the whole extent of ground (in their direction) from the back of the Pillars to the outer ditch of the Garden leased to Mr Townley is only 96ft. 6in, and consequently the Mooring must be kept within that Limit - this will render it necessary to adopt your plan of bending the Chains at their entrance into the Ground, and perhaps building a small piece of Breast Wall for them to bear against - I cannot give you a more exact length of the Chains than my last Section will furnish, and if you extend the horizontal distance from the back of the Pillars to 96ft . 6in you will have all I can furnish you with, on this point.

Ps. The Stone has not yet arrived -'.

The bridge was completed in 1826 according to Mr Swansborough's suggestion for the south side retained road approach, which can be seen in the copy of a contemporary print, and survived for 100 years.

A description of the bridge structure by W Watson 'Historical Account of Wisbech' 1827 gives all the important details.

> 'The bridge is one hundred and ninety feet long, and in breadth fourteen feet; the platform or road of the bridge springs two feet in the centre and five feet six inches above the general level of the bank, with a neat iron railing five feet high, and a three feet walk on each side for foot passengers. The bridge is supported by four principle suspending chains, driven twelve feet into the ground, rivetted end to end, and properly secured by coupling plates and bolts of proportional strength with proper circular suspenders supporting the lower bars on which the beams of the bridge rest; the suspension rods are of different length, being nineteen in number on each side. The foundation of the structure consists of sixteen strong piles of timber to each of the two piers, driven twenty one feet in the solid bed of gravel. A large iron plate, fixed twelve feet in the ground, forms a sort of bed, called the anchor, through which the chains run, and to which they are fastened. The piers of the brickwork are twelve feet high, and the cast iron piers twenty one feet making in all thirty three feet from the foundation to the top of the pier'

Suspension bridges had fired both public and authoritative imagination, also Gale Townley, whose awareness of events was considerable, and the completion of Brunel's Menai Bridge was just four months away; seven years after its commencement. Brown's ideas and methods had made that great project possible, as was succinctly put by C S Drewry (*A Memoir on Suspension Bridges - 1832*) '..The plan originally proposed had been the same as that for Runcorn Bridge (Mersey) viz. to make iron cables of small bars welded together and bound up in a bundle. This, however, was laid aside, and the chains were ultimately made as the plan brought forward by Captain Brown, viz. of straight bars, united by coupling bolts.'.

Telford's Conway Bridge similarly benefited from the adoption of the flat eye-bar link principle; also completed in 1826.

Brown's role in supplying iron-work for Menai may have been greater than hitherto believed, as in correspondence with Brown, William Chisholm wrote to him on April 6th 1830 about Clifton Bridge subscription matters, and concluded with the following sentence: '.. I was glad to hear from Mr Hume that you had nearly completed the repairs of the Bridge and that Mr Telford was well disposed on the subject of the accident.'..

Sometime during 1825 Robert Stevenson introduced Brown to one of the Seguin Brothers who had been appointed engineers for the Bridge of Suspension over the Rhone. In 1823, Messrs Seguin, of Annonay, suggested cable suspension methods to the French Government for a bridge of 278 feet span at Tournon over the Rhone, which was accepted, started in 1824, and opened during August 1825. Its success established the 'cable of Wires' method for suspension as a principle. In similar vein the French Government had sent M. Navier, Ingenieur en chef des Ponus et Chaussees. to England, with the object of gathering information from our engineers and their examples. Although the French interest was primarily in the use of wire cables and forming their ground anchorages over masonry pedestals to change the final direction vertically, there was still much to be learned. Brown had put forward the idea of changing the direction angle of back stays to ground anchorages in his 1817 patent for a one thousand foot span bridge, and Navier was to use Brown's flat eye-bar link method for his ill-fated bridge over the Seine, opposite the Hotel des Invalides. In that case it was a weakness of the foundation design which was exposed by a water main bursting nearby that caused failure, rather than the principle; it was pulled down and replaced in 1829 with a bridge very similar to that of Tierney Clark's Hammersmith.

It is of interest to note that French Government policy towards the subject of public works was entirely different from the British approach. By the middle of the 18th century France had recognised and established the need for sound mathematical understanding-and appreciation of the behaviour of materials which gave rise to the founding of the Ecole des Ponts et Chaussees in 1747. In Britain, the pace of practical industrial progress was directly related to the powers of imaginative individuals for whom commercial patronage was abundant: the government simply adjudicated in terms of Bills put to them which they either turned down or granted enabling Acts as appropriate and necessary. Within this framework Brown's practical approach in the development and use of ironwork satisfied both his creative and financial ambitions.

During all the activity, Brown's attention was drawn by the civil engineer Habberley Price who was concerned with the mail coach communication with Ireland by way of Milford Haven, the direct route of which faced crossing the rivers Severn and Wye. Two Ferries crossed the Severn near Chepstow, the Old Passage Ferry from Beachley to Aust, and the New Passage Ferry a few miles miles downriver from the Old Passage which resulted in some competition.

Beachley was at the tip of the land spit which separated the mouth of the Wye from the Severn, and the Ferry Association considered that a suspension bridge spanning the Wye at that point would overcome the distance from Beachley on the eastern bank of the Wye, through Chepstow to Crick. Brown had entered the field of discussion through correspondence with Mr Price by October 11th 1825, and on the 15th received a sketch '.., to give you an idea of the form of the ground where the bridge might be erected. I have sketched roughly on the opposite side my notions of the section of the Bank of the River at that point, the only part as yet measured is the distance across at high water; and if you can without giving yourself much trouble favour me with the sort of information I have described I shall feel obliged..'

Mr Price was seeking an approximate estimate of cost for the metalwork and platform '...within one or two thousand pounds.... and if found to be beyond the reach of the Association ... the probability is they will abandon the idea for the present, and proceed with a fly bridge, or even take an improved line to Chepstow and cross over the present bridge which is only about 2½ miles round ...'. Mr Price concluded the letter with an admiring reference to Brown's plan for the Tyne (Shields) bridge proposal.

In 1826 a Select Committee of the House of Commons considered the whole problem, which was set out in a booklet '.. The Improved Old Passage Ferry from Aust to Beachley near Chepstow, the most eligible point for the Milford Mail to cross the Severn '. Of the many improvements mentioned was a suggestion to improve the route from Beachley to Crick. by '.. constructing of a suspension Bridge over the river Wye near its mouth which is considered practicable by Mr Telford, Mr Nimmo and Mr Price but which perhaps be objectionable on account of the expense '.

Neither suspension or fly bridges were proceeded with, a decision which may have been influenced by the erection of John Rennie's cast iron bridge at Chepstow in 1816. The Ferries and the road to Crick through Chepstow remained operative until the opening of the Severn Suspension Bridge on September 8th 1966 to the design of Freeman Fox & Partners with a main span of 3240 feet.

Brown's 'Warden' bridge over the River Tyne at West Boat, Hexham was built, and enjoyed some seventy years of existence until 1903, when it was replaced with a stone arch bridge by Northumberland County Council. Little is known about its history other than it was erected in 1826 as a Toll Bridge of 310 feet span, and very similar to the Union Bridge with two tiers of twin round bar eye linked chains each side, but with the suspension rods secured by means of a coupled drop link at the shackle joints, almost identical to those surviving at Kalemouth, instead of the saddle method at Union and Brighton.

Fig 41 - Bridge over the River South Tyne at West Boat, Warden, Hexham

Broughton Suspension Bridge over the River Irwell by Broughton and Pendleton (Manchester) was opened in 1826, with a span of 144ft and 18ft roadway, paid for by John Fitzgerald, owner of Irwell Castle. Although attributed to Samuel Brown it is more likely to have been the work of Thomas Cheek Hewe, a local millwright.

The *Philosophical Magazine* 1831, pp 387-9 reported its collapse on April 12th 1831 resulting from 74 troops marching four abreast causing the failure of a bolt in one of the stay chains attached to the masonry of the ground anchor which, according to the report had been badly forged. With Samuel Brown's reputation for high quality iron and forging it seems unlikely that his firm manufactured the components.

The Bridge was repaired and used for a further 90 years until its replacement in 1924 with a Pratt Truss footbridge briefly mentioned in the *Manchester Guardian* on April 3rd 1924.

The reasons for the Broughton Bridge failure had more serious consequences in France on April 16th 1850 when a battalion of marching troops crossing the Angers Suspension bridge over the River Maine had added to the already swaying bridge influenced by a strong wind with considerable loss of life.

For some years after public confidence in suspension bridges faded.

On July 18th, 1829, the foundation stone of Brown's suspension bridge over the River Tees was laid for the continuation of the Stockton and Darlington Railway. Philip Thomas wrote to Brown from Newbridge Works on June 30th, 1830 confirming the receipt of plans for the Clifton Bridge competition and other related matters and, in reply to a letter from Brown, about delivery of the Stockton Bridge, stated that '..the additional work is now in hand and shall be forwarded without the least delay it shall be sent either by sea or canal in about 10 days..'

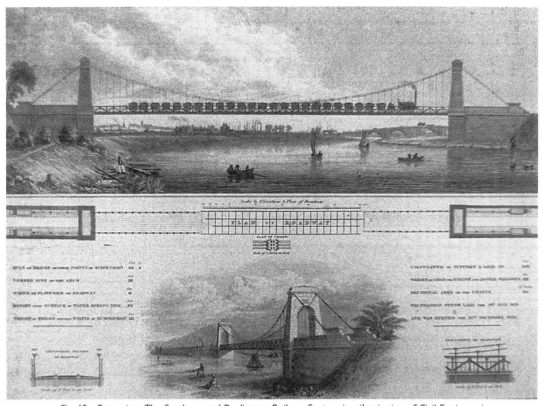

Fig 42 - Engraving: The Stockton and Darlington Railway Suspension (Institution of Civil Engineers)

It was a daring piece of work which was opened on December 27th 1830, but from the very beginning its unsuitability was recognised, and it only remained in existence for twelve years. Early in December, experiments were made to test the stability of the bridge. The first of these took place on the 9th, when a weight of 18 tons 1 cwt was placed on the centre of the bridge which resulted in a deflection of $9^{3}/_{16}$". This was followed on the 13th with 28 waggons weighing 37 tons which were drawn over the bridge by an engine and tender weighing 8 tons that produced a depression of $5^{8}/_{10}$". A further experiment with 16 waggons weighing 66 tons 12 cwts caused the masonry of both towers to be affected, and two cast iron retaining plates split. Other experiments were made to determine 'the best mode of distributing the weight which might prudently be taken across the bridge', with the result that four waggons connected together by means of chains with couplings which kept them nine yards apart was the considered limit. 'The failure of the bridge was a great disappointment to the Company, who had been led to believe it could support a weight of 150 tons. This was probably the first time that Brown experienced the reality of his structures being subject to loadings that he claimed they would safely take and it must have been a nasty shock.

In many ways it could be regarded as Brown's folly but it was the first time that a suspension bridge had been designed and constructed to carry a railway, and the riding effects of the rolling load transmitted through the rails to the platform was a condition that few engineers of the time would have appreciated. Brown had at least recognised the need for platform stiffness by providing a substantial diagonally-braced balustrade, but it was totally inadequate in restraining the wave motion that was induced in the track ahead of the locomotive. As a road bridge, it would have been admirable, having a span of 281 feet 4 inches, a versed sine of 28 feet, and main chains arranged in two tiers of triple circular section iron eye-bolts linked with shackles and bolt pins in the typical Brown manner. Suspension rods were bolt coupled to eyed links similar to those that were later used at Kalemouth.

The bridge was calculated to support a load of 150 tons uniformly, but anything like this weight acting as a moving point load introduced a different set of conditions. Given the particular loading circumstances and experiments that had been made in earlier years about the behaviour of catenarian cables and their shape distortion when subject to variable loading, it is surprising that Brown had not foreseen the likely problem. 1830,

Fig 43 - Engraving:The Stockton and Darlington Railway Suspension Bridge, (Institution of Civil Engineers)

however,saw the birth of railways in the true commercial sense with the opening of the Liverpool and Manchester Line. From this time, demands for increased speed and general improvements attracted greater locomotive and rolling stock weight. Until the locomotive trials at Rainhill in October 1829, the Directors of railways had been convinced that coal waggons were best hauled by horses. From the trials, George Stephenson's 'Rocket' emerged as an unimagined success, and the Liverpool and Manchester Line's future was thus assured. Before this event, the Directors had grudgingly accepted the use of standing steam engines for steep gradient hauls, but were at least open to be otherwise convinced: hence the trials. From 1822, when George Stephenson was appointed constructional engineer to the Stockton & Darlington Railway, he determined to shed the promoters idea of horse drawn waggons in favour of steam locomotion, This was accomplished in 1825, with the advent of his well known 'No 1 Locomotion'.

The purpose of the Stockton & Darlington Railway was to link the output from the collieries of the West Auckland District with Stockton and Darlington. Plans for a canal had been proposed by John Rennie and others, and there were arguments about the merits of railways and tramroads. All the diverse schemes and discussions occurred before 1800, but from 1816 onwards the positive idea for a railway strengthened, and in 1822 a 'committee' made the decision to use steam locomotives, and the Stockton & Darlington Railway was officially opened on September 27th 1825. At that time no commercial gain was envisaged for the export of coal, but in 1827 the situation changed when it was decided to extend the line over the River Tees to Middlesbrough and thereby obtain shipping facilities. Securing the necessary rights and purchase of land proved difficult, which delayed an early start of the project. The Tees Navigation Company would not accept the temporary obstruction of the river channel for the purpose of constructing bridge arches, which no doubt led the Directors to the idea of a suspension type bridge, for which Samuel Brown secured a contract in 1828 in the sum of £2,200. Land costs were another obstacle.The agents of the Bishop of Durham demanded £5073. 9s 3d. for the 6 acres 1 rood 26 perches of land required near Stockton which, after objection and an inquistion was reduced to £2000. All the problems were overcome and the formal opening of the bridge was a great occasion. The locomotive 'Globe' was specially designed by Timothy Hackworth with a four coupled wooden wheel arrangement which hauled waggons fitted with seats for passengers.

Those early four coupled locomotives were below 10 tons in weight, which was an important consideration in relation to the load that the cast iron track could support. This particular problem had been recognised by John Birkinshaw of Bedlington who in 1820 manufactured and patented the first malleable iron rails in lengths of 16 feet. Primitive as the situation was in 1825, railway engineers were a new and energetic breed, and by 1840 six coupled locomotives following the pattern set by Stephenson's 'North Star' of 18¾ tons weight entered the scene in 1837, and became an established type throughout the steam age.

These events were part of the progressive surge, that made keeping pace with developments an almost impossible task, and Stockton Bridge had come into being at a time when railways were rushing into a new dimension, which was not Brown's concern in 1829. The photographs shown are taken from a bcontemporary print at the Institution of Civil Engineers. Charles Stewart Drewry dedicated his *Memoirs on Suspension Bridges* (1832) to Samuel Brown 'By His Obliged Friend', and although he ignored mention of the Darlington Bridge, it is surprising that he did not take the opportunity of discussing the lessons that had been learned, unless he considered the subject painful for Brown.

The idea of using suspension bridges for carrying railways over rivers may not have been Brown's, as in the closing months of 1825 Robert Stevenson wrote to him '... I am to propose Chain Bridges across the Esk and Tyne in the line of the proposed East Lothian Railway. Will you therefore be so good as to get ready a survey made as to satisfy your self of the extent and quote in one (sense) the expense. Mr Slight can have access to the surveys made - but would still require to see the places perhaps. Should we get the bridge to do we will deduct your charges for personal trouble '.

The proposals were for taking the railway over the rivers Esk near Inveresk and Tyne at East Linton. As mentioned later, Brown claimed to have secured the contract for a road suspension bridge over the Tyne in April of that year, so the territory was not new to him. Stevenson received letters in reply on December 9th and 20th with estimates for the railway bridges, which were acknowledged on the 26th, with mention that the information would be contained in his Report on the subject. There the matter ended, and the railway did not get its suspension bridges. The seeds were sown, however, which resulted in the crossing of the Tees for the Stockton and Darlington Railway in 1830 which enjoyed a short and unsuccessful life, and apart from John A Roebling's crossing of Niagara for the railway in 1855, the principle of the method for that purpose was never again repeated.

The 'for and against' feeling in respect of railway development was really confined to the interests of commercial and industrial people, in which the attitude of landowners was very variable, but the mood of the nation was fired after the years of war which had plunged the country into a period of depression and unrest in the opening decades of the century. Thus, the opportunities for 'speculation' by all branches of society, with cash to spare or gamble, attracted a fascinated public.

By the end of 1829 Reports had been published by the respective engineers responsible for tie Liverpool and Manchester Railway, and subsequent 'Experiments' by Robert Stephenson and Joseph Locke, but a strong lobby of disapproval and concern was ever present. Just as 'Investigator' had battled with Samuel Brown over the Shields Bridge project, so did another 'Investigator' emerge in reply to the proposed Railway between Birmingham and London, entitled 'Beware the Bubbles'

'A strong tendency to speculate and embark in all manner of new projects is the principle which has given to England so many mechanical and commercial advantages for all the nations of the world; but just in proportion as this power is great and elastic, it calls the more for regulation, because without that, the very energy which does good would just as certainly do harm. There are abundant proofs of the necessity of this regulation, in all periods of our modern history, but more especially in that uncontrolled exercise of the spirit of speculation, which, in 1825 and 1826, brought about so fatal a crisis, involved so many in ruin, and enabled mere projectors, and their attorneys and other assistants, to put into their private pockets thousands, aye, millions of money; which, had the public mind been in a state of sober watchfulness, might have quietly been applied to an extension of the productive industry of the country, and thereby much of the distress which has since been felt might have been avoided '.

Such was the cynical, yet near truth, view of 'Investigator' in the climate of change, which did notarrest the experiments and successes of engineers like Samuel Brown and his mechanically minded counterparts in their respective enterprise and tenacity. Philip Thomas, in a June 1830 letter to Brown, also mentioned as a follow-on about the delivery of the Stockton Bridge'.. from this time the Soham Bridge is just forwarded and shall be shipped to London by the first Schooner that sail..' Soham is in the same Fenland area as Welney, and the bridge referred to is, apparently, Middle (or Middle Fen) Bridge between Ely and Stuntney on the Ely to Soham road, over the Middle Fen drain. The Cambridgeshire County Records Office has no reference to the iron suspension bridge ever having been built, but among the records of the Isle of Ely Quarter Sessions are documents relating to liability for maintaining the bridge and its unsafe condition, 1825-30. This, at least, suggests that an existing bridge needed replacement, but an Agreement was eventually reached, in 1827, between the Bedford Level Corporation, the County Justices, the Commissioners of Soham or Middle Fen District, and the Justices of Turnpike Roads for building a new bridge, which, according to the Agreement, was to be of '.. Good sound bricks and well tempered mortar and other proper materials.' A minute of the Special Sessions of the Justices of July 12th 1830 relating to payment of costs of litigation does, however, refer to it as '.a new iron bridge.' Could it be that the Trustees had a last minute change of mind in favour of a masonry structure, and faced a claim for costs?

Other than Union Bridge, Samuel Brown's suspension bridge over the River Teviot at Kalemouth Roxburghshire still exists without any design changes. By comparison the

Fig 44 - Kalemouth Suspension Bridge

example is small, 160 feet span and 14 feet overall width. It came into being through the desire of William Mein of Ormiston, who, according to Jeffrey the historian of Roxburghshire, '...greatly improved the lands, built a new house, and erected at his own expense, for the accommodation of the public, a suspension bridge, for carriages over the Teviot at Kalemouth...'

In most respects the bridge is very typically Brown, except for two features. It has every other suspension rod connected at the centre of each chain link bar by means of a bolted clamp attachment, in addition to the main coupled points of connection with the ends of bar links. From a design point of view this seems wrong, but is sound, and probably resulted from Brown's dedication to the use of long chain eye bars (which in this case are 10 feet) arranged as a single chain unit of twin-coupled bars each side. The platform suspension rods obviously needed to be spaced closer than 10 feet, and by simply engaging an intermediate rod a convenient and sensible solution to the problem resulted. The connection of the eye-bar links is an interesting feature, with the linking eyes formed exactly like those of Union Bridge and Brighton Chain Pier, but at that point the similarity ends. For this bridge Brown devised a 'T' shaped plate with a downstanding tail for the suspension rod attachment. It also served as a coupling which was located between the pairs of chain bar-eyes to act in unison with a pair of shackles at the outside faces. Linking pins with threaded ends were fitted with eight sided domed and step moulded nuts to complete the joints. It was a relatively simple answer to the problem, and represented a considerable advance over the cast iron saddle device of the earlier years.

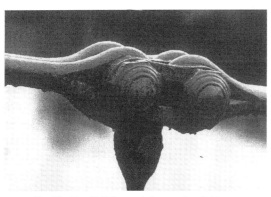

Fig 45 - Detail: Kalemouth Suspension Bridge

Fig 46 - Detail: Kalemouth Suspension Bridge

Fig 47 - Detail: Kalemouth Suspension Bridge

Fig 48 - Kalemouth Suspension Bridge

The symmetrical design has four independent tapered stone towers about 20 feet high. Suspension rods pass through the ends of the timber platform transoms with no longitudinal linking 'run-bar' as originally at Union.

The transoms are decked with a single layer of planks breaking joint forming an eight foot width carriageway, with timber kerb stringers that provide for stiffness and a form of demarcation between carriageway and footwalks at each side. Rigidity of the platform. was introduced by heavy wooden diagonally braced balustrading raised off a substantial edge plank connected to the transoms.

Another new feature was introduced into the Kalemouth bridge that allowed for a means of adjusting and tensioning the chains at one end. No records of this device have been made, but the apparatus is remembered by Mrs. Eileen Buist, who writes:

"....when we took over this very small, beautifully situated estate on Teviot banks in 1935, a well-built cottage (which had acted originally as a Toll House for the privately-built Bridge) was in ruins, and which we rebuilt, and in doing so, discovered a small stair leading to a vaulted chamber containing the Capstans where the steel cables were secured and cared for.

Alas: in spite of our protestations, the County Council covered in the little stairway and the beautiful vaulted chamber with the road surface leading onto this east end of the Bridge at the end of which Captain Brown's name was clearly to be seen and the date - all now flaked off the stonework through neglect."

Mrs Buist's memory was somewhat hazy about the date, and suggests that it could have been either 1830 or 1836.

Although 1835 is a recorded bridge completion date, the content of an email of May 23rd 2017 from Hans Seland CE suggests that 1830 is the correct date; it reads:

"Hans Seland of Kristiansand, Norway. I am a civil engineer, retired from longtime employment in the Norwegian Public Roads Administration, who has taken up the study of transport technology development and transfer between Western Europe and Scandinavia at the time when the Industrial Revolution gained momentum outside Britain around 1840. My case is Norwegian roadmaster and national director of canals and harbors Georg Daniel Barth Johnson (1794-1872) who, in 1838, went on an extended tour of the United Kingdom, Belgium, Germany, the Netherlands, Denmark and Sweden. His objective was to learn more about roads and bridges, harbors, canals and river/shore defenses in order to improve the quality of Norwegian public works. As most engineers of his time, Mr Johnson was educated as a military engineer and whenever he could, he detoured to see the famous forts and fortresses of the recent Continental wars. When he came home he published Norway's first textbook on his subjects in 1839 and named it "Handbook for Road Officials" ("Haandbog for Veiofficianter").

Mr Johnson arrived in Scotland as passenger on a small merchant ship, sailing from Kristiansand to St Andrews in July 1838. He travelled to Anstruther and Leith/Edinburgh and then by coach via Crichton, Dean, Lauder to Kelso where he admired and described Brown's chain suspension bridge crossing River Teviot at Kalemouth, a few miles to the south west of town. And he went on to inspect Brown's Union Bridge across River Tweed. In his "Haandbog" he appears very convinced that Kalemouth Bridge was built in 1830. I notice that British authors are more doubtful about the date, but Mr Johnson may be correct as he visited the site just 8 years later."

It could be that Mrs Buist's memory of the bridge plate earlier date of 1830 had always been right.

At the peak of Brown's interest and contractual involvement with suspension bridges he became deeply concerned with the projected idea for a high level bridge over the River Tyne at Newcastle. It was all part of the 'Important Improvement of the Great North Road by a Proposed Bridge over the River Tyne to avoid those steep and difficult Hills, the Battle Bank, Gateshead, and Dean and Mosley Street, Newcastle upon Tyne'. The bridge which had been erected after the destruction of the earlier structure by flood in 1771 was, in the words of Mr. B.R. Dodd, Civil Engineer, in 'Great jeopardy of Falling'. Mr. Dodd's report about the project considered the pendant and suspension systems of bridging for 'their economy and expedition over all others', but, as he was to relate '.... although the expense excepted, there can be no well-founded objections to a bridge of stone'. The site was surveyed and levelled in 1826 by Mr. J.M.Bell between Mosley Street Newcastle and New Road Gateshead, and seven years passed by before the proposed route was again examined. Brown was consulted, and in 1833 produced a design for a high level bridge of three rigid cast iron spans with intermediate masonry piers that was very much in the Telford mould. The design represented a radical departure from the type of bridge structure for which Brown had gained his reputation, and comprised arched masonry raised approaches with a central shallow arch cast iron span of 485 feet between piers of masonry at about 180 feet clear height above mean water level. Two side spans of about 220 feet and all of massive proportions completed the sketchily presented design proposal.

The choice of Brown as engineer for the proposed project seems strange, particularly in the light of his background, but he may only have been one of other engineers invited to submit schemes, and by 1833 the gamble of imaginative spark had given way to the return of conservative thinking by scheme sponsors. Telford's four-span masonry Dean Bridge over the Leith at Edinburgh had impressed Mr. Dodd, and the committee responsible for the project were thereby influenced in favour of a durable bridge with long life expectancy.

Fortunately the project was abandoned, for Brown's design was not pretty or expressive of its type by Telford standards, and with the development of the railway line north, the Tyne was eventually graced with Robert Stephenson's High Level Bridge work in 1849.

Of all the solicitations Brown received during 1825 for costs of Bridge ironwork, the one from John

Anderson (possibly of Leith Walk Foundry, Edinburgh) on November 12th and 24th eventually led to a positive result: '... I send you plan of an Iron Bridge proposed to be thrown over the river Dee...'

Other parties were to undertake the construction and provide wood and stone. Mr Anderson sent very scant information, and although enclosing a drawing (not discovered) his committee was uncertain about the carriageway width '.., they think 8 feet sufficiently broad, but I told them 10 or 12 feet was the very least they should possibly think of. It is for ordinary county purposes, tho' the traffic upon it is very inconsiderable, the greatest trial will be once a year cattle going over it - the Ground on both sides of the Water is nearly level - No vessels pass under it, and the height is calculated above the highest floods..'.

Only Brown's note of costs on the margin of the letter, in his own hand exist in reply, and it seems that some 27 tons of wrought iron at £35 per ton was required with cast iron platform beams recommended amounting to 19 tons.

It was not before time as the town authorities had projected the need for a bridge over the Dee at the Craiglug in 1448 where the river channel narrows and deepens and passes through rocky projections but sufficient money was not forthcoming.

The erection of a new parish church, at the expense of the heritas of Nigg (County of Kincardine and Presbytery of Aberdeen) gave reason for influencing the Road Trustees of the district to improve approaches and in consequence, a Parliamentary Bill was promoted in 1829 for a bridge at Craiglug. It included for a new line of Turnpike road from Stonehaven Road near the Moss of Cairnrobin to the proposed bridge: the Act was passed on May 14th 1829. In August 1829, the Trustees entered into contract with Captain Brown for the construction of the bridge with Robert Mearns appointed as the local builder. The bridge was completed and opened for foot passengers in November 1830 and to carriage traffic in May 1831 following completion of the new road approaches.

The bridge was named 'Craiglug' and was renamed 'The Wellington Bridge' by a resolution of the Bridge Trustees on March 3rd 1831 as the noble Duke '… was still a conspicuous figure in public life'.

The bridge structure was in the true Brown mould with massive arch pierced granite towers 215 feet apart (230 feet centre to centre of the towers) with a carriageway width of 15 feet and a footpath each side of 2' 6" width in addition. The platform is suspended from four main chains of 3" x 11/8 " section flat eye bar links having three bars in each joined together by side plates and bolts every 10 feet; the two tiers each side arranged vertically above each other; the joints staggered for the suspension rods between chain

Fig 49 - Wellington (Craiglug) Bridge, Aberdeen

SAMUEL BROWN AND UNION CHAIN BRIDGE

couplings and the cast iron deck transoms which provided load distribution. Timber planking bolted to the transoms formed the primary decking to which was spiked transverse planking coated with a composition of coal-tar pitch and broken stone. Substantial timber balustrades were provided each side of the deck with vertical posts and diagonal bracing, similar to those surviving at Kalemouth Bridge. The braced balustrade was used to assist in overcoming wind induced movement but its inclusion attracted considerable local criticism as being 'out of character' with the general style of the ironwork structure. The final cost of the bridge was greater than first envisaged which, together with the approaches, amounted to £9,815.00 This was a result of the carriageway width being made 15 feet wide instead of 10 feet in Brown's original specification, the enlargement and design change of links which passed over the tower saddle bearings and related additional masonry and timbering. The bridge remains very much in its original form except for the timber balustrading which was removed in a major deck reconstruction in 1930.

In the twilight of Telford's life he was invited to assess entries in a competition for a suspension bridge over the Clifton Gorge. The success of Menai, and the existence of an accumulated fund left by William Vick in the eighteenth century, enabled the magistrates of Bristol, in 1829, to form a company with the intention of carrying out the task. A Bill was quickly presented to Parliament to a secure the necessary Act, and subscription lists opened, in which Brown was quick in taking up a £50 share. A considerable number of entries was received, including one from the young I K Brunel, which Telford strongly reacted against, and dismissed all others, including an entry from Samuel Brown. C S Drewry recorded that: '.. A very bold design was also proposed by Captain S Brown. The dimensions of Captain Brown's bridge were to be:

Span	780 feet	Carriage-way	20 feet
Height above high water	220 feet	Two footpaths, each	5 feet
Breadth of platform	30 feet		

The towers were to be masonry, raised on the cliff tops with a very shallow catenary chain curve, and offered for the lump sum price of £30,600, and to be completed in four months after completion of the masonry towers. Brown was so keen to secure the contract that he had full size sample eye bars and links made up in his Newbridge works and shipped to Bristol accompanied by his works manager Philip Thomas to explain the intricate details, but all was to no avail.

Fig 50 - Drawing of Brown's proposal for Clifton Suspension Bridge 1830

Telford's reaction resulted in the launch of another competition, and an entry from Telford, which was for a Gothic towered design with the towers rising from the river level. It was accepted by the bridge committee, but public outcry changed their minds, and a scheme put forward by Brunel was finally accepted in March 1831. It has to be remembered that Telford was in his late seventies and Brunel just 25 years old, but it was 1836 before work began on the 702 foot span bridge, to be followed by 20 years of frustrating delays, and Brunel died in 1359, before the structure was eventually completed.

With Menai completed, and in every sense a delight of architecture and engineering, it is difficult to appreciate Telford's feelings towards the Clifton project. It may have been his earnest desire to win and secure the contract that thrust the lingering, but still fashionable, picturesque 'Castle Style' into his mind; believing that the taste of Clifton people would relish his ornate and decorative offering, which was all too reminiscent of William Forden's spikey cathedral style for the Earl of Grosvenor's Eaton Hall in Cheshire, and the fantasy of Nash's Brighton Pavilion for the Prince Regent. The slim lofty towers rising the full height of the gorge reflected an antithesis of all Telford's pragmatic philosophy towards design, in complete contrast with Brown's adventurously 'bold' concept, which was very close in form to Brunel's ultimate scheme.

Either through the influence of the Clifton experience, or simply the fashion for the 'Castle Style' in the Highlands, Brown's design for his Findhorn Bridge at Forres opened November 30th 1832 reflected the Gothic idiom with arch connected castellated octagonal towers, but in common with his developed method of supplying the structural design and ironwork, the masonry architecture may well have been outside his brief. His bridge over the Spey at Delfur 'Boat o'Brig' (1830) came first, however, in the more restrained and orthodox style, but both bridges enjoy a related history.

For differing reasons, the idea of new bridges over the River Spey at Boat O Brig and the River Findhorn, Strathdearn, became very active in the minds of local people in 1825 and 1829 respectively. Two centuries earlier, the wooden bridge of St Nicholas, over the Spey, had decayed and disappeared - ".. and the passage of the river became a Ferry.." Before that, it was an ancient river crossing for the route over the hills between Delfur and Knock More on the east side of the river, where the Hospice of St Nicholas is recorded to have existed before the thirteenth century. It is mentioned in the Charter to Walter de Moravia *"Mea confirmasse Deo et beato Nicholae et hospitali ejusdem sito juxta pontem de Spe"*.

The columns of the *Elgin Courier and Province of Moray Advertiser* of June 17th 1829 recorded: '..The public spirited resolution of the Hon Col. Grant of Grant, M.P. and other proprietors in the neighbourhood..' .., decided to erect a '..Bridge of Suspension - at their own risk,' and continued '..We understand that the accomplishment of this great object, so long desired and projected, the country is much indebted to the exertions of Mr Stewart of Aurhlunkart..'.

Samuel Brown secured the contract and built a bridge with with a span of 235 feet and a deck span of 16 feet with his Union bridge-type arch, pierced stone towers, and chain cable arrangement at a cost of £3500; *The Courier* carried the opening announcement on December 10th 1830 ; and to put

Fig 51 - Bridge at Findhorn (Forres)

SAMUEL BROWN AND UNION CHAIN BRIDGE

everyone's mind at rest stated that the '.. iron work has been proved to sustain a surplus weight of eighteen Tons, over the weight of 1420 persons, being the greatest number of persons who can have standing room on the bridge at one time. The appearance of the bridge is singularly light and airy, notwithstanding the massive granite towers from which it appears to be suspended, and the great strength of the chains..'.

The Road and Bridge Bill for the County of Elgin enabled Trustees, in 1830, to proceed with a proposal for a new bridge over the River Findhorn, and an appointed bridge committee received, and considered, a Report from the civil engineer William Hughes at a meeting held on October 1st 1830 '.. as to the most eligible site for its erection..'. On the grounds of cost, Mr Hughes recommended that a cast iron bridge should be erected on the site of the five arch stone bridge, built in 1799-1800, which had been swept away in Moray floods of 1829. As this recommendation was in '.. direct opposition to that given by Mr Jardine.', the committee felt that they were not competent to take a decision.', although '..fully persuaded that a bridge at the old site will, if practicable be the most advantageous for the public, and the most likely to pay a productive pontage '. Mr Hughes' opinion resulted from his investigation into the failure of the stone bridge in relation to the behaviour of the river and the nature of its banks. An influence was also the lack of a suitable local stone for a single span arch form, whose abutments would have to '..overlap the rock at least twelve feet on each side, making a span of 170 feet.' He made the point that if granite were to be brought from Aberdeen for such a span the cost - '.. would amount to £10,700.', whereas, '.. A cast iron arch, the same span including stone abutments would cost £6,600..'.

With Boat o' Brig (Delfur) built, and Mr Jardine having been consulted, it is not surprising that Brown entered the field for the Findhorn contract for the supply of iron work. The costs involved were a major issue for those responsible, and while Boat o' Brig was being constructed the Trustees for Findhorn 'Moved that the committee be instructed to draw up a memorial to the Lords of the Treasury praying that they would issue a loan towards building the Bridge..', they further added

Fig 52 - Bridge at Findhorn (Forres); engraving W Rea

'.. And this instruction to be extended to the committee for the Spey Bridge (Boat o' Brig) with a recommendation that both committees do act in concert in this matter..'. Resistance was voiced by some of the committee members against '.. any part of the county or Turnpike funds being appropriated towards defraying the expenses incurred by the committees for the bridges of Spey and Findhorn, but that they shall be defrayed out of the peculiar funds desired from the respective pontages..'.

Brown's proposal was put to the committee in the first week of August 1831; '.. The style of the Building is Castellated Gothic and in point of beauty and elegance would surpass all other ever executed..'. He quoted for a span between towers of 270 feet and a platform width of 23 feet, including all bulwarks for the sum of £6,400. This was a sum 'considerably' in excess of the committee's anticipation, and Brown was asked to reduce the platform width and related work accordingly with the object of arriving at an overall figure between £5000 and £5200. The *Elgin Courier* expressed regret for such a decision but the final design did result in a span of 270 feet between towers, a deck span of about 250 feet, and a total length including approaches of 441 feet

6 inches. The width of roadway was 16 feet 2 inches within an overall width of 22 feet, and the distance between tower arches 14 feet 2 inches. The Gothic towers were constructed with sandy freestone. Before the bridge was demolished details of the ironwork were recorded by the county engineer.

'Main chains composed of three parallel bars, each 4 inches deep and 11/8 inches thick, held at the connections by crosspins 2½ inches in diameter ... From the main chains are 51 suspending rods on each side, 11/8 inches diameter, each capable of supporting 24 tons. These rods have eyes at each end and are secured to the main chains and tops of the girders on each side of the carriageway by crossbolts 11/8 inches diameter ... As originally constructed the carriageway was suspended by suspension rods. It consisted of cast iron cross-under beams to support the roadway and along each side was a wooden beam 2 feet 4 inches deep and 3 inches thick for the purpose of distributing weights over the cross girders. There was a cast iron protection rail on each side. The suspending rods were fastened to the ends of the cross under girders by cotter pins and the surface of the carriageway was constructed on these girders of timber planking and asphalt.'.

Drewry's published account (1832) about the bridge size and its principal structural elements gives more detailed information: although the overall dimensions differ.

'The span is about 300 feet. The breadth of the platform is 23 feet: and the bridge is calculated to bear 250 tons in load, besides its own weight. The main chains will contain twelve lines of bars 9 feet 8¾ inches long, out and out; 4 inches broad by 11/8 inches thick = 49½ square inches of iron in all, united by coupling plates 18¾ inches long, and bolt pins 2½ inches diameter. The coupling plates are 5¾ inches broad in the middle, and 7¾ inches broad across the ends, where the bolt holes are drilled out, so as to allow 25/8 metal all round the holes. The ends of the main chains will be held by keys rounded on one side, 2 feet long, 3 inches broad and 4 inches deep. The entire weight of iron work suspended will be about 76 tons.' The chains were arranged in two tiers of triple-connected bars each side of the bridge.

Apart from expected deterioration of the timber decking, the bridge suffered little until the advent of the traction engine and, like Welney bridge, with their heavier rolling loads, the platform and suspension members succumbed, although the main chains sufficed. In 1881, the County Road Trustees employed George Cunningham, an Edinburgh civil engineer, "...to report on the bridge and suggest what was necessary for it to carry the heavier loads." Mr Cunningham in turn employed William Arnol, later of Forth Bridge fame, to advise him as to the condition and requirement of the bridge. The cast iron girders were condemned and the present fish-belly wrought iron girders inserted instead. Wrought iron parapet girders were not attached to the tops of the girders as at present, but were continued down and attached to the ends of the cross-under girders. This reconstruction, however, was a failure, for on April 26th 1883, a traction engine and two waggons caused the carriageway of the bridge to depress to such an extent as to buckle and warp the girders which had been recently erected along each side.

Mr Cunningham suggested an expenditure of £60 for strengthening the side girders but the Trustees took Counsel's Opinion about the matter. He exonerated the contractors, Messrs James Abernethy of Aberdeen, and for diverse reasons felt that Mr Cunningham could not be held responsible for the failure of the design. The Trustees then employed another civil engineer, Mr Willet, from Aberdeen, to report. He recommended the substitution of the side girders with stronger members and the attachment of suspension rods to the top of the side girders. The work was accordingly carried out and the bridge tested with a weight of 30 tons and "...pronounced capable of safely carrying a rolling weight of 25 tons."

Findhorn Bridge was taken down in 1938 and replaced with a less romantic structure. The photograph showing the final stages of demolition clearly shows the platform structure. Boat o' Brig lasted another twenty years until it was closed on June 27th 1957 and replaced.

The *Carmarthen Journal* gave Notice, on September 9th 1831 (p.164) to Engineers, Iron Masters, Masons, and others 'That the Committee appointed by the Llandovery and Lampeter Turnpike Trust for the purpose of contracting for the erection of a Suspension Bridge over the river Towy near the town of Llandovery in the county of Carmarthen was ready to receive proposals for the erecting of the said bridge, according to the plans deposited with Mr. William Garner Clerk to the Trustees of the said trust at the town of Llandovery who will produce the same and that a meeting of the said committee will be held at the Magistrates Room in the town of Llandovery on Wednesday 19th October next for the purpose of consulting for the erection of the said bridge. The Notice attracted 'Phillip Thomas, of Ynysangharad, the engineer and Superintendent for Messrs Brown, Lenox, and Co, of London, the Contractors duly reported in *Y Cymmro ("The Welshman")* on April 13th 1832 (p.3(4).) 'On Wednesday last, the Ceremony of laying the Foundation Stone of

Fig 53 - Bridge at Findhorn (Forres) under demolition

the new intended Suspension Bridge over the River Towy, at Llandovery, was performed by the chairman of the bridge Committee, Col. Gwynne and when the gallant Colonel had fixed it by the truly Masonic blows of the hammer he named it the Clarence Suspension Bridge, in commemoration of our present beloved and patriotic Queen, ... '

The bridge was erected under a private Act of Parliament and had a span between piers of 215ft. The piers were independent cast iron tapered ladder in form, unlike Samuel Brown's heavy masonry structures, supporting single pairs of bar iron chains (Photograph: Carmarthenshire Records Office). The *Carmarthenshire Notes* Vol.11, 1890 mentions that '.. Owing to the ravages of time upon the iron-work, apprehension as to its safety were entertained a few years ago, and some of the county authorities would mend it, whilst others would end it '. the latter opinion prevailed, and the present substantial stone structure was erected in its stead '.

According to *Pages from the history of Llandovery* p.399 the bridge structural components lived on when in 1883 they went to Buckland, the Breconshire mansion of the Gwynne-Holford family of Cilgwyn, Myddfai, and were re-erected and some of the chains were used for a small bridge in the grounds of Blaenos mansion near Llandoverey.

Road improvements in Ireland included bridging the Kenmare River, County Kerry, between Kenmare and Bantry. Roadworks started in 1834. The Marquis of Lansdowne had offered to build at his own expense a "floating chain or fly bridge". William Bald FRSE, by invitation, produced designs including multi-arch masonry designs and suspension but without success – for some reason, nothing was seen as acceptable until Brunel had examined all the proposals, to no avail. Although it may seem obscure, two architects – John and Thomas Smith of Darnick, near Melrose in the Scottish borders, had proposed a single stone arched bridge in 1838, their fame following publication of a paper relating to suspension bridges published in the Architects Journal in 1835. Sir Samuel Brown entered the scene in 1839, with a comprehensive "Specification for a Suspension Bridge proposed to be built across the Sound at Kenmare by Sir S. Brown", a handwritten two-page document signed "Sir Samuel Brown", together with a well-detailed drawing showing in elevation a half-span width from the central tower some 50 feet+ high above low water level and details of the flat rectangular bar chains. After all the local shenanigans between the Board of Works and other interested parties, Sir Samuel Brown offered to supply all the ironwork etc for £6,150.00 and the Board of Works undertook all other aspects of construction including the central tower wing walls etc completed in 1841. Glamorgan Record Office holds considerable information about the bridge (ref D/D BL 25/1). As was and is the case about most bridge designing, the effects of excessive traffic took its toll and in 1932 the bridge was declared unsafe and soon demolished. It was replaced with a 2+150 feet span reinforced concrete parabolic bridge in 1933, designed by L G Mouchel and Partners, following the pattern of the 1410 feet 4 arch reinforced concrete span Royal Tweed Bridge at Berwick-upon-Tweed.

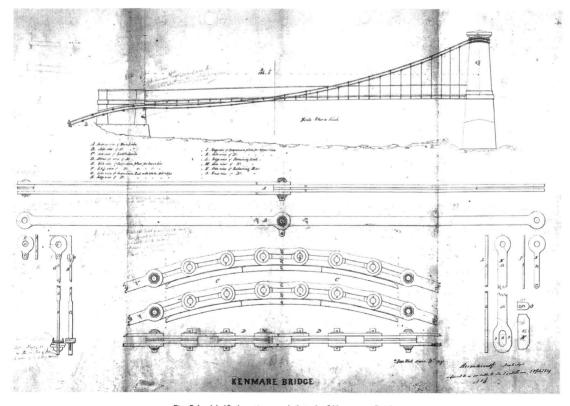

Fig 54 - Half elevation and detail of Kenmare Bridge

Fig 55 - Specification for Kenmare Bridge

Kenmare c. 1839

Specification for a Suspension Bridge *proposed to be built across the Sound at* Kenmare *by Sir S. Brown. Com. R.N*

The Masonry & Carpenters work in Platform & railing to be provided by the Commissioners of Public Works, according to the plans prepared by the Boards Engineer, & approved by Sir S. Brown, who will superintend the execution of the same, so far as it is necessary to insure its being substantially performed & adapted to the purpose for which it is required ___ Every other portion of the Bridge which is included in this specification and shewn by the drawing herein referred to are to be provided fixed & completed by the said Sir Samuel Brown wh is to be responsible for its stability for two years after the Bridge is opened for the use of the public.

The work is to be performed according to the drawings referred to in this specification and to be constructed as follows Viz.

Plan No 2. The Bridge is to be supported by eight Chains each Chain to consist of two Bars four & one half inches wide and one and one quarter inch thick And three bars of four and one half inches wide and inch thick connected by bolts of two and one half inches diameter as shewn by figure 10 +

note by S.B. + This I expect will be altered to two Bars close together in the centre joined by two side bars which will make all bars alike Viz.

the sectional area of which will be forty four square inches they will be extended in two parallel lines over each other passing over the central Tower and continued through the counter abutments as shewn in drawing No 11

Figure 14 the joints of the upper Chain with part of the suspending rod attached, these rods to be three quarters of an inch thick by one & one half inch wide the lower plates of the suspending rods supporting the ends of the beams or transverse bearers are shewn at P figure 9 and by the dotted line Cf on the sides of the Bridge.

Figure 11 the joints of the Chains to be 10 feet from centre to centre the upper bars at the Tower to be only five feet from centre to centre of the joints in order that the joints of the upper Chain may be in the middle of the lower Chain so that the suspension rods which are laid to the joints of the main Chain may support the

Continued over …

to the cast Iron retaining Plates, the cast Iron retaining plates to be of the size
shewn by figure 3 at B and accurately fitted to the surface of the stone (but the
links of the chains) DD shew the toggel or retaining Bolts for securing the extremities
the Chains. F, figure one shews the construction of the joints of the upper chains
rest upon the cast Iron plate F these are to be supported by the stones GG and the
chains on the front of the breast work are to rest on the cast Iron plates H in the section
and shewn in the front elevation of the breast work H H figure 5 +

Note by Sir SB + figure it is not correctly drawn the saddle or bearing plates are 12 Inches apart
shewn in the section K   figure 3, below this is also a little wrong but these err
do not affect as they will be corrected in the masonry I would prefer the saddle links
be a little longer in order to join the upper bars clear of the Tower and prevent an elbow
the neck.

Figure 4 Is a section of the Tower shewing the chains resting on the cast Iron
and K is a cross section of the same

Figure 5 Is a front elevation of the breast work shewing the main chains rest
on the Iron plates II

Figure 6 Is an elevation of part of the side of the Bridge which is eighteen
wide &3 Inches thick — A is a curt or cordon twelve inches wide & 6 1/2 inches thick
(figures 6, 7 & 9) extending the whole length of the bridge on both sides the under
edge forming a covering over the side to be bolted down flush with the planking
upper edge of the side with six of 3/4 In bolts clenches above & below as shewn at B
figures 6 & 7. — C figure 6 shews the scarf of the sides each of which are
bolted down by 6 of 3/4 In bolts riveted over washers —

To provide wood transverse bearers of sufficient strength to support
road way in lieu of the cast Iron bearers as shewn by elevation D Suspendin
rods as H to be fied over the ends of the wood beams passing through the curt of the
platform and supporting its ends. — The whole of the work to be executed in a substan
& workmanlike manner with materials the best of their several kinds to the satisfaction
the board engineer and everything to be done that is necessary for completing the Bridge
notwithstanding the same may not be mentioned in this specification as shewn by the
drawings with the exception of the masonry & carpenters work in platform which is to
executed by the board of Public Works and forms no part of the contract with Sir Sam
Brown

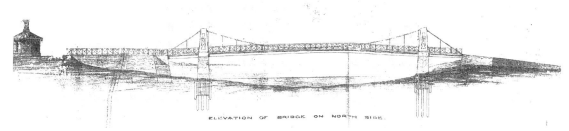

Fig 56 - -Earith Bridge, plan

Earith Suspension Bridge was completed on August 7th 1846, when Samuel Brown reported to the Justices of the Peace for Huntingdonshire and the Isle of Ely that Messrs Fox Henderson & Co. of the London Works near Birmingham had completed the majority of the work in a satisfactory manner. Its design expressed his ultimate type, and was probably a final constructional exploit, having cast iron independent towers mounted, from deck level on masonry piers which, in turn, were raised upon timber pile clusters sunk into the river bed. The superstructure comprised a main clear span of 120 feet with two shore spans each of 20 feet. Suspension chains were of the flat wrought iron eye-bar type, four coupled to each side of the bridge with wrought iron circular suspension rods at a fifteen foot spacing arrangement to suit and connecting with cast iron transverse girders. Seven rows of timber binders mounted over the girders were decked with three inch planking, and a central carriageway of 8' 4" width was covered with one inch thick Elm boarding and surfaced with a one inch layer of tar, lime and sand mixture, contained within Oak curbs.

The original agreement for the erection of the bridge between the Clerks of the Quarter Sessions of Huntingdonshire and the Isle of Ely, and Charles Fox and John Henderson (contractors)of London Works near Birmingham, was entered into according to the specification of Captain Sir Samuel Brown RN on September 22nd 1843. It is one of the few discovered contract documents which had been engrossed, and the parts setting out the structural requirement are transcribed for the interest of its detail and manner of description.

The contract sum was £1,503 : 10s to '... Build, erect and finish the said intended Bridge including the alterations and temporary additions to the present Bridge..'

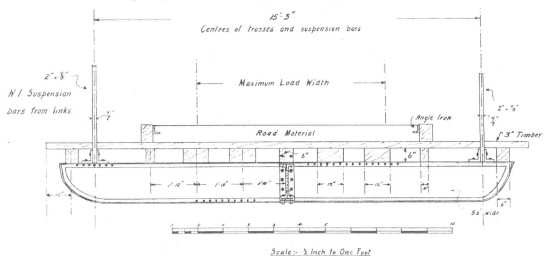

Fig 57 - Earith Bridge, cross section through suspension span

To Excavate the Ground where necessary for performing the works and deposit the same where directed by the said Engineer for forming the Roadway and Embankments between and around the retaining and Wing Walls - If there be more ground than is required for these purposes the Contractor will not be required to cart away the same but will be allowed to deposit it on the adjoining ground within fifty feet of either end of Bridge as may directed - If the ground to be excavated for the insertion of the back stay chains be of a looser or lighter description than that excavated at other parts the space is to be filled in again with the latter instead of the former and well rammed.

Foundations to Main Piers
No.6 Bearing Piles to each of the four piers of Fir 12 by 12 with wrought Iron Shoes at least 28 lbs weight each and strong wrought Iron Bond Hoops for securing the heads every pile is to be driven (if possible to the depth shewn in the drawing and each one so much further below these levels as the said Engineer may deem necessary for the work.)

Security of the Work (they shall therefore be provided in lengths as may be directed for this purpose) - All timber required for extra depth of piling will be paid for at and after the rate of 3s/- per foot Cube but if the Piles cannot be driven to the depth shewn a deduction of 3s/- per foot Cube will be made for the deficiency in this respect but no addition or deduction shall be made for labour or other matters or things concerning the same - The Piles are to be cut off at the level shewn and secured on four sides with a Waling Timber 12 by 6 notched to Piles (partly out of each) and secured at each place of contact with g wrought Iron bolt and the ends bevilled off to clear the guide Piles as shewn in drawing -

Sheeting Piles - No 4 Guide Piles of Fir 9 by 9 to each pier with four Waling timbers 9 by 6 notched to Piles (partly out of each) and well secured with g wrought Iron bolt at each place of contact as shewn the Piles to have wrought Iron Shoes at least 20 lb weight each and strong wrought Iron Bond Hoops - Sheeting Piles of 3 plank pointed and driven to the depths shewn the heads bonded with them strong Iron hooping - If any irregularity or defect arise in the driving of any of the Piles the same is to be rectified by drawing them and redriving the same or others or drawing additional ones as the said Engineer may direct without any extra being allowed for the same -

If from the state of the Floods the sheeting Piles be required higher than shewn they must be of greater length when driven and an inner Waling 6 x 3 bolted to the inner face of Piles with ½in wrought Iron bolts at distances not exceeding 2 feet apart and they must be subsequently cut off at the level shewn when the Floods permit -

The ground within the Sheet Piling and to 18 inches beyond the footing in the rear (where there is no sheet piling) to be removed to 2 feet below the heads of bearing Piles and the space thence up to the underside of planking filled with a concrete of 8 parts by measure of shingle and one part stone lime -

The ground is also to be removed to an average of 2 feet 6 inches deep and 3 feet wide around the four sides of main piers and this and the space between the sheet piling and brickwork and also an average of 3 feet by 1 ft 6 inches round the outer face of the retaining and wing walls to be filled with the concrete as above described with the addition of Rubble Stone average at least 4 inches diameter embedded in the upper surface -

Two shoulders to be cut in the sides of each bearing pile and 6 inches fir sleepers fixed thereon) notched and closely fitted to the piles and spiked with 12in wrought iron spikes to the Waling timbers – Upon the sleepers a platform of 1in planking is to be laid over the whole surface within the sheet piling and to the distance back-ward as shewn in drawing closely jointed and fitted to the sheet piling around.

Main Piers and retaining & Wing Walls
The Main Piers from the planking up to the platform of Bridge and the Walls at the ends of platform with the various footings offsets buttresses etc., as shewn in drawing to be built with bricks bedded in Roman Cement and clean sharp sand – except the parts hereinafter described as Stone -

The work to be laid with neat close joint in English or Flemish Bond as the said Engineer may direct and the external faces of work to have the joints neatly struck - And the whole is to be well flushed in at every course and all the interstices between the bricks completely filled -

Stone Work to Main Piers
A 6 York landing 4 feet by 3 feet with hole cut for couplings to be laid in at the position shewn - The top of the piers immediately under the Iron Towers to be covered with a 9 " portland landing moulded on four sides as shewn in drawings with bolt holes cut or drilled for the various nuts bolts and attachments shewn in drawing under this a 12 in course of Portland Stone Ashlaring consisting of two entire stones on the shorter side of piers 18 in thick and a central stone on the two wider sides 9 in thick to complete the course on the four sides of piers from the last mentioned course to the bottom edge of wood fascia

A 9 in portland stone ashlaring with a central Bond stone 18 in into the work - to the outer face of each pier - All the angles of the four Piers commencing at an average of 2 feet above the footings up to the portland Ashlaring are to have quoin Stones of Bramley-fall in courses not less than 15 deep each stone averaging $\frac{2}{6}$ x $\frac{1}{2}$ with one entire course of 15 Bramley-fall to each pier inserted at about 8 ft below the said portland Ashlaring in not more fan 2 Stones to each Pier - Portions of the (toing) and retaining Walls are to be of Bramley-fall stone equal to an average of two 12 in courses 18 in thick of the whole length of front and side walls at each end of platform - The stone work described of average dimensions" are to be such sizes abd used at such respective parts as the Engineer may direct provided the same do not exceed in the whole the average scantling and quality - At all the Quoins the stones are to be secured with two Slate Dowels to each bed 2in x 2in - A portland stone course 18 by 4 from each corner of the retaining wall up to and upon the return piers where the chains enter the ground with circular top and circular ends and corners as shewn securely plugged and run with lead and holes cut for railing in.

The Towers above the stone base on top of piers to be of cast Iron each side cast in one piece with the flanges braces and other parts shewn in drawing the whole to be an average thickness of 14 in in every part up to the Saddle rests where the thicknesses are increased as shewn by drawing to form a bed to receive the Saddles the sides of Towers rising above the Saddles beds to be $\frac{7}{8}$ with rim 1¼ by $\frac{3}{8}$ on the edges –

The ties next the saddle plates and the braces and ties at the lower part to be of cast-Iron average thickness of each part ¾in there are to be two of each to each Tower as shewn in Drawing secured with ¾ Bolts to the Towers each Tower is to be secured with No. 2 1" bolts to the stone base and with No. 2 wrought Iron Rods with eyes and couplings and links as shown in Drawing the Rods to be round 1½" diameter the eyes and links 1½ by 1 at every part - Wrought Iron Bolts 2¼ diameter the upper ends round with heads washers and pins and the lower ones flattened on one side to bear against the retaining plates the latter to be of Cast Iron 1in thick in the central part chamfered off as shown to ½in The upper end of Rod to have nuts 4in deep and the Rod left 3in above the Bolts The Saddles to be of Cast Iron average 1½ thickness in all their parts these to have uniform and level beds and to be carefully wedged in all round - Tops of Towers to be covered with sheet Iron 2lbs to the foot super -

The Suspension Chains to be of Wrought Iron consisting of eight rows of bars (four on each side of Bridge.) each Bar to be 3in by ⁷⁄₈ in at the central part and 2in by ⁷⁄₈ in at the Bolt hole or eye with enlargements at the connections between central part and eyes as shown the eyes to be all carefully drilled and accurately fitted to the Bolts –

The Couplings to be formed with wrought Iron round Bolts 2¼ diameter with cast Iron heads and caps and wrought Iron keys ⁵⁄₈.

The Suspending Rods are to be of round wrought Iron 1¼ diameter with eyes to receive the Coupling Bolt of Chains 1 by 1 around same enlarged at connecting parts as shown in drawings and the lower ends formed into double suspending straps 3¾ by ⁵⁄₈ each to receive the Girders under which are to be placed gibs and wedges through the double strap to secure the girders in the positions required - The part of Chains passing over the Saddle to be formed of curved links 14 " long 6¼ wide and ⁷⁄₈ thick with Bolts caps heads and keys as the other parts of Chain and a washer in the centre 4¼" diameter 1" thick - The Back Stays are the same in every respect as the parts of Chains between the Towers except only where no suspending rods occur washers are to be inserted as described for the part passing over Saddles at the extreme ends there are to be long eyes formed in the last two sets of Bars with gibs wedges a central link as washer and intermediate blocks secured with pins or wedges as may be found necessary for adjusting the length of Chains -

The coupling Bolts at end of Back Stays to be of wrought Iron 2½ diameter and the eyes of Back Stay Chains around d°/, to be 2¼ by ⁷⁄₈ the central one of the horizontal retaining Chains to be 3 by 1 the two outer ones 3 by ⁷⁄₈ the parts around the eyes to be respectively 2 by 1 and 2 by ⁷⁄₈ the retaining bolts to be 2½ diameter with one side flat the other round as shown 2 bars 3 by ⁷⁄₈, to each pair of retaining piles with parts around upper bolts 2¼ by ⁷⁄₈ and around lower bolt 2 by⁷⁄₈ - 2¼ bolt through piles with Caps Heads and Keys as to suspending Chains - No.8 L shaped Cast Iron Retaining Piles each average 20ft long and 16in supersection in area throughout - Retaining Plates - 4 Cast Iron plates 2ft 6" 1½ thick in centre chamfered off to ¾ at the outer edges -

Girders - The Girders to be of Cast Iron extreme depth in centre 11in and 8in at the ends 7/8 thick - upper and lower ":'ebbs or Flanges 2" wide and 1¼ thick bevelled 14 brackets for binders (10 with bolt holes) to each girder and a bracket formed at each end of Girder with Stay at Back of d°/. ⁷⁄₈ thick at each part and one bolt hole and one screw hole on d°/.

Platform - Insert Fir plate 8 by 4 in the face of each retaining Wall and fix a tier of Fir bibders 8 by 4 on each side of the Bridge from Girder to Girder the entire distance between pier and pier and thence to the plates above mentioned - Fix two other tiers of Fir binders 10 by 4 and one d°/. 10½ x 4 from Girder to Girder the entire length of Bridge from one retaining wall to the other secured to the plates on retaining Walls and Flanges of Girders above mentioned with ½ wrought Iron Bolts - The whole surface of the Bridge from the back part of one retaining Wall to the back part of the other to be covered with 3" planking and well spiked to the 7 Rows of Binders - Along the entire length of the Platform a space of 8ft 4" wide is to be covered with 1" Elm Boards as a wearing surface for Carriageway and coated with a composition 1" thick of Hot pitch Coal Tar Lime and Sand - On each side of the Elm Boarding an Oak fender Curb 5 ft(sic) by 4 [should have been 5" x 4"] of the form shewn in drawing is to be well spiked to Platform the inner face to be covered with wrought Iron ¼" thick screwed to same - Fix 3 inch deal fascia on each side of Bridge with cross tongued joints the upper part bolted to binders with $2^5/_8$ Bolts to each space between the Girders and the lower part with a $^5/_8$ in bolt to the brackets at each end of Girders - The Fascia to be wrought one side and all edges - 4" deal wrought and rounded nosings 3" deal wrought and chamfered strings under d°/. - Oak Curb to receive the railing on either side of Bridge with dovetailed returns at every second standard projecting 9" (to receive the Stay Bars to Standards) - The Curb and returns to be wrought the Top circular weathered and the ends of returns rounded off and the whole securely Bolted or screwed down - Apertures are to be neatly made in Platform wherever the suspending Rods pass through and holes bored at all parts where directed for allowing the water to pass from the surface of the Bridge or for any other purposes connected with the Works herein mentioned or referred to -

Iron Railing - An Iron Railing 2ft 10in high to be fixed on the top of Oak Curb on each side of Bridge from one end to the other and thence per continued and returned on the Stone Curb as shewn in drawing - Top Rail of wrought Iron average 2 by $^3/_8$ rounded - 1¼ Cast Iron standards as per drawing secured with wrought Iron rivets to top rail and with plates at the bottom screwed on each side of standard into the Oak Curb -

Rounded wrought Iron Stay Bar 1½ by 1 curved as shewn in drawing rivetted to Standard. and to a bottom rail 2 by ¼ which is to be screwed down to the returns in Oak Curb (see Carpenter works) and thence pass across the Curb and have a strong screw at the outer end - At the Stone Curb there are to be no bottom rails to Standards but ties of round wrought Iron 1" diameter and the Standards and Stay Bars are to be let into Stone Curb 1½ and the panel 1" and run with lead -

Retaining Walls - At each end of Bridge (beyond the retaining and Wing Walls at the extremities of Platform) a retaining Wall is to be formed of Concrete composed of 7 parts Shingle and 1 of Stone Lime each Wall to be 30 ft long 10ft high and 4ft thick with No. 4 6 " York Landings 4ft 6in by 4ft ft 6in to receive the bearing plates -'

It suffered an early fracture of a cast iron deck beam in 1848, and another in 1856, followed by other repairs in 1857. A steam threshing engine passed over it in 1864 hauling its tackle which resulted in a number of cast iron members cracking and causing the county authorities considerable concern for the future of the bridge. In similar vein to that of the Tees bridge for the Stockton and Darlington Railway, the erection of Earith Bridge coincided with the rapid development of the steam traction engine, which effectively started life with Howden's 6 n.h.p portable engine of 1839, quickly followed by other budding manufacturers during a period of mechanical development and excitement. The offending machine may well have been a Burrell-Boydell engine and threshing machine of 1856 which caused the havoc with a unit weight of 112 tons, but twenty years earlier few people would have predicted the advent of mechanical road transport:

It is somewhat ironic that owners of Brown's ill-fated Tees Railway Bridge responded to an advertisement in the *Railway Times* during March 1843 which invited tenders for the Earith Bridge. Their company Engineer and Treasurer respectively addressed letters offering their Bridge to the joint Huntingdonshire and Isle of Ely committee. The Engineer, in his letter, pointed out that '.. I consider that although of much wider span than the Bridge you contemplate erecting, it may nevertheless, (if the nature of the Country will admit of it) be made available for your purpose..' The Treasurer, Mr Pease, was much more to the point, and on behalf of the company directors expressed '.. their willingness to sell on very moderate terms - their suspension bridge... . The structure is handsome and complete according to the original design by Sir Samuel Brown RN - and I submit is well worthy of your notice - An increase of traffic and weight has compelled the Co, to erect a New Stone Bridge.' Nothing came of this overture.

The ironfounding and contracting firm of William and James Garforth of Dunkinfield near Ashton under Lyne were contracted on August 19th 1864 by the County of Huntingdon to strengthen the bridge, which they carried out with sensible skill, and extended its life until 1962. The work entailed the addition of arched 'top booms' between the heads of the existing cast iron piers, and the provision of wrought iron bars connecting the chain suspension points with booms in a diamond formation; new suspension rods to replace the original, the removal of back chains and the complete replacement of the deck, all resulting in the conversion of the suspension form into that of a Bowstring structure.

A condition of the Articles of Agreement for the work stipulated that:
'The Bridge when finished must be tested by sending one of Bray's heavy traction Engines over it several times which test must be made in the presence of the Engineer or by an assistant appointed by him..' This engine was popular with Fen farmers, being the creation of William Bray, an engineer from Folkestone whose first engine patent granted in 1856 was developed and '..achieved the distinction of becoming the world's first showman's engine..'. By 1864 Bray's engines weighed up to 10 tons, with a hauling capability of 20 tons, so the old bridge was required to be subject to severe test.

The replaced platform was recorded in a survey drawing made by the County Engineer (fig 57) Mr J S Todd, in his report upon the bridge dated July 31 1939. It shows an adherence to the original design concept, but with stiffened cast iron primary platform structure and improved suspension connections.

The bridge survived in its changed form until 1962, when it was replaced with a new bridge.

Construction of Charles Labelye's Westminster bridge, was completed in 1750, but, owing to extensive pier subsidence failure, was replaced by Thomas Page's wrought iron seven arch bridge opened in 1862. Their existence slowed proposals for a bridge at the Lambeth - Horseferry site although an enabling Act of 1809 existed until 1828 permitting either a stone or chain suspension bridge but again shelved until 1836 with an Act incorporating the Metropolitan Suspension Bridge Company. All was to no avail until 1847 when Sir Samuel Brown sought authority of Parliament to establish a Toll for a suspension bridge over the Thames from Westminster to Lambeth, which he offered to construct and maintain at his own expense. The merits of the proposition were inquired into by Captain Vetch of the engineers -' who has entered upon the investigation with the assistance of Captain Washington, one of the tidal Harbour Commissioners. The estimated cost, including structure, approaches, and the purchase of property, is £90,000, but this estimate has been made on granite - and the material is now intended to be either iron or stone. The width of water at high tide where the bridge is intended to be built is 858 feet - at low water 828 feet. It is intended to have two piers, each of which will intercept 45 feet of water. The erection of the Bridge to be finished in 2 years from its commencement.'

Nothing happened until 1861, nine years after Sir Samuel had died, when the Lambeth Bridge Act resulted in P W Barlow's stiffened suspension type with twisted wire cables. By 1879 their deterioration through oxidation coupled with severe rusting of girders rendered the bridge unsafe leading to its closure in 1910 and eventual replacement in 1932.

In Brown's Letters Patent, *'Improvement in the Construction of a Bridge A.D.1817 - No.4137'* in emphasising the qualities of bar iron for chains he makes the point '35"... A bridge of wires, being the most complicated of any, is the most objectionable. The want of durability is of itself an insuperable objection to wire bridges, as well as all others constructed of such slender filaments. The immense surface exposed to the action of the atmosphere would infallibly cause a rapid decay, and the common preventatives of corrosion could not be made generally beneficial,...'

In 1817 he was aware and deeply concerned about the threat to bar iron posed by French engineers work with wire cables and felt justified in emphasising his critical reasoning. Had he lived, Barlow's bridge may not have been constructed but, in any event. Brown's predictions were well founded.

Any anxiety would have faded following the success of Union Chain Bridge as bar iron was either used or proposed for some 17 projects in the following decade.

By 1830, or thereabouts, Brown Lenox and Company no longer found the financial rewards of their -manufacturing easy to maintain at the levels previously enjoyed. After that date considerable localised competition existed and while the cost of transport became a seriously influencing factor, such practical matters alone were only part of Brown's worries. From its beginning the Brown Lenox relationship was far from smooth as disagreements were deep rooted - Brown was the eternal adventurer, almost a gambler, and his cousin a sound headed financier.

Brown was a keen business man who never lost the flush of enthusiasm for anything within his grasp. The comforting thought of his established chain manufactory enabled his excursions into project ventures, most of which and for various reasons were not carried out, but so far as Brown was concerned it was all good for business and kept his name to the forefront. Examples of his work that have been described in some detail reflect known information rather than any particular order of merit, but they do however serve to typify the range of design limit that Brown reached. Other examples given in the chronology of bridge structures that were either built or projected, or in which Brown played some part, made no further progressive design contribution.

In 1822 Samuel Brown married Mary, daughter of Mr. John Hume of Edinburgh, writer to the Signet. An 1896 description of Samuel given by a Miss Sarah Gurr, simply says, 'He was of medium height, not strongly built; had a ruddy complexion, and his hair was iron grey. Owing to some injury or defect, he walked somewhat limping, with the assistance of a stick'.

Fig 58 - Netherbyres, Eyemouth, built by Samuel Brown sometime after his marriage in 1822

Fig 59 - Additions to Netherbyres in course of construction after Samuel Brown's move to Blackheath, London

Sometime after his marriage, Samuel Brown bought the estate of Netherbyres, near Eyemouth, from the Crow family, who had been in continuous ownership since about 1550. He promptly demolished the old building and built the house that now exists, which has also been subjected to alterations and extensions. While living at Netherbyres, Brown put an experimental bridge across the Eye to provide a new access to his property, which he referred to as a 'Tension Bridge, being supported by, instead of suspended from, the chains.' A contemporary account referred to '...a magical transformation on the place.' Brown's coat of arms remains on the gable face over the upper front window. The bridge remained in existence until 1951, when the late Sir Christopher Furness, owner of Netherbyres, had it removed for reasons of safety.

Royal recognition came in January, 1835, when William IV made him a knight (3rd class) of the Hanoverian Guelphic Order. In 1838 he attained the rank of Knight Bachelor, and in the same year Queen Victoria conferred on him the honour of Knighthood. Some recognition came early, when in 1814, Brown was elected a member of the Society of Arts, now the Royal Society of Arts, in whose building Naysmith's painting of Union Bridge still hangs[1]. Samuel Brown's principles of suspension, based upon his chain design and manufacturing techniques, undoubtedly influenced Telford and other engineers throughout the Victorian era, but his own engineering ambitions never drifted far from the 'chain', as an element and its application. Although he was not a member of the Institution of Civil Engineers, Brown enjoyed the respect of its President Sir John Rennie, who in 1846 acknowledged his great contribution to engineering.... 'to Capt. Brown, however, who had previously brought chain cables into use for ships may be attributed the introduction into England of the improved system of the bar-link which is now so generally adopted.' Samuel Brown died on

Fig 60 - Netherbyres entrance hall in 1975, with 'companionway' gallery approach to first floor rooms

125

March 15th 1852, at Vanbrugh Lodge, Blackheath, London, where he lived in later life, leaving a widow but no issue.

The *Kentish Mercury* of Saturday March 20th 1852 recorded: 'DEATH OF CAPTAIN SIR SAMUEL BROWN,K,H - This gallant and scientific officer died on Monday last at his residence in Vanbrugh Fields, at the age of 76 years. He entered the navy in 1794, but although seeing much service and being engaged in different actions, his promotion went on slowly. He was first-lieutenant of the Phoenix in her brilliant action with the French frigate La Didon, and was with Sir Richard Strachan in capturing the four French line-of-battle ships that escaped from Trafalgar. This was in the year 1805, and yet, although in the capture of the Didon he was second in command, he was passed over and not made a commander until 1811. In May 1842 'sic' [1812] unable to secure further promotion he accepted the rank of retired captain. Of late years the deceased has been better known in the arena of science. He did not leave his monument for others to erect. The bridge across the Tweed and the Chain Pier at Brighton are unmistakable testimonials to his memory. Instead of trusting to monumental stone he carved his own name upon iron; and with many useful inventions -including chain cables, suspension bridges and piers - will the name of Sir Samuel Brown be transmitted for the admiration and veneration of posterity.'

1   Nasmyth's painting of the Union Bridge was subsequently acquired from the RSA by The Paxton Trust and is now displayed in Paxton House.

Fig 61 - Netherbyres, Eyemouth, Arms of Captain Sir Samuel Brown RN
Dexter: Gules, three fleur de lys
Sinister: Vert, a lion rampant argent
Crest: a lion rampant
Motto: Floreat majestas

Fig 62 - Chronological list of Samuel Brown's significant activities

Chronological list of Samuel Brown's significant activities including suspension bridges either built, proposed, considered or in some way involved.

1805   Residing at Dove Court Lombard Street London
1808   Residing at Castle Court Watling Street London
1813   Isle of Dogs Factory
1817   Runcorn Gap
1820   Union Bridge
1821   Trinity Chain Pier
1823   Montrose Brighton Chain Pier
1824   St Catherine's London Kingston upon Thames
1825   Hammersmith London Shields Beachley
          Annan & Dryfe Dumfries

Initial experiments with ideas for wrought iron chains
Secured Patent for Ships Standing Rigging and Ground Tackle of Chains

Experimental Bridge constructed Suspension Bridge proposal

Built at New Water Ford, Paxton First successful road bridge that remains in use.

Built at Newhaven, Edinburgh
A landing pier in the Firth of Forth - Collapsed in 1896

Built over river South Esk replaced in 1931

Brighton Chain Pier - Built and destroyed by storm in 1896

Design proposals to bridge the River Thames between Little Tower Hill and Bermondsey

In letter to Robert Stevenson expressed feelings of likey bridge contract at Kingston and for prefabricated bridges exported to India

Designed by W Tierney Clark assisted by Charles Blacker Vignoles specialist advice and ironwork supplied by Samuel Brown & Co.

Proposal to link North and South Shields over the River Tyne

Tentative idea for bridging the River Wye between Beachley and Crick South Wales

Surveys carried out for proposed suspension bridges over the River Annan between Lockerbie and Lochinabar and nearby over the Dryfe Water Annandale Borders

Quotation 'in general terms' for a suspension bridge over the River Nith

Ruswarp Ford - Built over the River Esk by Ruswarp Mill North Hiding Yorkshire. Destroyed by flood in 1928 - re-built and finally destroyed by flood in 1880

East Lothian Railroad - Exchange of correspondence between Robert Stevenson and Samuel Brown as to costs of providing a suspension bridge over the Rivers Esk and Lyne

1826   Menai Straits - Samuel Brown's ideas and methods adopted by Telford in the construction of the suspension bridge viz. of straight bars and coupling bolts supplied by Brown's company

Warden Chain Bridge - built over the South Tyne near Hexham Northumberland - replaced early 20th century

Welney Chain Bridge - Built over the Hundred Feet River Welney Norfolk - replaced about 1926

Broughton - Built over the River Irwell (Manchester) Attributed to Samuel Brown but most likely the work of Thomas Cheek Hewe local Millwright

1829   Montrose Bridge - Built over the South Esk River Aberdeenshire - collapsed in 1830, rebuilt and destroyed in 1838 gale - again rebuilt and finally replaced in 1931.

Whorlton Bridge - Built over the River Tees near Barnard Castle Co. -Durham by John Green of Newcastle upon Tyne with a span of 173 ft using flat bars similar to Samuel Brown's Patent - Extant

1830   Kemeys Commander - Built over the River Usk near Kemeys Commander, Gwent - replaced in 1906

Stockton & Darlington - Built over the River Tees for the Stockton & Darlington Railway - replaced in 1842

Soham - Designed for bridging Middle Fen Drain near Stuntney but not built

Wellington Bridge 'Crailug' - Built over the River Dee Aberdeenshire Flat section eye bars and remains in original form apart from balustrade

1829 Clifton - built over the River Avon at Clifton Gorge to the design of I K Brunel - result of competition judged by Telford - 'a bold design proposed by Captain S Brown' (Drewy)

1832 Llandovery - Built over the River Towy near Llandovery. Designed by Philip Thomas - Messrs Brown Lenox & Co. Contractors Replaced 1890.

Findhorn Bridge - Built over the River Findhorn near Forres, Scotland - replaced in 1938

1833 Newcastle upon Tyne - Proposal to bridge the River Tyne in the line of the Great North Road with three rigid cast iron spans on masonry piers

Isle of Sheppey - Proposed design for a suspension bridge over the River Swale at Kings Ferry Kent

1834 Netherbyres House - Tension Bridge built over the Eye Water at Eyemouth Berwickshire for Samuel Brown's own use - removed in 1951

1835 Kalemouth - Built over the River Teviot near Kelso Roxburghshire and remains unaltered

1838 Kenmare - Built over Kenmare Sound, Kerry, Ireland replaced in 1932

1846 Earith - Built over the Great Ouse, Huntingdonshire replaced in 1932

1847 Westminster to Lambeth - Proposal to bridge the River Thames

'Alphabetical Index of Patentees of Invention' 1617 - 1852
The British Library Science Reference, Extract from pages 72,73.
Patentee 'Brown,Samuel 'until Progressive No.8994 when his name is recorded '
Brown, Samuel, Sir'.

No 2107 - 1808 Feb 4
'Rigging of Ships or Vessels' Lt. RN. Castle Court, Budge Row, Watling St. City of
London.

No 3888 - 1815 Feb 28
'Rudder, and Apparatus connected therewith' Cdr, RN. Mark Lane, London.

No 4090 - 1816 Dec 19
'Chain Manufactured by a new Process; and apparatus and improvements in
performing and executing the same. Cdr, RN. Mark Lane, London.

No 4137 - 1817 July 10
'Construction of a bridge by the formation and uniting of its component parts' Cdr,
RN. Mark Lane, London.

No 5929 - 1830 Apr 24
'Making Bolts and Chains' Cdr, RN.

No 6045 - 1830 Dec 6
'Drawing up Ships and other Vessels from the water on to the 'Land; Moving ships,
vessels, and other bodies on land, from one place to another' Cdr, RN. Billiter
Square. City of London.

No 6994 - 1841 June 19
Drawing carriages or other machines along inclined planes, railways and other
roads, and drawing or propelling vessels in canals, rivers, and other navigable
waters' Sir Samuel Brown Cdr, RN. Knight of the Royal Hanovarian Guelphic Order
Netherbyres House Ayton, County of Berwick.

No 9680 - 1843 March 27
'Construction of breakwaters; constructing and erecting lighthouses and beacons,
fixed and floating; apparatus connected therewith; anchors for mooring the same,
applicable also to ships' Sir Samuel Brown,Cdr, RN. Blackheath in the County of
Kent.

No 10,790 - 1845 July 29

'Formation of embankments for canals, docks or sea-walls; propulsion of locomotive engines and other carriages or bodies on canals and other inland waters, and on rail and other roads; Propelling vessels on the ocean and navigable rivers' Sir Samuel Brown, Cdr, RN. Blackheath in the County of Kent.

No 11,295 - 1846 July 14

'Railways and Railway Carriages; construction and arming of ships or vessels' Sir Samuel Brown, Cdr, RN. Blackheath in the County of Kent

No 11,887 - 1847 Oct 7

'Propelling and steering vessels; mariner's compass' Sir Samuel Brown, Cdr, RN. Blackheath in the County of Kent.

ANNO QUINQUAGESIMO NONO

GEORGII III. REGIS.

****

Cap. lviii.

An Act for more effectually making, amending, and
maintaining certain Roads and Bridges in the
Counties of *Durham* and *Berwick*, and Liberties
of *Berwick-upon-Tweed*; for repairing and maintaining certain other Roads therein mentioned;
and for improving the Entrance to the Town
of *Berwick-upon-Tweed.* [14th *June* 1819.]

WHEREAS by an Act paſſed in the Forty-ſecond Year of theReign
of His preſent Majeſty, intituled *An Act for the more effectually* 42G.3.c.117.
*amending, widening, improving, and keeping in Repair the Road
from the Turnpike Road at* Buckton Burn, *in the County of* Durham, *through*
Berwick-upon-Tweed *to* Lammerton Hill, *and alſo ſeveral other Roads therein
mentioned, lying in the ſaid County and within the Liberties of the ſaid Town
of* Berwick; *and alſo for erecting Two Bridges over the River* Tweed; *and
for making Two Roads from the ſaid Bridges to the Road leading from*
Berwick *aforeſaid to* Cornhill *in the ſaid County of* Durham; certain Perſons
therein deſcribed were appointed Truſtees for putting the ſaid Act into
Execution; and certain Powers and Authorities were given to them for
the more effectually making, amending, widening, improving, and maintaining the ſaid Roads, and for making, erecting, and maintaining the
ſaid Bridges, and, for putting in Execution all the other Powers by the
ſaid Act granted: And whereas by another Act paſſed in the Fiftieth 50 G. 3. c.61.
Year of the Reign of His preſent Majeſty, for amending the ſaid Act,
[*Local.*] 17 I the

the Powers of the said former Act were further enlarged : And whereas, under the Authority of the said Acts, the said Roads and the Bridges thereon have been made and repaired (excepting the Bridges by the said recited Acts authorized to be made over the River *Tweed*, and Roads of Communication therewith, which have not yet been made), and considerable Sums of Money have been advanced or borrowed on the Credit of the Tolls and Duties thereby authorized to be levied, which Sums of Money are still due and owing; and the said Roads and Bridges thereon cannot be effectually amended, widened, improved, and kept in Repair, nor the said Bridges over the River *Tweed*, and Roads of Communication made, nor the Sums of Money so advanced or borrowed, and the Interest thereof still owing be repaid, unless Powers be given to levy increased Tolls and Duties thereon : And whereas the following Roads lying in the County of *Durham*, *videlicet*, the Road from the *Cornhill* Turnpike Road by *Grindon* to the *Etal* Turnpike Road at or near *Felkington*; the Road from the said *Cornhill* Turnpike Road at or near *Longridge* to the said *Etal* Turnpike Road at or near *Murton*, and from thence by *Murton* and *Unthank Moor* to the *Wooler* Turnpike Road at or near the *Oxford* Limekilns; the Road from the River *Tweed* at or near *Norham* by *Shoresflood* to the *Etal* Turnpike Road at the *Folly*; and the Road from the River *Tweed* at or near *Norham* to the *Cornhill* Turnpike Road at *Velvet Hall* Bridge, and by *Thornton* to the *Folly*, are in bad Condition; and it is expedient that the same should be effectually made, improved, and maintained : And whereas it would be of great Utility to the Public, if Powers were given to improve the Entrance into the said Town of *Berwick-upon-Tweed* from the South : And whereas it is expedient that the said recited Acts should be repealed, and that more extensive Powers and Authorities should be given in relation to the same and the Purposes aforesaid : May it therefore please Your Majesty that it may be enacted; and be it enacted by the King's most Excellent Majesty, by and with the Advice and Consent of the Lords Spiritual and Temporal, and Commons, in this present Parliament assembled, and by the

Recited Act repealed. Authority of the same, That from and after the passing of this Act the said recited Acts of the Forty-second and Fiftieth Years of the Reign of His present Majesty shall be and the same are hereby repealed; and from thenceforth the several Tolls, Powers, Penalties, Forfeitures, Exemptions, Clauses, Matters, and Things in this Act contained, shall be put in Execution, and shall continue in force during the Term herein mentioned, for the Purpose of making, amending, improving, and maintaining the Roads hereinafter specified, and for the other Purposes in this Act mentioned.

Tolls made subject to the Payment of Monies due by recited Acts or this Act. II. Provided nevertheless, and be it enacted, That all the Tolls and Duties which are hereby authorized to be levied shall, under the Conditions and Provisions herein-after mentioned, be and the same are hereby made subject and liable to the Payment of all Sums of Money now due and owing on the Credit of the said Acts hereby repealed, and shall also be liable to the Payment of all Sums of Money which may hereafter be borrowed on the Credit of this Act, and of all Interest due or that may become due thereon, as fully and effectually to all Intents and Purposes as if such Money had been borrowed or become due and owing on the Credit or on account of **Debts to Trustees.** this Act; and that all and every Person and Persons owing any Sum or Sums of Money to the Trustees for executing the said recited Acts hereby repealed, or either of them, shall be liable to the Payment thereof to the Trustees under this Act; and all Conveyances, Covenants, Agreements,

5 Con-

Contracts or Securities entered into by any Person or Persons to or with the Trustees for executing the said recited Acts hereby repealed, according to the Provisions and Directions thereof, shall remain in full Force and Effect, and be, and continue available, in all Courts of Law and Equity until the same are fully satisfied and performed on account and for the Benefit of the Roads and Bridges under this Act; and all Mortgages, Bonds, Conveyances, Lettings of Tolls, Orders, Contracts, and Agreements duly made or entered into by the said Trustees for executing the said Acts hereby repealed, or either of them, shall so far as the same are not altered or avoided by this Act remain in full Force and Effect, and be observed and kept by the Trustees under this Act, according to the Terms and Stipulations thereof respectively; and that all Tolls and Duties due, and Penalties and Forfeitures incurred, in virtue of the said recited Acts hereby repealed, or of either of them, shall be held to be due and incurred, and shall be exigible by the Trustees under this Act; any Thing herein contained to the contrary notwithstanding.

All Contracts, Securities, &c. by virtue of former Acts, continued.

III. And be it enacted, That *Alexander Allan, George Adam Askew, Henry Askew, Thomas Grey Alder, William Rowland Alder,* the Honourable *Henry Grey Bennett,* Sir *Francis Blake* Baronet, *Robert Dudley Blake, George Baillie, George Baillie* junior, *Thomas Wentworth Beaumont,* the Mayor, Recorder, and Vicar of *Berwick* for the Time being, *George Buchan, Thomas Boswall, John Bell* of *Ninewar, Matthew Bell, Andrew Bonar, John Bonar, William Berry, William Burrell, James Grieve Burn, Thomas Bates,* Sir *Thomas Clavering* Baronet, Sir *William Purves,* Hume *Campbell* Baronet, *Henry Collingwood, Anthony Compton, Ralph Compton, Alexander Christie, William Clark, Matthew Culley* of *Fowberry, Matthew Culley* of *Akeld, James Dickson, Henry Dinning, Robert De Lisle, John Strangeways Donaldson, John Strangeways Donaldson, John Miller Dickson, John Dickson, George Dickson* of *Bellchester, Cuthbert Ellison, Thomas John Fordyce, Matthew Forster, James Forster, Ralph Forster* of *Downham, Thomas Forster* of *Lucker, Anthony Gregson, William Grieve* of *Ord House, James Grieve* of *Ord House, Burnett Grieve, John Grey* of *West Ord, John Grey* of *Berrington, James Grey, George Grey* of *Middle Ord, Stephen Fryer Gillum,* the Honourable   *Grey* commonly called Lord Viscount *Howick,* Sir *Carnaby Haggerston* Baronet, Sir *James Hall* Baronet, *Thomas Haggerston, Thomas Haggerston* junior, *Joseph Hume, George Home, William Hepburn, George Hogarth* of *Marshall Meadows, John Hall* of *Dunglass, Abraham Home, George Hogarth* of *Hilton, William Hay, James Home* of *Broomhouse, William Jeffreys, Robert Johnston, Hume Johnston, Thomas Kerr* of *Tone, John George Lambton, George Logan* of *Edrom, George Logan* of *New Edrom, William Stow Lundie, David Low, George Logan* of *Burnhouses,* Sir *John Marjoribanks* Baronet, Sir *Charles Miles Lambert Monck* Baronet, *Joseph Marshall, William Moile, James Murray,* the Honourable *William Mordaunt Maitland, Henry Morton, Thomas Marton,*   *Murray* of *Bellevue,* the Vicar of *Norham* for the Time being, *Robert Nisbet, Robert Nicholson* of *Loanend,* the Honourable *Charles Augustus Bennett* commonly called Lord *Ossulston, Daniel Ord, George Frederick Ord, Robert Ogle* of *Edlingham, Leonard Shaftoe Ord, John Bertram Orde,* the Honourable *William John Frederick Vane Powlett,* Sir *John Pringle* Baronet, *William Pattison, John Pratt* of *Bellshill, John Pratt* of *Melkington,* Sir *Matthew White Ridley* Baronet, Sir *James Riddell* Baronet, *Alexander Renton, Robert Romer, Mark Riddell, William Riddell,*

Trustees.

Riddell, John Robertson, William Robertson of *Ladykirk, Robert Robertson, David Renton,* Sir *James Stuart* Baronet, Sir *Thomas Stanley Maffey Stanley* Baronet, Sir *Horace David Cholwell Saint Paul* Baronet, *Henry Heneage Saint Paul, John Swinton* of *Swinton, John Swinton* junior of *Swinton, John Swinton* of *Broad Meadows, Henry Collingwood Selby, Prideaux John Selby, John Sibbit, Francis Sitwell, Grieve Smith, Michael Angelo Taylor, George Taitt, James Thomfon* of *Eamflaw, George Taylor* of *Chefwick, Richard Taylor* of *Chefwick,* the Honourable *John Vaughan, Richard Wharton, John Allan Wilkie, James Wilkie, William Waite, Robert Wilkie, John Wilfon* of *Cumledge, John Wauchope,* His Majefty's Juftices of the Peace for the Counties of *Durham* and *Berwick,* and their Succeffors, to be elected in Manner herein-after mentioned, fhall be and they are hereby appointed Truftees for the Purpofes of making, amending, improving, and maintaining the Roads herein-after fpecified, lying in the County of *Durham; videlicet,* the Road from *Berwick-upon-Tweed* to *Buckton Burn* in the County of *Durham,* being the Great Poft Road from *Berwick* to *Newcaftle* and *London;* the Road branching from the laft-mentioned Road near *Scremerfton,* and leading through *Ancroft* to the *Lickerburn,* being the High Road towards *Wooler,* in the County of *Northumberland,* and commonly called the *Wooler* Turnpike Road; the Road from the High Toll Gate at *Tweedmouth* in the County of *Durham,* through *Duddo,* to the Brook called *Horn Burn,* being the High Road from *Berwick* towards *Etal* and *Ford* Bridge, in the County of *Northumberland,* and commonly called the *Etal* Turnpike Road; the Road branching from the laft-mentioned Road and leading through the lower Part of the Village of *Eaft Ord,* through *Twifel* and *Cornhill,* to *Deddo Burn,* being the High Road from *Berwick* towards *Coldftream, Kelfo, Jedburgh,* and *Hawick,* and commonly called the *Cornhill* Turnpike Road; as alfo the Roads herein-after fpecified, lying within the Liberties of the Borough of *Berwick-upon-Tweed; videlicet,* the Road leading from *Berwick* aforefaid to *Lammerton* in the Shire of *Berwick,* being the Great Poft Road from *Berwick* to *Edinburgh;* the Road branching from the laft-mentioned Road at the Bottom of the *Calf Hill,* and leading by the South Side of the *Hallidown Hill* to the *Bound* Road at *Mordington* Toll Bar, being the High Road from *Berwick* to *Dunfe,* in the Shire of *Berwick;* the Road branching from the laft-mentioned Road at a Place called the *Alder Bufh,* and leading acrofs the River *Whitadder* to the *Bound* Road at *Paxton* Toll Bar; as alfo the Roads herein-after fpecified, lying in the faid County of *Durham; videlicet,* the Road leading from the *Cornhill* Turnpike Road, by *Grindon,* to the *Etal* Turnpike Road at or near *Felkington;* the Road from the *Cornhill* Turnpike Road at or near *Longridge,* to the *Etal* Turnpike Road at or near *Murton,* and from thence by *Murton* and *Unthank Moor* to the *Wooler* Turnpike Road, at or near the *Oxford* Limekilns; the Road from the River *Tweed* at or near *Norham,* by *Shorefwood,* to the *Etal* Turnpike Road at the *Folly;* the Road from the *Tweed* at or near *Norham,* to the *Cornhill* Turnpike Road at *Velvet Hall* Bridge, and by *Thornton* to the *Etal* Turnpike Road at or near the *Folly;* and for repairing the Bridges and neceffary Works on the fame; for erecting the faid Bridges over the River *Tweed;* for making the neceffary Roads of Communication therewith; for improving the Entrance into the faid Town of *Berwick-upon-Tweed* from the South; and for putting in Execution all the other Powers and Authorities by this Act given and granted.

IV. And

Power to make Bridges.

XXII. And whereas the Powers and Authorities by the said recited Acts granted, for building Two new Bridges across the River *Tweed*, and making Roads of Communication thereto, have not hitherto been carried into Execution; and it is expedient that such Powers and Authorities should be continued; be it therefore enacted, That the said Trustees, or any Three of them, may and they are hereby authorized and empowered to build or make, or cause to be built or made, of such Materials and Construction as they shall think fit, a Bridge across the said River *Tweed* in the most convenient Situation that can be found for the same, at the said Town of *Norham*, or within One Mile on either Side of the Market Cross thereof; and also another Bridge across the said River *Tweed*, in the most convenient Situation that can be found for the same, at the Ford or Place called *New Water Ford*, or within One Mile on either Side thereof; and to dig and make proper Foundations in the said River and on the Lands on each Side, for the Piers, Abutments, and Landings and Fixtures of the said Bridges, and each of them, and to cut and level the Banks of the said River in such Manner as shall be necessary and proper for the said Bridges, and to cut, remove, and take away all the Trees, Roots of Trees, Beds of Gravel, Sand, Mud, or other Impediment whatsoever, which may anywise hinder the erecting, making, and completing the said Bridges, or either of them, and to erect and make in and over the said River and the Lands adjoining or near the same, any Campshots, Trenches, and Landing Places, and from Time to Time and at all Times hereafter to do all other Matters and Things necessary or convenient for making, erecting, maintaining, or supporting the said Bridges, and for executing the Purposes of this Act; and that the said Trustees shall also, and they are hereby authorized and empowered to make or cause to be made Two or more new Roads in the most convenient Direction from the said Two Bridges to the *Cornhill* Turnpike Road, or to repair and amend any old Roads in the same Direction, and also to make and form a sufficient Communication between the North Ends of the said Bridges, and the next most convenient public Roads in the said County of *Berwick*; and for those Purposes to contract and agree for the purchasing of any Lands, Tenements, Ferries, Hereditaments, or Heritages, or other Property whatsoever, which the said Trustees or any Three or more of them shall think necessary to be made use of upon Account of the said Bridges, or either of them, or the said Roads of Communication therewith, or the Execution of any of the Powers of this Act; and also to treat, contract, and agree for the Loss or Damage any Person or Persons may sustain whose Lands, Tenements, Ferries, Hereditaments, Heritages, and other Property whatsoever, shall be really and truly encroached upon, or damaged or destroyed by or on account of the building of the said Bridges, or either of them, or the Roads of Communication therewith, or the Execution of any of the Powers of this Act; and out of the Monies arising by virtue of this Act, or out of any Money to be raised on the Credit thereof, to pay for the Purchase of such Lands, Tenements, Ferries, Hereditaments, Heritages, or other Property whatsoever, or for such Loss or Damage, such Sum or Sums of Money as shall be agreed upon between the Owners and Occupiers thereof and Persons interested therein, and the said Trustees or any Three or more of them, and also the Costs and Charges attending such Agreements and Purchases respectively.

15

XXIII. And

XXIII. And be it further enacted, That it shall be lawful for the said Trustees to cause a Turnpike and Toll House to be erected at such Place or Places upon or at either End of or near to each of the said respective Bridges herein-before mentioned and directed to be made or built, as they shall think proper, at each of which respective Turnpikes there shall be demanded and taken, by such Person or Persons as the said Trustees or any Five or more of them shall from Time to Time appoint for that Purpose, before any Persons, Horses, Cattle, or Carriages shall be permitted to pass through the same respectively, over and above the Tolls leviable on the said Roads in Manner herein-before mentioned, the Tolls following; (that is to say), *Tolls on or near the Bridges.*

For every Foot Passenger, One Penny:

For every Horse, Mule, or other Beast whatsoever, drawing any Coach, Landau, Chariot, Barouche, Berlin, Chaise, Hearse, Calash, Chair, Taxed Cart, or other such Carriage, One Shilling:

For every Horse, Mule, Ox, or other Beast whatsoever, drawing any Waggon, Wain, Cart, or other such Carriage, Sixpence:

For every Horse, Mule, or Ass, or other Beast of Burden, laden or unladen, and not drawing, the Sum of Sixpence:

For every Score of Oxen, Cows, or Neat Cattle, or young Horses, unshod, the Sum of One Shilling and Eight-pence, and so in proportion for any greater or less Number; and,

For every Score of Calves, Hogs, Sheep, Lambs, Goats, or Kids, the Sum of Ten-pence, and so in proportion for any greater or less Number.

XXIV. And whereas, for the Purpose of keeping the said Bridges and the Roads leading to and from the same in good Repair, and to render the Tolls to be collected thereon or near thereto productive, it was found necessary and expedient that certain Bye Roads leading to and from the said River *Tweed*, and the Ferries and Fords herein-after mentioned, should be shut up, stopped, and discontinued, and Powers and Authorities were by the said recited Acts granted upon the Erection of the said Two Bridges to shut up, stop, and discontinue such Bye Roads, Ferries, and Fords; and it is expedient that such Powers and Authorities should be continued; be it therefore enacted, That as soon as the said Bridge authorized to be built across the said River *Tweed*, at or near *New Water Ford* aforesaid, shall be erected and made passable, the Passage over and through the said River at *New Water Ford* aforesaid, and also the Bye Roads leading from *Gainslaw* and *West Ord* to the said River *Tweed*, and across the same, and also all other Bye Roads leading to and from the said River, and all Ferries and Fords over and through the same, between the Ford called *Upsetlington Ford* and *Berwick Bridge*, shall thenceforth be shut up and stopped, by building up the Passages to the said several Ferries and Fords and the said several Bye Roads with Stone and Lime, making Ditches across the same, or in such other Way and Manner as shall appear to the said Trustees most effectual for answering that Purpose; and it shall not be lawful, after the Time aforesaid, for any Person or Persons to cause or allow any Carriage, Horse, or Cattle, to pass through, across, or over the said River, at any Place situate between *Upsetlington Ford* and *Berwick Bridge* aforesaid, (except along the said Bridge at or near *New Water Ford*); and also that as soon as the said Bridge authorized to be built across the said River at or near *Norham* shall be erected and made passable, the Bye *Ferries and Bye Roads to be discontinued.*

Bye Roads leading from *Upfetlington* and *Norham* to the faid River *Tweed*, and acrofs the fame, and alfo the Bye Road leading from the Road at or near *Lennel Hill* to the faid River *Tweed*, and acrofs the fame, and all other Bye Roads leading to and acrofs the faid River, and all Ferries and Fords over the fame, between the Bridge called *Coldftream Bridge* and the faid Ford called *New Water Ford*, fhall thenceforth be fhut up and ftopped in fuch Manner as aforefaid; and it fhall not thereafter be lawful for any Perfon or Perfons to caufe or allow any Carriage, Horfe, or Cattle, to pafs through, acrofs, or over the faid River, at any Place fituate between the Bridge called *Coldftream Bridge* and the faid Ford called *New Water Ford*, except along the Bridge fo to be built at or near *Norham*; and alfo that when and as foon as both the faid Two Bridges herein-before authorized to be built fhall be erected and paffable, all Bye Roads leading to and acrofs the River *Tweed*, and all Ferries and Fords over and through the fame, between the faid Bridges called *Coldftream Bridge* and *Berwick Bridge*, fhall be ftopped, fhut up, and difcontinued in fuch Manner as aforefaid; and that it fhall not thereafter be lawful for any Perfon or Perfons to caufe or allow any Carriage, Horfe, or Cattle to pafs through, acrofs, or over the faid River *Tweed*, at any Place or Places between the faid Bridges called *Coldftream Bridge* and *Berwick Bridge*, except along the faid Bridges hereby authorized to be built, or either of them; or acrofs the Bridge authorized to be erected by an Act paffed in the Fifty-firft Year of the Reign of His prefent Majefty, intituled *An Act for making and maintaining a Railway from or near* Spittal, *in the County of* Durham, *to* Kelfo, *in the County of* Roxburgh; *and for erecting and maintaining a Bridge over the River* Tweed, *from the Parifh of* Norham, *in the County of* Durham, *to the Parifh of* Coldftream, *in the County of* Berwick; and if any Perfon or Perfons fhall, after the refpective Times aforefaid, ride, lead, or drive any Carriage, Horfes, Cattle, or Sheep, or caufe any Carriage, Horfes, Cattle, or Sheep to be ridden, driven, or led through, acrofs, or over the faid River, contrary to the Directions herein-before contained, whereby the Payment of any of the faid Tolls or any Part thereof fhall be avoided, or if any Perfon or Perfons fhall pull down, deftroy, or fill up any of the faid Walls or Ditches when fo made or erected as aforefaid, every Perfon fo offending in any of the Cafes aforefaid fhall for every fuch Offence forfeit and pay any Sum not exceeding Five Pounds: Provided always, that the Owners and Occupiers of all Lands, Houfes, Fifheries, and Hereditaments or Heritages, fituated and being adjoining or near to the faid River *Tweed*, and their Servants, Horfes, and Carriages, fhall be allowed free Paffage by fuch of the faid Bye-roads as lead thereto, on the fame Side of the River.

Tolls how to be levied in cafe of Non-payment.

XXV. And be it further enacted, That the faid refpective Sums of Money by this Act granted fhall be demanded and taken as for or in the Name of Toll; and if any Perfon or Perfons fubject to the Payment of any of the faid Tolls fhall after Demand thereof neglect or refufe to pay the fame, it fhall be lawful for the Perfon or Perfons appointed to collect the faid Tolls, to levy the fame by Diftrefs of any Horfe or Horfes, or other Cattle or Carriage, upon which fuch Toll is by this Act impofed on fuch Perfon or Perfons, with the Harnefs or Accoutrements thereof refpectively, (except the Bridle or Halter apart from the Horfe or other Beaft); and if fuch Toll and the reafonable Charges of making and keeping fuch Diftrefs fhall not be paid within the Space of Five Days after fuch Diftrefs fhall be made
and

and taken, the Perfon or Perfons making fuch Diftrefs may, under the Authority of a Warrant under the Hand of any One Juftice of the Peace of the County or Liberty wherein fuch Diftrefs fhall have been made, (which Warrant any fuch Juftice is hereby empowered to grant); fell the Horfes, Cattle, or Carriages, with their Harnefs or Accoutrements fo diftrained, returning the Overplus (if any) upon Demand to the Owner thereof, after fuch Toll and all reafonable Charges fhall be deducted.

XXVI. And be it enacted, That it fhall and may be lawful for the faid Truftees, or any Three or more of them, at any General Meeting affembled, whenever they fhall deem it expedient, to leffen and reduce the Tolls and Duties hereby granted, and made payable, and again to advance the fame, fo as every fuch Reduction be made with the Confent of the Perfon or Perfons entitled to Three-fourth Parts of the Money, then due on Security of the faid Tolls, and fo as the fame do not at any Time exceed the Tolls and Duties granted and made payable by this Act. *Power to reduce the Tolls and raife them.*

XXVII. Provided always, and be it further enacted, That no Perfon who fhall have paid the Toll by this Act impofed, for paffing through any of the Gates or Turnpikes erected or to be erected by virtue of this Act, fhall be fubject to the Payment of any Toll for returning through fuch Gate or Turnpike the fame Day, before Twelve of the Clock at Night, with the fame Cattle, or with the fame Horfes or other Beafts of Draught or Burden, drawing the fame Coach, Waggon, or other Carriage, or bearing the fame Perfon, but fhall pafs Toll-free, upon producing to the Collector or Collectors at fuch Turnpike or Turnpikes refpectively a Note or Ticket, which the Collector to whom the faid Toll fhall have been paid is hereby required to give *gratis* upon Receipt of the Tolls, and fuch Tickets fhall fpecify the feveral Gates freed by fuch Payment : Provided always, that no Perfon or Perfons fhall be liable to pay Toll more than Once for any Horfe, or other Beaft of Draught, drawing any Cart or other Carriage, Once going for and returning loaded with Coal or Lime, and that without Regard to the Hour of the Day or Night, at which fuch Horfe or other Beaft with the Cart or other Carriage fhall pafs and repafs. *Tolls to be paid but once a Day.*

XXVIII. And be it enacted, That it fhall and may be lawful for the faid Truftees to continue and erect, or caufe to be erected, One or more Gate or Gates, Turnpike or Turnpikes, on the Side or Sides of the aforefaid Roads hereby directed to be repaired, and acrofs any Lane or Way leading out of the fame, and alfo a Toll Houfe or Toll Houfes at each fuch Gate or Turnpike, and there to take or receive fuch Tolls or Duties as are by this Act granted and made payable ; but fo as that a Ticket received at any fuch Side Gate fhall entitle the Receiver thereof to pafs Toll-free through the next Gate or Turnpike upon the Roads hereby directed to be repaired, if within Six Miles, on the fame Day, to be computed as aforefaid. *Side Gates.*

XXIX. Provided always, and be it enacted, That in cafe of any Difpute as to the Payment of any of the faid Tolls and Duties, it fhall be lawful to any One or more Juftice or Juftices of the Peace for the faid Counties of *Durham* or *Berwick*, or Town of *Berwick-upon-Tweed*, upon Complaint made in relation to the fame, to grant Warrant for fummoning the *Power to Juftices to decide in Difputes as to Toll.*

[*Local.*]   17 N   Party

said Street shall be flagged and paved by the Person or Persons, Body or Bodies Politic, Corporate, or Collegiate, subject or liable to flag or pave the Footways of the said Town, in such Manner as the Footways of the other Streets of the said Town are flagged and paved.

Quay Gate to be shut up, and new Way to the Quay to be made.

XLVII. And be it further enacted, That for the Purpose of improving the said Street the said Trustees shall have full Power and Authority to cause the present Passage and Gateway leading from the said Street of *Bridge Street* to the Quay to be contracted so as to be sufficient for and used by Foot Passengers only, and not less than Five Feet in Width, and in Place of the present Passage for Horses and Carriages, to make another Road or Passage for Horses and Carriages, from that Part of the Street situate between the Bridge Gate and the Garrison Wall adjoining the Quay, or in some other convenient Place; and for that Purpose to purchase the Fish House on the Quay now occupied or used by the old Shipping Company of *Berwick*, and the Block-maker's Shop, occupied by *Robert Lyall* and Company, and to cause the same to be wholly or partially removed, and to pay for the same in Manner aforesaid, and to use the Scites thereof or Part thereof for the said Passage, and the Ground so used shall for ever after be deemed to be a Public Common Highway: Provided always, that the Consent and Approbation of His Majesty's Honorable Board of Ordnance, or Barrack Board, as the Case may require, be previously obtained for the making of the said new Passage and Road, and for widening or altering the said Bridge Gate, and that the same be done under the Direction of the Officers of the said Boards respectively; and in future the said Road or Passage shall be repaired and maintained by the said Trustees.

Power to repair Twisel Bridge, Haggerston and Gainslaw Bridge.

XLVII. And be it enacted, That the said Trustees shall and may apply so much of the Money which shall be collected at the said Toll Gates as they shall from Time to Time judge necessary for keeping in Repair the Bridges called *Twisel Bridge* and *Haggerston* North and South Bridges, and also the Wooden Bridge over the River *Whitadder* at *Gainslaw* within the Liberties of *Berwick* aforesaid, but they shall not be bound to rebuild or renew the said Bridge at *Gainslaw*.

Subscribers to be obliged to pay Subscriptions.

XLVIII. And be it enacted, That if any Person or Persons who hath or have already subscribed towards the Expence of obtaining and passing this Act, or for any of the Purposes herein mentioned, or any other Person or Persons who shall hereafter become such Subscriber or Subscribers, their respective Executors or Administrators, shall after Twenty Days previous Notice in Writing under the Hand of the Treasurer or Clerk to the said Trustees for that Purpose, to him, her, or them given, or left at his, her, or their Dwelling House or usual Place or Places of Abode, refuse or neglect to make Payment of the respective Sums by him, her, or them subscribed, or agreed to be subscribed, or such Part or Parts thereof as may be required in such Notice, it shall be lawful for the said Trustees to bring or cause to be brought in the Name of their said Clerk, any Action of Debt or on the Case, Bill, Plaint, or Suit, against such Person or Persons so neglecting or refusing as aforesaid, his, her, or their Heirs, Executors, or Administrators, in any of His Majesty's Courts of Record at *Westminster*, wherein no Essoign, Protection, or Wager of Law, nor more than One Imparlance, shall be allowed, or in the Court of

5   Session

Seffion in *Scotland*, by way of Summary Complaint or Petition; and after Proof of fuch Perfon or Perfons having fubfcribed or agreed to fubfcribe, and that fuch Notice was given as aforefaid, fuch Perfon or Perfons, his, her, or their Heirs, Executors, or Adminiftrators, fhall be compelled to pay the Sum or Sums of Money fo by him, her, or them fubfcribed, or agreed to be fubfcribed as aforefaid, together with full Cofts of Suit.

XLIX. And be it further enacted, That the faid Truftees may and they are hereby empowered from Time to Time to contract and agree with any Perfon or Perfons for the making, repairing, altering, turning, or amending the faid Roads, Bridges, and Works therewith connected, or any Part or Parts thereof, in fuch Manner as the faid Truftees fhall think proper; and that all Contracts and Agreements in Writing, entered into purfuant to an Order made at any Meeting by the faid Truftees, fhall be binding on all Parties who fhall fign the fame, his, her, or their Heirs, Executors, and Adminiftrators; and that Actions and Suits may be maintained thereon, and Damages and Cofts recovered againft the Party or Parties failing in the Execution of fuch Contracts or Agreements.

Truftees may contract for repairing the Roads, &c.

L. And be it enacted, That the faid Truftees are hereby authorized and empowered, at any Time or Times during the Continuance of this Act (in cafe they fhall think it neceffary), to turn, alter, or widen the Courfe of any Part or Parts of the faid Roads, or to turn or lead any Part or Parts of the faid Roads another Way or any other Ways, and for that Purpofe fhall have full Power and Authority from Time to Time to contract and agree with the feveral Owners and Occupiers of and Perfons interefted in any Lands, Hereditaments, or Heritages lying by, contiguous, or near to any Part or Parts of any of the faid Roads for the Purchafe or Exchange of any fuch Lands, Hereditaments, or Heritages, or for the Lofs or Damage any fuch Owners, Occupiers, or Perfons interefted fhall or may fuftain by fuch turning, altering, or widening of any Part of any of the faid Roads, (provided always, that fuch Part or Parts of the faid Roads as fhall be fo widened, turned, or altered be not thereby made of greater Breadth than Sixty Feet, including the Ditches), and out of the Tolls and Duties by this Act granted, and out of any Monies already borrowed or to be borrowed on the Credit of this Act, to pay for fuch Lands, Hereditaments, and Heritages, and for fuch Lofs and Damage, fuch Sum or Sums of Money as fhall be agreed upon between fuch Owners, Occupiers, and Perfons interefted as aforefaid and the faid Truftees, and alfo the Cofts and Charges attending fuch Agreement: Provided always, that it fhall not be lawful for the faid Truftees, in turning, altering, or widening the Courfe of any of the faid Roads, to deviate more than One hundred Yards from the prefent Line or Courfe thereof, nor to take or pull down any Dwelling-houfe, or other Building, or to take in or make ufe of any Orchard, Garden, Yard, Paddock, Park, Planted Walk, or Avenue to a Houfe, or any inclofed Ground planted and fet apart as a Nurfery for Trees, other than and except the Houfes, Buildings, and Grounds mentioned in the Schedule hereunto annexed, without the Confent in Writing of the Owners or reputed Owners and Occupiers for the Time being of the Lands, Hereditaments, and Heritages which may be affected by any fuch Diverfion, Alteration, or Widening.

Power to widen or alter Roads.

Not to deviate more than 100 Yards, without Confent of Owner and Occupiers.

LI. And

The Need for the Bridge and Reason for Suspension

In a meaningful sense, the Industrial revolution never came to Berwickshire or North Durham but its influence did impact upon agricultural production in the region, with price rises for barley, wheat and oats – in turn, land values soared. It also created a high demand for lime. To an extent, limestone existed over the whole district but coal, the vital ingredient for limestone kiln burning, only existed south of the River Tweed in the coalfields of North Durham, in which areas it was economic for the processing to occur. Transportation of the final kilned product in either slaked or lump form was expensive – a problem well recognised by government and, in particular, George III, who showed great interest in agricultural and transport problems. As in England, Scotland was involved with a massive programme to provide metalled roads and bridges that would suffice obvious neds and wider trade expansion.

The ford between Tweedhill and Horncliffe was an ancient crossing of the River Tweed, some 5.25 miles upriver from the 17th century bridge at Berwick – recorded as New Water Ford since 1542. The name originates from the Scottish salmon water and, before the Treaty of Berwick in 1639, Charles I camped his army on the high English bank overlooking the ford against the Covenanters. Hollar's contemporary map shows the crossing point as King's Ford, a name long since forgotten.

The Berwick and North Durham Turnpike Trustees secured the authority of Parliament to bridge the river in 1802 and years of inactivity caused a further enabling Act to be passed in 1819. *(Fig 64)* However, decisions had been made to proceed with both roads and bridge well before this date within the powers of the earlier Act. William Willoby, clerk to the trustees, published a Notice "in terms of a special order of the House of Commons" in the *Berwick Advertiser* on March 20th and April 3rd 1819, the main contents reading:

> "An Act for the more effectively Amending, Widening, Improving and keeping in Repair, the Road from the Turnpike Rad at Buckden Burn in the County of Durham, through Berwick-upon-Tweed to Lamberton Hill, and also several other Roads therein mentioned lying in the said county, and within the liberties of the said town of Berwick; and also for Erecting Two Bridges over the River Tweed, and for making Two Roads from the said Bridges to the road leading from Berwick aforesaid to Cornhill, in the said County of Durham; " and also of an Act passed in the Fiftieth Year of the Reign of His present Majesty, for amending the said Act; and also for the Amending, Widening, Improving and Keeping in Repair, the Road from the Cornhill Turnpike, by Grindon, to the Etal Turnpike, at or near Felkington; the Road from the said Cornhill Turnpike, at or near Longridge, to the said Etal Turnpike, at or near Murton, and from thence by Unthank Moor to the Wooler Turnpike Road at or near Oxford Lime Kilns; the Road from the River Tweed at or near Norham by Shoreswood, to the Etal Turnpike at the Folly, and Road from the Tweed at or near Norham, to the Cornhill Turnpike, at Velvet Hall Bridge, and by Thornton to the Folly; and for levying and collecting certain Tolls on the several last mentioned Roads, the said several Roads and Bridges being within the Township and Parish and in the Parishes of Ladykirk and Hutton, in the County of Berwick, and in the several Townships of Tweedmouth, Spittal, and Ord...." etc

The Act clearly provided for those existing Turnpike Roads to be improved which formed the triangle between Berwick, Wooler in the south and Cornhill by Coldstream to the West. At the time, bridges existed at Berwick and Coldstream at a river distance apart of some 15¾ miles, and a reliance upon fords provided hazardous points of crossing.

New Water Ford was an obvious site for bridging as approach routes satisfied both commerce and people. News of the possible bridge created tremendous local enthusiasm as it would remove the danger to movement across the river created by freezing in the winter, a rapid rise in the level with rain – apart from the tides adding yet another difficulty. All too often, those conditions were compounded by the deep river channel on the English side, catching out waggon drivers with fatal consequences.

The position of the bridge was both needful and splendid in concept. Below Ladykirk, the Tweed winds in a series of majestic reaches past the heights of Norham Castle, Greenhill and Horncliffe until New Water Ford where the river line is almost north/south and its crossing east/west. In recent years a long narrow island has appeared at the old Ford position forming a main and secondary river stream, but in 1819 only the main stream existed and the banks rose more gently on both sides than in any other nearby position up or down river. But in times of flood the river width was twice the norm.

Paxton House had stood for some 75 years on the Scottish side, a half mile due north of the Ford and the long river reach with commanding views from its one hundred feet high elevation over wooded banks and silvery water.

Four years before the bridge was built, a young American visitor to Paxton House etched his feelings upon a bedroom window glass that overlooked the Ford:

"If human hearts were formed of glass to show the thoughts that through them pass How seldom would that prospect be So fair as what through this we see".
W.B October 4 - 1816 (W.B. – Will Blair)

In 1791, a map was prepared from survey and carries the title: "Plan of the roads in the County of Berwick proposed to be repaired by Turnpike laid down on a scale of two inches to a mile from an Actual Survey and measure 1791…NB the waters are determined at random except where they Cross the Roads Survey'd…"

The interest in this map is the line of road between Fishwick and over the Ford to Loanend Township that passes over Tweedhill before the house was built. Armstrong's Map of Northumberland 1769 also shows the river Ford crossing in similar position, and Robert

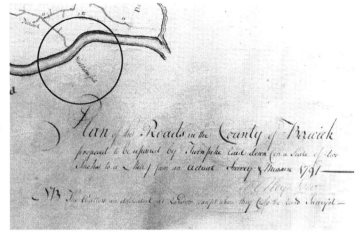

Fig 65 - Detail: Plan of the Roads in the County of Berwick 1791

Rule's Map of Norham and Islandshires 1842 shows the change in road line on the Scottish side owing to the eventual bridge position and the building of Tweedhill House. This map also shows the old Ford road down to the river at Bank Head, although the ferry quickly went out of use.

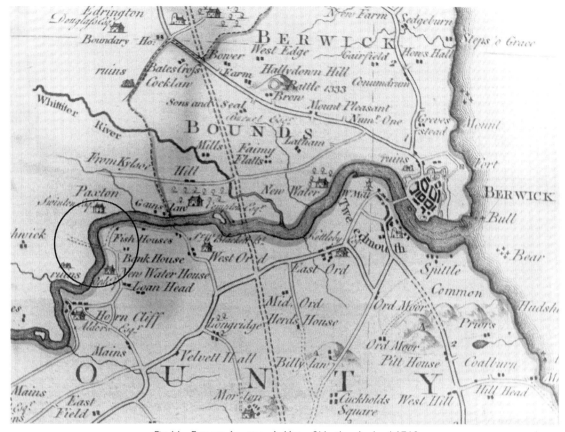

Fig 66 - Extract: Armstrong's Map of Northumberland 1769

In the early days of the bridge's existence, farmers and others attempted to overcome payment of tolls by driving by-pass routes and threatening the gatekeepers, but all were effectively dealt with under the powers of the Act and the newly-established routes reluctantly became accepted. The merit of a suspension bridge is its comparative low cost, as the design allows a greater load to be carried in relation to the self-weight of the bridge than with traditional masonry arch forms. However, the suspension bridge is a very special and exciting form of structure which alone answers very specific types of problem, not least the ability to span considerable distances without piers.

As is the case today, Samuel Brown wanted to bridge gaps with economy and durability that would carry the loads required and remove obstruction to river flow. His thoughts were also on the financial benefits that would derive from the use of circular bar iron, the perfection of its quality and proven technology then well established, not least the confidence gained from the success of his experimental bridge at the Millwall works.

Fundamental problems are inherent in suspension bridges and Samuel Brown must have been aware of most. The American, James Finley, had paved the way to a logical understanding of the basic principles in 1801 with a 70 feet single span, 13 feet width, over Jacob's Creek, Fayette

County, Pennsylvania. It was paid for, by agreement of Fayette County and Westmoreland County, to erect an iron bridge over Jacob's creek; local industry providing the ironwork. He patented the system in 1808. Finley's interests most likely developed after a stay in Philadelphia between 1790 and 1799, very much a scientific centre.

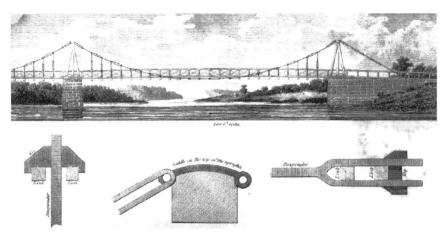

Fig 67 - Drawing:"View of the Chain Bridge invented by James Finley Esq"

Finley's main realisation was the need for a stiffened road deck to overcome wind and rolling loads; the deformation of a suspended deck when subject to a moving load is a large proportion of the whole allowed for. An added problem is the behaviour of the road deck, which rises as a wave in front of a moving load. This condition produces much greater stresses than would result from a weight at rest. Sam Brown was concerned about this and wanted to fit the roadway with iron rails to distribute load and reduce wear of the timber decking, but cast out the idea.

Wind is another factor and greater destructive force, producing oscillations in the whole structure, causing the road deck to lift and twist, resulting in intense strains. These effects may be reduced by stiffening the deck lengthwise and laterally by tying the ends to the abutments. Brown had knowledge of such activity, accounting for the diagonal bracing that interlaces around the ends of deck beams at each side. The bars making up this bracing are not attached to the bridge deck in any way; only to abutments at each end.

These bracings do not seem to serve any other purpose than act as longitudinal restraining members upon movement of the bridge beck vertically, yet their looseness of fitting would permit considerable flexing. Their contribution to the stability of the deck is not assessable.

During the 1974 restoration work, early means of tying the bridge deck ends to the abutments was discovered. From what remains, it appears that a form of sliding prongs with slip joints was employed, permitting longitudinal expansion of the deck and preventing the deck end from lifting.

James Finley, born 1762 of Scottish Presbyterian descent, eventually settled in Fayette County, Pennsylvania, very much a frontier region. His education and outlook was totally different from that of Samuel Brown; from the outset, following Presbyterian teaching with enthusiasm for the "three R's" and science and philosophy. The social structure required everyone to accept and knuckle down to the tasks of farming, building and making all and everything necessary for survival. Finley enjoyed a relatively high social standing. He had an intense interest in the local industry and the infrastructure of the area; transport, roads, canals, bridges etc. and in a sense, at the time, little different from that in Britain. According to the French engineer Joseph Cordier, who had toured America seeking technology information, some 18 suspension bridges were built to Finley's design principle between his first at Jacob's Creek and 1820. Finley's majestic Essex -Merrimack Bridge had endured hard use conditions, snow, oxen-hauled carts and, in later years, electric street cars. In 1909 it was replaced by a wire-cable suspension bridge.

Although it would be churlish to make like-for-like comparisons, it would be reasonable to say that Samuel Brown's concept of shackle pin connections for eye bar chains was superior to Finley's long-link chains, although modified by builders from time to time.

Union Bridge has survived for almost 200 years with little change to the primary structure but the future for suspension bridges undoubtedly lies in the wire cable developed by John A Roebling, the German-born American civil engineer, after his replacement for the Essex-Merrimack in 1909.

Samuel Brown's idea for a 1000ft span suspension bridge clearly set out in his Specification Patent 4137 AD 1817 was an ambitious proposal, mindful of future bridge projects likely to fall within such scale of operations. Based upon detail contained in the Specification, reasonable load assessments and calculations can be made:

Summation

Overall suspended dead weight	530 tons with a dip (d) of 40ft
Parabolic chain profile tension at lowest point due to dead weight only amounts to some…	1656 tons ft
Max tension at piers	1677 tons ft
Max stress in 8 chains	8.73 tons/inch^2
Shear stress in each coupling (double shear)	5.45 tons/inch^2
Bearing stress	15 tons ft/inch^2
Assuming a yield stress of 12.5 tons/inch^2 Stresses at yield point in suspension chain	228.8 tons ft
Deck area = 1000 x 30 sq ft; therefore superload to produce yield in bars of chain	510lbs/ft run of bridge
Chain bolts – shear stress at this superload	7.8 tons/inch^2
Bearing stress at this superload	21.5 tons/inch^2
Total load/rod	0.73 tons ft

In ideal calm weather conditions all would be well but wind loading in addition to above would lead to worse stresses compounded by vibration problems with critical consequences.

A.D. 1817 . . . . Nº 4137.

SPECIFICATION

OF

SAMUEL BROWN.

CONSTRUCTION OF BRIDGES.

LONDON:
PRINTED BY GEORGE E. EYRE AND WILLIAM SPOTTISWOODE,
PRINTERS TO THE QUEEN'S MOST EXCELLENT MAJESTY :
PUBLISHED AT THE GREAT SEAL PATENT OFFICE,
25, SOUTHAMPTON BUILDINGS, HOLBORN.

Price 1s. 1d. 1856.

A.D. 1817 . . . . Nº 4137.

Construction of Bridges.

BROWN'S SPECIFICATION.

TO ALL TO WHOM THESE PRESENTS SHALL COME, I, SAMUEL BROWN, of Mark Lane, in the City of London, Commander in His Majesty's Royal Navy, do send greeting.

WHEREAS His most Excellent Majesty King George the Third, by His
5 Royal Letters Patent under the Great Seal of Great Britain, bearing date at Westminster, the Tenth day of July, in the fifty-seventh year of His reign, did give and grant unto me, the said Samuel Brown, His especial license that I, the said Samuel Brown, my executors, administrators, and assigns, or such others as I or they should at any time agree with, and no others, during
10 the term of years therein expressed, should and lawfully might make, use, exercise, and vend, within England, Wales, and the Town of Berwick-upon-Tweed, my "INVENTION OR IMPROVEMENT IN THE CONSTRUCTION OF A BRIDGE, BY THE FORMATION AND UNITING OF ITS COMPONENT PARTS IN A MANNER NOT HITHERTO PRACTISED;" in which said Letters Patent there is contained a
15 proviso, obliging me, the said Samuel Brown, by an instrument in writing under my hand and seal, particularly to describe and ascertain the nature of my said Invention, and in what manner the same is to be performed, and to cause the same to be inrolled in His said Majesty's High Court of Chancery within six calendar months next and immediately after the date of the said
20 recited Letters Patent, as in and by the same, reference being thereto had, will more fully and at large appear.

NOW KNOW YE, that in compliance with the said proviso, I, the said Samuel Brown, do hereby declare that my said Invention or Improvement consists of a bridge or bridges of suspension, in the construction of which,

Brown's Improvement in the Construction of a Bridge.

instead of using metal chains formed of links, wires, or by other methods, as heretofore practised, I employ a combination of straight bars, bolts, or rods, joined or united at their ends either by side plates and bolts, coupling boxes, welding, or other suitable methods, so that these bars, bolts, or rods so joined become in effect one entire length or piece the whole extent or length 5 of the bridge, and support their proper proportion of the tension in the direct line of the curve which they assume or partake of, and these constitute my main lines or means of suspension. The number and consistency of these main suspending lines must depend on the extent of the span or opening, and the general magnitude of the design of the bridge, and each of the main sus- 10 pending lines may be formed of a single series of bars, bolts, or rods joined in the manner and direction before-mentioned, or they may consist of a lateral combination of several entire lengths of bars, bolts, or rods bound securely together by hoops or other suitable means; and I do hereby declare that the following description, and the Figures hereunto annexed, contain a true account 15 of various methods by which my said Invention or Improvement may be carried into effect.

To enable the public more fully to appreciate the merits of these designs, it will be necessary for me to make some observations on the principle and effect of bridges of suspension which have been in use prior to this Invention. The 20 most common are those composed of chains suspended from elevated points, either of natural rocks, or some edifice of stone or wood, on either side of the river or valley to be passed. There are others, more recently formed, of wires suspended in this manner, but those are merely intended for the convenience of foot passengers. In all bridges of the Catenarian order there must be some 25 similarity in the principle of forming the pieces, the points of suspension, and securing the extremities of the chains, of whatever form these may be, and as I propose, in framing this my Specification, to be very explicit on those important parts of the design, I shall at present refrain from any observations on this head, and proceed to explain the defects and imperfections which I 30 conceive my Invention is calculated to obviate or remedy.

It is universally admitted that all materials will support the greatest compression in a perpendicular position; so their cohesion, or the power by which they resist being pulled asunder, is greater when acted upon in a direct line against the force applied; and that the measure of strength of any 35 material, whether granulous or fibrous, is always in proportion to the area of its section, provided the part which is subject to the action of a receding force is uniform in its texture. It must necessarily follow, that the Catenarian curve, composed of links, not only possesses great superfluity of weight, but that the

material is placed in a situation much less favorable for resisting the strain than one constructed of straight bolts, bars, or rods supporting the tension in the direction of their length, which is the nature and principle of my Invention, as before stated. It will not be necessary to enter into any theoretical
5 reasoning on the subject, as the comparative weight and strength of chains, bolts, and bars have been accurately found, by numerous corroborative experiments at my manufactory, near Poplar, and an account of them, as well as of the machine by which they were performed, is to be found in Mr. Barlow's late work, published in London, intitled "An Essay on the Strength and Stress
10 of Timber." I shall, therefore, confine myself to the description of two of the above experiments as sufficiently illustrative of the fact. A cylindrical bolt of Welsh iron, denominated No. 3, or cable iron, measured two inches in diameter and twelve feet six inches long, weighed one hundred and thirty-two pounds, and required a force of eighty-two tons and three quarters to tear it asunder,
15 and it stretched during the operation eighteen inches and a half. A bar of the same description of iron measured three inches in depth and one inch in thickness, twelve feet long, weighed one hundred and twenty-four pounds, and required a force of seventy-two tons and one quarter to pull it asunder, and stretched thirteen inches in the process. Both the bolt and the bar are parts
20 of the Invention marked in Figures 3 and 4 in the accompanying Drawing. A chain of the same sort of iron, one inch and a half diameter, twelve feet six inches long, weighed two hundred and forty-one pounds, was broken by a force of seventy-nine tons, and stretched during the process twenty-three inches; thus the excess of weight was nearly double and the strength barely equal, and
25 as every portion of the chain between the points of suspension, indeed within the extremities where they are fixed, operates against its strength, the additional weight must be considered as so much actual loss of support. It is further to be observed, that bridges, of whatever denomination, are usually public works, and that the chains would, in all probability, be obtained by public contract;
30 but from the manner in which they are usually manufactured throughout the country, they will not bear more than one-third of the strain of those made and proved at the works before-mentioned; and as a bridge of chain of any magnitude must consist of many thousand links, one superficial or unsound sheet or welding might prove fatal to the whole fabric. In all bridges of sus-
35 pension, whether constructed of chains, wires, or bars, it is of the utmost importance that every part should maintain its due portion of the tension and weight to which the whole is subject, and the fewer the parts which compose the great Catenarian lines, the greater is the certainty of accomplishing this essential point. A bridge of wires, being the most complicated of any, is the

most objectionable. Where they are intended merely for the accomodation of foot passengers they may be easily contrived and constructed; but one composed of such slender and ductile materials, of sufficient strength to support the weight of loaded carriages, must consist of such a multiplicity of parts that an united effort by their proper adjustment is not to be expected. The want 5 of durability is of itself an insuperable objection to wire bridges, as well as all others constructed of such slender filaments. The immense surface exposed to the action of the atmosphere would infallibly cause a rapid decay, and the common preventatives of corrosion could not be made generally beneficial, because it is impossible to apply any composition to the interstices and crossings 10 of the wires or seams of the filaments where they are most liable to be effected; and as the defects cannot there be observed, the bridge might be in a state of dangerous insecurity, while it indicated no appearance of decay. The plans which I have adopted for removing and remedying the foregoing objections have not been hastily formed, but have been deduced from a series of experi- 15 ments which I made on the comparative strength of bolts and bars and chains of different descriptions in the year One thousand eight hundred and eight. About that period I made drawings and calculations of the strength of bridges of suspension on the precise principle of the design which is the subject of the above recited Patent. A variety of important engagements prevented me from 20 making any experiments upon the design itself on a scale commensurate to its importance till One thousand eight hundred and thirteen, when I constructed a bridge of straight bars for this purpose on my own premises, where it still remains. The span or extent of this bridge is one hundred and five feet, and although the whole of the iron work weighs only thirty-seven hundred weight, 25 it has supported loaded carts and carriages of various descriptions.

Having stated the constituent principle of the Invention, I shall now proceed, in as concise a manner as the nature of the subject will admit, to describe the several methods of combining the component parts together, whereby the whole is completed.   30

Fig. 1 represents a general view of a bridge upon my plan of a span or extent of one thousand feet. It consists of eight principal double lines of suspension, the situation of which are seen at A, A, A, A, and B, B, B, B, in Fig. 7, and four lower lines of bars for the support of the roadway, the situation of which are seen at E, E, E, E, in the same Figure, the greatest point of 35 deflection, or versed sine of the curves, in the lines of bars A and B, in Figure 1, being forty feet below their respective points of suspension C and D. The undermost line of bars E, on which the platform or roadway is laid, are suspended by the perpendicular bars, a few of which are marked F, *f*, from

Brown's Improvement in the Construction of a Bridge.

the upper lines A and B. Any tension on the lower lines of bars E will be injurious unless they are extended with the same degree of curvature, or are parallel to A and B, in which case they would sustain their due proportion of the strain, but then the piers and abutments would require to be con-

5 siderably and inconveniently heightened. I do not, therefore, allow these under bars to draw upon the abutments; but I prefer convexing them into an easy curve upwards, whereby they are made of important service in counteracting the effect of undulatory motion, which, without the reaction of such a reversed curve or arch, is to be apprehended during the violent

10 storms and gusts of wind to which these bridges may be exposed. The reversed curve or arch I recommend to rise or have a versed sine, in the proportion of twenty feet in a thousand feet of length, which is adjusted by the suspending bars F, *f*. Figure 2 represents a view of one side pier and part of the same bridge on an enlarged scale. In order to produce

15 an equal bearing on all the great Catenarian lines, the perpendicular suspending bars F, *f*, F, hang alternately, by means of double key heads on the first lines A and the second lines B. For example, the perpendicular bar No. 1, which carries the first joint or length of the roadway bars, passes between the double bars B, and rests equally on the double lines of bars A at *m*, and the perpen-

20 dicular bar No. 2 rests on the double lines of bars B at *n*; the perpendicular bar No. 3 passes between the lower bars B and rests on the upper bars A at *o*, and so on, throughout the structure. In this Figure the double lines of bars cannot be shewn, but will presently be explained by N and O in Fig. 3. G, in Figure 3, is one of the longitudinal bars of which the great Catenarian

25 lines of suspension A and B are composed, it is six inches deep by two inches thick, and I recommend to be about fourteen feet long, or of other suitable lengths. The platform or roadway bars E are of the same shape, and united in the same manner as the principal suspending bars A and B, but as they are free from tension they do not require to be stronger than to support the

30 ends of the platform beams without bending, and are half the length of the bars above them. The ends of all the bars are to be upset or swelled out, so that when the bolt hole is punched the surrounding metal may rather exceed the quantity in the common section of the bar. H is one of the plates by which the bars are united; the section of these plates should rather exceed

35 half the section of the main bars, the metal round the bolt hole to exceed the general section, as in the preceeding case. I, section of a round bolt, three inches and an half in diameter, shewn in elevation at K; by these the coupling plates, and the bars are attached, and are then keyed tight by the usual mode

of forelocks and washers. L, hoops, which are driven tight over the ends of the coupling plates to bind the whole together, making the joint as stiff as the main bar; *l*, side view of the hoop; M, M is a side view of two bars coupled together, shewing the situation of the side plates, bolts and hoops. N is a bird's-eye view or plan of two pair of bars as they lay together in the construction *r, r,*   5 the key head of a perpendicular suspending bar F bearing across the plates; two such lines of these bars form one main line of suspension. O is a section through the last Figure at *r, r,* shewing the form of the suspending bars F, with the double key heads above and below, and the manner in which these rest upon the main suspending bars and support the platform bars.   10

Second Plan, Figure 4. The platform bars in this design are the same as Figures 2 and 3, and the great Catenarian lines are similar, except that cylindrical bars are used, containing the same quantity of iron, with eyes welded instead of holes being punched, in the manner before described. The coupling plates are also welded in the side, and made of cylindrical bolts, flattened in   15 the interior where the sides collapse. P represents a single cylindrical bar with its eyes; Q, a coupling plate; R, R, section and elevation of the joining bolts, as before; S represents two of these cylindrical bars united by their side plates and bolts.

Third Plan. Figure 5 shews the method of forming a continuation of bolts   20 or bars lengthways, without welding, punching, or joining by bolts or coupling plates. T is a bolt or bar, of fourteen feet, or other suitable length, upset at the ends; V is one side, or the half of a pair of iron clams, with sockets reversed to receive the heads of the bolts; U is a corresponding half, shewing the ends of the two bolts in the sockets; W is a view of the two bolts secured in the   25 clams by placing them together, and driving the two hoops Z, Z, firmly over their two ends to prevent their separating; it is in this manner that bolts or bars are fixed at my works when their tenacity is tried by the action of opposite forces, and I find they never break or draw in the joints so constructed. By the above means a continuation of bolts or bars may be formed to any desired   30 length; the number and arrangement of the principal suspending lines, and the platform, bars, &c., being the same as before described.

Fourth Plan. The same principle of forming the Catenarian bars may be effected by a lateral combination of many small bars, either flat or square, but the fewer the divisions in the section the better, because an uniform and   35 equal degree of tension is thereby more likely to be accomplished than by the adjustment of a multiplicity of rods. In the present case I propose the same numbers of principal suspending lines, composed of bars to be twenty-five feet

Brown's Improvement in the Construction of a Bridge.

long and seven-eighths of an inch square; other lengths, diameters, or dimensions may, however, be used. Sixteen of these bars piled or laid together form a section of 3 and $\frac{1}{2}$ inches square; each of these bars is united by a hooked scarfed joint, and constitute an entire length from one extreme
5 point to the other. The joints of these bars need not have any distinct binding, because the whole pile is to be secured together by hoops as at X; and this or other proper methods of binding the bars or rods together is to be adopted wherever a joint occurs, or at intermediate distances, if necessary, and the joints are to be placed alternately opposite the centre of every division,
10 which will be effected by beginning with bars of different lengths, so that no two bars shall be joined between the same pair of hoops. The perpendicular suspenders in this case hang by their key heads, before described, equally on both the great suspending bars, which I recommend to be always used in pairs, although single bars may in some cases be adopted, and are included in
15 my Invention. The platform bars are the same as before-mentioned. Durability is an object of great importance in all public works, and from the simplicity of the construction of this bridge, there is at all times an opportunity of applying the usual preservatives against any decay; but the period, however remote, must arrive when it may be requisite to renew the materials, and it
20 will be obvious that no plan was ever executed or proposed to be executed that affords the same opportunity of a complete and perfect restoration without any interruption to the passage. On referring to Figure 6 it will be seen that all the bars may be removed and new ones introduced into their places, by which means the structure may be maintained for ever. Y is a side
25 view of one of the temporary side plates, which extend the length of the three bars, and which embrace or bear upon the ends of the coupling plates, and are secured by hoops in that situation; the holes in the sides are for the purpose of withdrawing the bolts. The bar *e* and the coupling plates may now be removed and new ones applied in their places; the temporary plates
30 are then shifted and fixed on the next division, as before, so that each defective plate or bar may in successsion be renewed.

The fourth or last mentioned of the plans of my Invention does not allow of the same facility of renewal as the three preceding ones, and as it consists of a greater number of rods or bars there is a greater surface exposed to the
35 action of the atmosphere, which will not fail to penetrate into the interstices and joints of the section in defiance of any paint or plastic composition whatever; it is therefore indispensably necessary to apply a more effectual or permanent remedy; the bars should therefore first receive a coat of some

anticorrosive composition, and the seams should, as far as is practicable, be
stuffed with the same, and then each of the principal suspending lines should
be enclosed with sheet lead, the seam being undermost and soldered, so as to
form an entire pipe completely water-tight the whole length of the bridge.
The parts of those principal bars which are carried through mason's work 5
I inclose in cast-iron pipes of the shape of the bars, and of sufficient strength
to withstand the pressure, but not to be attached to the bars, so as to be subject
to any tension; these cases should also be secured with lead in the joints and
made water-tight.

Although I have specified the foregoing plans as the most eligible and 10
effectual for carrying the Invention into effect, yet it admits of others without
any deviation from the principle; the main suspending bars, for instance, may
be placed all parallel to each other in four upper lines, instead of the upper
and lower lines A and B, and the alternate arrangements of the perpendicular
bars be the same; but the lower ones, which bear upon the main lines B, in 15
the examples already given, will, however, require to be considerably lengthened in this case. In some cases, also, when the points of suspension are
naturally much elevated, or when they can be conveniently heightened, a more
relaxed curve may be used; and it is one of the merits of the system, that in
the combination of its constituent parts there is a great latitude of choice for 20
the architect or civil engineer.

The platform or roadway I construct of wood. In the example given in the
Drawing it consists of three divisions, viz., two side roads for carriages and
horses to pass in opposite directions, of twelve feet each, and a centre path for
foot passengers, of six feet; but these roadways may be varied in number or 25
dimensions or positions, to suit the convenience of the situation. It is formed
of beams laid crossways the whole breadth of the bridge, which rest on the
upper edge of the platform bars, before mentioned, and of planks laid lengthways upon these; but instead of using solid balks of timber as beams, I make
them of two planks laid edgeways, twelve inches deep and three inches thick, 30
or such other dimensions as the weight may require. These planks are connected by chocks at intermediate distances, which keep them about three inches
asunder; the chocks and planks so disposed are bound and secured together by
hoops, screw bolts, or any other suitable means. The boarding or planks for
the platform or floor are to be three inches thick, or of such substance as the 35
case may require, and are spiked or bolted down firmly to the beams, the
whole being in a great measure similar to the construction of a ship's deck.
The lower sides of the beams are held in their places by strong cleats or

hanging knees, which fit the inside surface of the platform bars and keep
them firmly in their places; they may have straps or braces to confine them
downward upon the bars if necessary. On each side of each carriage roadway
there is a triangular piece of timber bolted down, which extends the whole
5 length, to prevent carriages from getting out of the proper track of the road,
as may be seen in section at *a, a,* in Figure 7; and the part which is exposed
to the wheel is to be covered with thin oak plank or sheathing, and iron bars
placed lengthways to prevent the main timbers from being worn away; the
centre part is also to be covered with a thin oak sheathing to save the principle
10 planks, and thin plates of iron must be nailed across it, not only for its
preservation, but to produce a firm foot hold for the horses. The platform is
completed by bolting securely a strong piece of timber to the ends of the
beams and upper edge of the plank the whole length of the bridge, covering
all the butt ends and edges of the upper planks and beams, a part of which are
15 seen uncovered by this last-mentioned piece of timber at *p, p,* in Fig. 2.

The most favorable positions for building the piers of suspension are those
where the declivity of vallies or the banks of rivers are naturally formed of
rocks; they afford the greatest stability for the builder's works, and the most
secure fastening for the extremities of the main lines of suspension. The
20 height of the piers will depend on the extent of the span, and the description
of ships, vessels, or other objects that may have to pass under it. To
form a passage over rivers which are not navigable, it will be merely necessary to lay the foundations of the piers, and form the roadway beyond
the reach of the highest floods; in this case the height of the piers and
25 points of suspension will depend altogether on the extent of the span. As
there is nothing materially new in the manner of erecting the piers, whether
of stone, wood, or other materials, they cannot be considered as forming a
principle in the Invention in any other light than as being a connection or
application of a known mode of building to a new purpose. It will not there-
30 fore be necessary to enter into the minutiæ of masons' or carpenters' work, but
briefly to state, that as the strength of all the main lines of suspension which
pass over the different columns or divisions of the piers greatly exceed the
strain which they will be subject to, they may be considered as inextensible,
so the materials and the workmanship must be of that substantial nature as to
35 be incompressible by the weight which they have to support, and as the bridge
itself admits an entire renewal in future times, they must also be of the most
imperishable description. The piers, represented in Figure 2, are composed
of stone, the foundation rock a substantial wooden building, on a secure

artificial foundation, although less preferable will, however, answer the purpose.
The lines X through one of the piers shew the iron cases or trunks which
inclose the main suspending lines; those iron cases, as before stated, are to be
of sufficient strength to resist the internal pressure of the iron bars, bolts, &c.
which compose the Catenarian lines, as well as the outward pressure of the 5
materials which may rest upon or surround them. Y, beyond this pier, in
Fig. 1, represents the rock from which the piers are founded and carried out;
the dotted lines Y, Y, are channels cut through this rock in the direction that
the bars obtain on the different divisions of the piers. These channels receive
the various main suspending lines, and the extremities are secured by strong 10
bolts, passing through the ends of the bars, and bearing against cast-iron plates,
which are fixed as a facing to the rock. The ends of each of these cast
lengths of the Catenarian lines are provided with several bolt holes, so that
the curve of each line can be adjusted or set tight with the greatest degree of
accuracy. The most convenient mode of erecting or throwing over my bridge 15
of suspension is as follows:—I build a strong wooden framing upon the top of
one of the main piers on both sides, directly over the trunk or iron case, in
which the main line of suspension is to be placed. This frame is to be about
six feet higher than the front of the pier or point of supension, and continued
sloping parallel with the pier to the rock or termination of the abutments. 20
In front of this framing I fix a strong cast-iron roller, and at convenient
distances there are other rollers on the top of the framing, over which a chain
of suitable strength is to lead or travel. Behind the abutment I fix a capstan,
windlass, or other suitable purchase; I then begin with joining the platform
bars at the extremitiy of the abutment on the opposite side, and continue them 25
over the top of the framing, and if the situation is a navigable river I join the
bars on board of a suitable vessel, beginning immediately under the pier.
I employ the chain and purchase before mentioned to heave the vessel across
as the bars are fixed, letting what seamen term the bight or the united parts
hang overboard. When the bars are all fixed, and the vessel hove over as far 30
as the line of bars will allow, I continue to heave on the purchase and draw
the bars over the rollers on the top of the framing, and finally secure the ends
at the termination of this abutment. I previously fix at four equal distances
on this line of bars a purchase of pullies, the lower block hanging down to the
decks of four vessels moored for the purpose of heaving the bars up. I then 35
proceed to secure one of the main suspending bars at its extremity, and lay it
in the trunk under the temporary framing, and fix each individual bar on
board of the vessel, and heave them across by the before-mentioned purchase.

Brown's Improvement in the Construction of a Bridge.

I then attach the tackles to corresponding distances, and by simultaneous operation of all the purchases, heave this main line of bars up to its proper elevation, and having previously fixed the opposite end and laid the bars in the iron trunk, I unite them at the front of the pier, and then gradually relax

5 the purchases and remove them from this main line; this is done by means of a travelling stage, which is suspended to the upper lines of bars. Having drawn up the corresponding line and fixed it in its place, I remove the framing, purchase, &c. to the next pier or division and proceed as before. When all the main lines of suspension are drawn up and secured, I take down

10 the platform bars which I have employed to raise the others. As has already been stated, I allow no tension on the platform bars; I therefore have only occasion to use a commodious travelling stage hanging from the main suspending bars, and join the bars one by one, and introduce the perpendicular suspenders in their corresponding situations. I then proceed to lay the beams

15 across and complete the platform, agreeable to the plan already described. The first three plans may be erected in this way, but it will be necessary in the last of those three plans to have a joint in each main suspending line at the point of suspension, also one at the water edge, to allow the bars to be fixed in a horizontal direction across the river, and those two joints may be

20 formed in the same manner as in the cylindrical line of bars. In the fourth plan, the bars may be drawn across singly, and each of the scarfed joints should be secured with clasp hoops to keep them in one entire bar; and when the lateral combination of all the bars in each line is formed, they should be hooped tight, as already stated, and the clasp hoops in the joints may be

25 removed, which will permit the bars to be more closely connected. The platform bar used in the preceding cases will be required in this, but principally for suspending the moveable scaffold or stage, which will be required to fix the hoops, &c., which done they may be taken down, as before, and the travelling scaffold may be slung to the main suspending lines for

30 joining the platform bars and arranging the perpendicular suspenders. I have only to add, that I strongly recommend Lieutenant Shouldham's (R. N.) improved blocks for the purchases, as possessing very superior power, with the least possible friction, and affording peculiar convenience in requiring a smaller fold than any other description of pully.

35 In witness whereof, I, the said Samuel Brown, have hereunto set my hand and seal, this Ninth day of January, in the year of our Lord One thousand eight hundred and eighteen.

SAMUEL BROWN. (L.S.)

A.D. 1817.—N° 4137.

Brown's Improvement in the Construction of a Bridge.

AND BE IT REMEMBERED, that on the same Ninth day of January, in the year above mentioned, the aforesaid Samuel Brown came before our Lord the King in His Chancery, and acknowledged the Specification aforesaid, and all and every thing therein contained, in form above written. And also the Specification aforesaid was stamped according to the tenor of the Statute 5 in that case made and provided.

Inrolled the same Ninth day of January, in the year above written.

LONDON:
Printed by GEORGE EDWARD EYRE and WILLIAM SPOTTISWOODE,
Printers to the Queen's most Excellent Majesty.   1856.

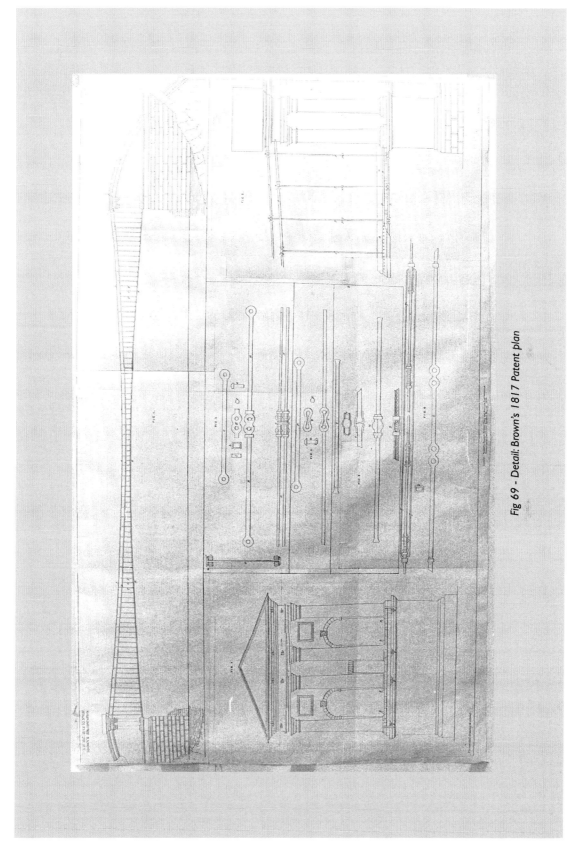

Fig 69 - Detail: Brown's 1817 Patent plan

SAMUEL BROWN AND UNION CHAIN BRIDGE

Fig 70 - Detail: Brown's 1817 Patent plan

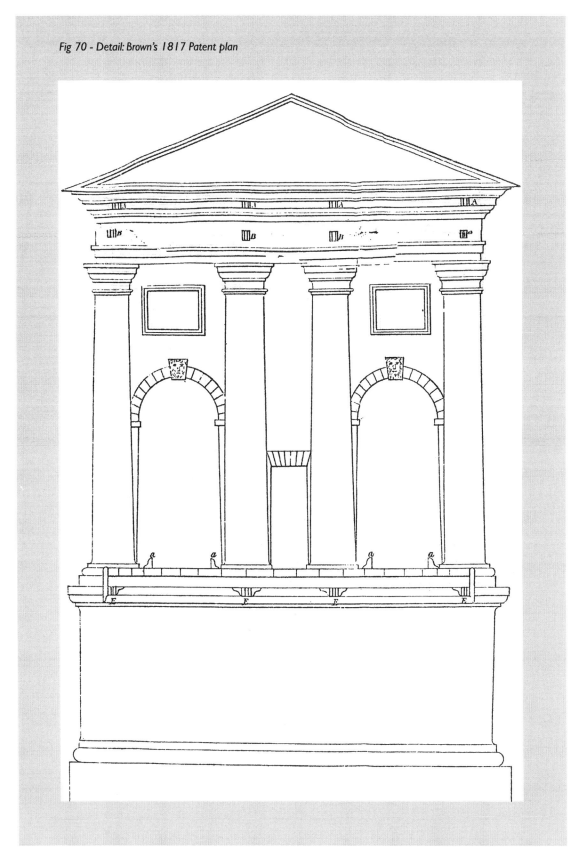

Fig 71 - Detail: Detail: Brown's 1817 Patent plan

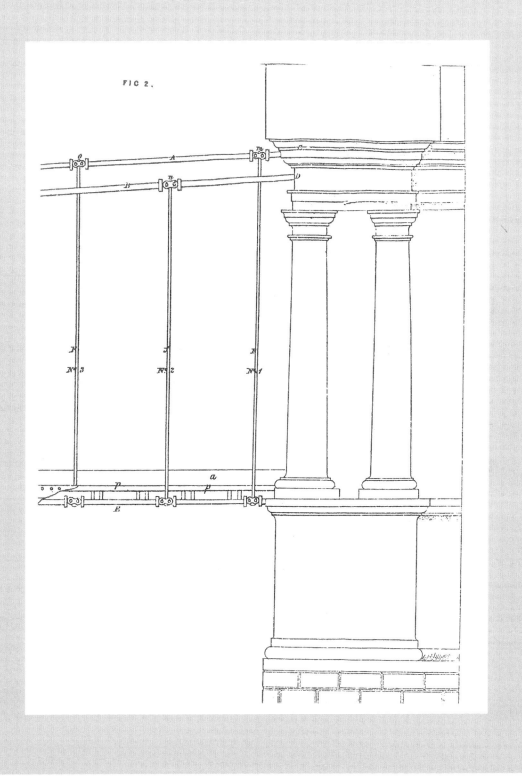

Fig 72 - Detail: Detail: Brown's 1817 Patent plan

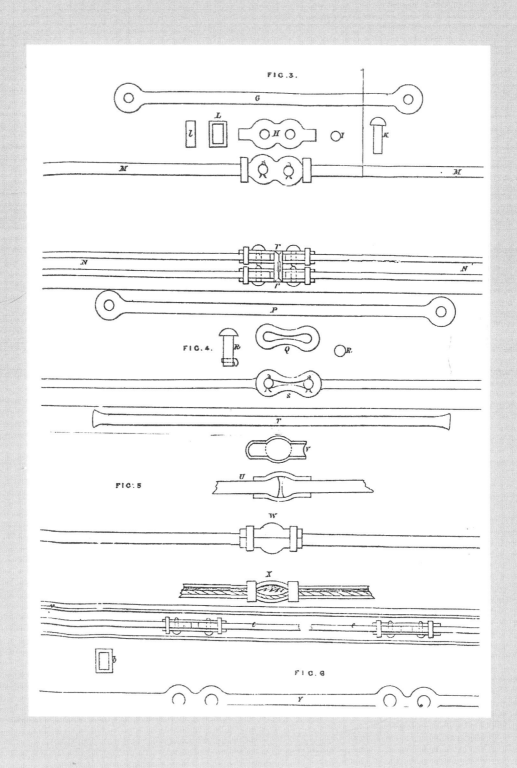

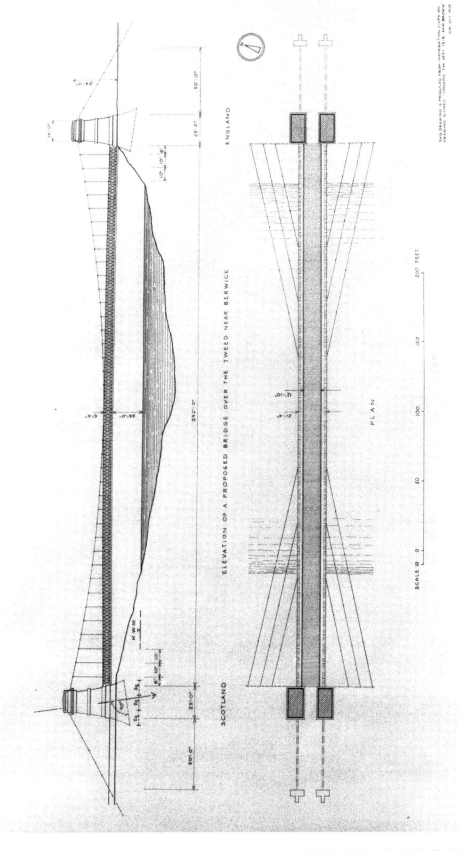

ELEVATION OF A PROPOSED BRIDGE OVER THE TWEED NEAR BERWICK

PLAN

SCALE 10 0   50   100   150   200 FEET

Fig 73 - Author's drawing from Sam Brown's original of September 7th 1818

165

~ 4 ~
The Proposed and Final Designs

A drawing signed by Samuel Brown, and dated September 7th 1818, became part of an 'Agreement' or contract, for the Union Bridge on August 21st 1819. No written form of agreement or other documents have been found which explain why the bridge, as ultimately built, differed both in design and related siting from the 'Agreement' drawing, but by examination of some known facts and an amount of speculation on my part, will, I hope, be of value in determining the possible course of events.

There is little doubt that Samuel Brown was influenced by John Rennie's criticism of his Norham bridge design, as the Union 'Agreement' drawing clearly pays regard to Rennie's two main points which are for the inclusion of 'side gyes' and the shape of piers to respect the 'Action of the Chains to pull them together..'. Having received a proposition from Brown, William Molle promptly referred it all to John Rennie, for his opinion on September 9th, who replied on November 11th 1818. On this occasion, Rennie was prudent enough to consider the desirability of a meeting with Brown before, as he put it, '..delivery of my sentimants..', to which William Molle agreed. There was, apparently, more than one meeting which led to Rennie's expressed opinion that '..several alterations in the design he approving of (referring to Brown) a new set of plans has been made out which, with those you sent to me, are transmitted by the Mail of this evening to the Red Lion Inn Berwick.' The amended plans have not been discovered, but by the nature of Rennie's comments, they did not necessarily relate to the final bridge design or its location, nevertheless, the alterations suggested are of interest, which were in his words:

"First That the abutments should be strengthened.

Second That the platform suspended to the Bearing chains being on one level, no effectual resistance was derived from thence in keeping the abutments from coming together, and that as the chains expanded by the heat this platform would become Hollow and consequently it would be shortened in Horizontal length, and therefore the Scheme of this platform should be altered.

Third That as the Chains passed over the top of the Abutments resting only on a Plate of Iron, their tendency was to derange the Masonry as the expansion or Contraction of the suspending Chains varied from the State in which they were originally adjusted, and this should be obviated.

Fourth That as the Towers on which the Chains rest were placed at a considerable distance from the River and strengthened by Buttresses on the River side the Span of the Chains and consequently the carriage platform was necessarily the width of these Buttresses more than the breadth of the River required. And, Lastly, that the Towers being perpendicular on their sides, had not sufficient strength to counteract the lateral action of the Chains."

Rennie then continued and summed up the situation in the light of design amendments which had been effected after some discussion with Brown.

"These various imperfections I trust are obviated in the designs which accompany this Report. For the Masonry of the abutments, if I may be allowed to use that expression for Masses that support the Chains are by the present Plan materially enlarged, both in the direction of the suspending Chains and laterally, by which their strength is greatly increased, but in doing this a much greater quantity of Masonry will be used than in Capt Brown's original design. On this account the expense of those abutments will be more than doubled - Capt Brown informs me the sum he put for the Abutments was £600. I doubt those I have advised will cost £1330, thus leaving a deficiency of £730.

Secondly, I propose that the carriage platforms shall have a rise in the middle of about three feet, which will be attended with this advantage, namely, that when the chains expand by heat the platform will descend a little, and its ends will act on the Abutments in part as an Arch, and that when it ascends by the contractions of the Chains, the inclined front of the Masonry in the Abutments will come in contact with the platform and thus always presume a certain action of it against the Masonry.

Thirdly, I propose that in the Iron plates to be placed on the Tops of these abutments there shall be rollers over which the Chains may move while lengthening or contracting and thereby they will adjust themselves to any state of the Atmosphere with little tendency to derange the Masonry.

Fourthly, The Masonry in Capt Brown's Towers on which the suspending chains rest were placed 11 feet further from the River than necessary: by the Plan of Abutments I have proposed this 11 feet will be saved on each side, by which the Span of the Chains and Carriage platform will be lessened 22 feet without abridging the Waterway - this will make a saving on the Iron and Woodwork as well as a strengthening of the Bridge by diminishing the Span, but as the Rollers and additional works on the Abutments will occasion some extra expense, the total saving in this department will be small.

Lastly, the Abutments have a batter on each side by which their strength to oppose the lateral shake is increased, and therefore they are more suitable to such a Bridge than those of Capt Brown. With respect to the suspending Chains and other Iron work, they are entirely on Capt Brown's own line, and of course I have not ventured to make any material alterations in them, and moreover as I am not locally aquainted with the Spot where the Bridge is to be erected, I can give no opinion as to the nature of the foundation or the manner of fixing the ends of the Chains - all I can say is, that if all these matters are properly attended to, my opinion is that the Bridge will be a durable and useful structure, and as he takes the responsibility on himself I see no reason why the Trustees should not enter into a Contract with him - all the extra expense incurred by the alterations I propose are on the Abutments, and if these are approved of by the Trustees, it will be for them to consider what extra allowance should be made for this increase - this extra in my opinion should be liberal, as I think he undertakes the Work more for the sake of introducing Bridges of this sort into general use than from any profit he can derive from this undertaking."

In considering the involvement of John Rennie, the content of correspondence, the 'Agreement' drawing, and their respective dates, some anomalies exist which although cannot be fully explained, are worth identifying: but first, the sequence of events:

January 6.1818	John Rennie comments upon Brown's Norham Bridge proposal
September 7.1818	Date of Samuel Brown's proposal drawing which became the subject of 'Agreement'
September 9.1818	William Molle writes to John Rennie seeking his advice about Brown's Bridge proposal
September 27.1818	William Molle confirms his agreement to a meeting between Rennie and Brown at Rennie's instigation
November 11.1818	John Rennie writes to William Molle with his Report upon Brown's proposal
July 3.1819	The Formal formation of a 'Body of Trustees'
August 21.1819	Brown's proposal drawing of September 7 1818 became the 'Agreement' drawing; engrossed by the Trustees

As to the anomalies. Brown's proposal and 'Agreement' drawing clearly shows the towers as not being 'perpendicular on their sides, as stated by Rennie in his letter, nor 'strengthened by buttresses' or 'placed at a considerable distance from the River'. Rennie's second point that the 'suspended platform is level is not evidenced in the drawing, but his further point about the chains 'passing over the top of the abutments resting only on a plate of Iron' is relevant. As the proposal drawing was in William Molle's hands and forwarded to John Rennie within two days it is difficult to understand how and when the variations were effected, if, at all. Let us consider the drawing in its own right. In the bottom right hand corner it bears in Brown's own handwriting 'London 7th Sept.1818 Sam Brown' and written at the top of the drawing:

> "Berwick 21st August 1819
> This is the Plan referred to in an Agreement dated this day
> Sam Brown
> R.Johnstone
> W.Molle
> J.S.Donaldson
> W.Pattison
> Anthy Gregson
> Thos G.Alder
> Thomas Boswall
> John Sibbit . . ."

The Agreement drawing is drawn in ink line with water colour wash on cartridge paper at a scale of 1:96 (1/8" to 1') and shows a symmetrical span arrangement. By scaling the drawing, the distance between tower abutment faces at platform level is 392 feet: each tower is 23 feet, and the back chain cable distance on the horizontal to the point of contact with the ground is 50 feet, making an overall length of 538 feet. Photographic copies from the original are illustrated, also a drawing showing the essential information taken from the original.

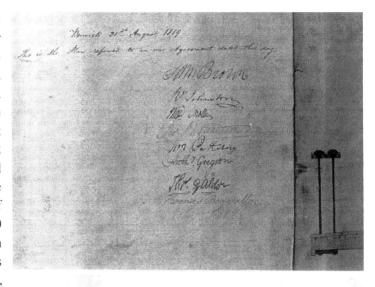

Fig 74 - Detail: Signatures from contractual engrossment "London 7th Sept 1818"

Rusticated ashlar piers are shown with strongly emphasised joints and arch voussoirs, the piers having pronounced concaved sides, which are in style reminiscent of James Finley's Potomac River suspension bridge. The 'section of pier' clearly shows the foundation base plane as being inclined at a raking angle, off the horizontal, the perpendicular of which would approximately correspond to the bisector of the chain angles each side of the pier. This alone would have meant doom for the pier stability, and ignored basic foundationing principles, and the idea may have stemmed from the effects of different possible methods of passing chain cables over pier bearings, or saddles. A thick line on the drawing suggests a crude form of bearing plate and if this was the principle intended, then the pressure on the pier would only have been vertical if the chains left the pier head at permanently equal angles, a system advocated by James Finley. The proposed profile outline of the piers does suggest that allowance was being made to accommodate a variation in the pressure angle planes without recourse to a more heavily constructed pier with straight inclined sides. On the other hand it may have been a stylistic whim or Finley's influence. Elevation 'D' shows a difference in angles that the chains make each side of the piers, but in the detail sections the angles are drawn as being equal. Brown obviously had misgivings about this part of the structure, but very little sense of engineering was being displayed about the design of the pier foundation shape which, with its proposed inclined plane would have created a condition of overturning or slip. The actual base width of piers as drawn would have adequately allowed for both vertical or inclined pressure lines to fall within the theoretical 'middle third' area for pier stability, which may have also influenced the general pier shape, to provide the necessary base spread. Two sets of chains, arranged in horizontal pairs, were proposed for the main catenary cables, with eye-bolt saddle joints providing for single platform

Fig 75 - Detail: : Plan attached to contractual engrossment

hangers connected at their lower ends with an iron plate or 'run bar' which supported the platform transoms. This iron plate was intended to be continuous over the whole platform length; and the platform additionally stiffened by a lattice ironwork balustrade. Platform transoms are shown cambered, from the centre, over the carriageway width; the inclination slightly increased from the roadway ribands or kerbs, to the extreme edge. The roadway decking is shown in the detail as single layer planking, laid longitudinally over the transoms, with a suggested surface layer of maybe tar and stoning over the road width, but the deck plan suggests a transverse surface layer of planking. Sway bracing cables are shown on the 'half plan' to arrest possible lateral movement and sketched pencil lines at the pier head also show Brown's thoughts about the number of chains that would be required, and those illustrated on the 'section of the pier' as three sets, were eventually employed in the final design.

General and detail drawings would have been prepared for the final design, particularly 'shop' drawings that would have been necessary for the manufacture of ironwork, but they all remain either hidden somewhere or lost for all time. Although the original proposal does not relate to the final bridge siting, it must have been destined for a position within about 350 yards north, down river, nearby the New Water Ford and ferry boat crossing. Nevertheless, it may be assumed that instructions to Brown from the Berwick Turnpike Trustees would have been to bridge the river in the most practical and economic manner in relation to the existing road system. The ancient Ford crossing would have suggested relatively shallow water with a firm bed, and in all probability suitable conditions for pier foundationing and cable anchorages. The drawing provides three clues in speculation about the intended bridge siting, the platform span of 392 feet, apparent raised road approaches, and the deep channel river bed section that scales 30 feet at high water mark mid-stream.

Some 300 yards exists between the meeting of the respective old Scotch and English roads with the river, and within this distance the river increases in width from 300 feet, by the approach from Fishwick, to 500 feet by the road descent from Bankhead, and the deeper channel changes from the English to Scotch side. The direction of the old Ford

Fig 76 - Detail: Plan attached to contractual engrossment

line over the river laid at an angle across the broad reach, and about 100 feet of the width being shallow water over a shingle shoal bank on the English side. On the Scotch side the deeper channel was however, relatively shallow, being a condition which resulted from the build-up of shingle deposited from the scouring of the comparatively narrow channel a little upstream.

Brown may have considered a bridging point near the English side road link by raising the tower off the shingle bank, which would have entailed elevating the approach road over flood arches. However, the river bed section shown on the drawing very closely relates to the situation by the Boat House. From a constructional point of view this was a good site, but the need to raise the platform from 24 to 27 feet above high water mark must have been the final influence upon Brown in choosing the ultimate site. It also meant a change in bridge design, but the alternative necessitated more expensive and complex road raising operations and the economics in relation to the revised platform level requirement became the deciding factor. It is understandable that Brown may have been initially put off considering a site more up river. 300 yards above the Ford a 60 foot high Sandstone outcrop terminates a continuous steep bank that runs from Norham, and is the reason why the old road that descends to the Ford skirts its way round the craggy situation. Brown's initial scheme was obviously based upon known physical information, upon which he based his ideas and prepared a design and estimate which was submitted to the Trustees before the facts of foreseeable new flood levels had been made known to him. The information was decisive in influencing the choice of site that would sensibly allow for the higher platform level, but it was also a decision that was to leave Brown financially wanting at the termination of the contract.

Eleven months passed between the dated drawing and its engrossment as a contract document on August 21 1819, and even this was a month after the foundation stone was laid, on July 26, at the final site. Faith and confidence were being displayed by the Trustees, for here was a bridge being started on a site to which the contract drawing did not relate. Doubtless the Trustees were satisfied, for they had contracted to pay an agreed lump sum price for the bridge, which carried guarantees, so in a sense they could not lose. In any event, the Trustees were enthusiastic about the experiment. Brown's task really began after he had secured the contract. He had complete confidence in the strength of the chains, but anchorages were another matter, and suitable sub-strata for both these and piers needed to be located. With the evidence of rock outcrops and a shingle river bed, Brown may have jumped to the conclusion that bed-rock generally existed

Fig 77 - Detail: Plan attached to contractual engrossment

below the surface but in fact, the subsoil of the sloping ground adjoining the Ford is of clay, to a considerable depth. An additional hazard at this position would have been the need to raise the level of approach roads, particularly on the English side, thereby forming an obstacle to water flow in times of flood. From an engineering point of view it would have been possible to overcome such difficulties but greater cost would have been involved and Brown, influenced by the economics, was anxious to get started at the most practical situation. The site finally chosen was not without difficulties, for although the rock face of the English bank presented good anchorage possibilities, a new approach road involved an inclined cut and fill down the bank for a considerable distance and also meant a right-angled junction with the bridge.

The Scotch side posed no problem other than the need to elevate the approach and because of the inside bend of the river, no flood water problems would arise. Approach road costs were, fortunately, outside Brown's contract sum, and although the platform length was to become slightly less than originally anticipated, the catenary chains would be about the same relative length overall. Everything considered, the final site was a good one, and is a major reason for the continued existence of the bridge.

Brown's initial design proposal illustrated all the essential information that the Trustees really required to know, and included an overall elevation with river bed section, half plan, pier elevation and section, showing the iron chains bearing, and a detail 'transverse' section of the road platform and parapet rails. Of particular interest is the relatively naive constructional methods that the

SAMUEL BROWN AND UNION CHAIN BRIDGE

drawing indicates, and it is therefore surprising that the ultimate bridge was such an advance in design and technical realisation.

Fig 78 - Detail: Plan attached to contractual engrossment

The delay of almost a year between the projected scheme and final agreement did however provide time for exchanges of views between Brown and other engineers. We know of Rennie's opinion, and at some time, the civil engineer Robert Stevenson entered the scene.

Immediately after signing the contract Brown started work on the bridge design and had the ironwork manufactured and shipped to site during the December of 1819. The winter weather was extremely bad which hindered progress with earthwork and masonry construction, and also prevented Brown from visiting the site as often as he would have liked. Stevenson was anxious to know about progress and wrote to Brown on March 9th 1820 "What is doing about the Bridge of Chains over the Tweed." to which Brown replied on March 14th, "I have been restricted by the severe winter from visiting the Bridge of Suspension over the Tweed, as you know that nothing is so adverse to the masonry as frost The chains have been down at the spot 3 months ago and I am informed by the builders that the piers will be high enough for

Fig 79 - Detail: Plan attached to contractual engrossment

suspending the bridge by the first week in April and I have no doubt in having it possible by the middle of June. It is an undertaking of the greatest magnitude and had I not have had the means of conducting or rather executing the whole of its component parts I would not upon any consideration have taken on me the heavy responsibility of the ultimate success of the design. I do not mention this from a presumption that I am the only person that could carry through so great a work, but from having the control of every branch of the manufacture and the power of rejecting any part of the iron work even upon the slightest appearance of defect, which I could not have done had I contracted for the Iron work through any other quarter, because I know well enough that the main point with smiths (of whom I may say that I have had more experience than most men of the present day) is not to detect faults but to conceal them, and there is no manufacturer that I know of where deception is less liable to discovery. The Union Bridge will be 440 ft. span without any support in the centre and it is calculated to carry over all the traffic of counties chiefly consisting of coal and lime and as it is broad enough for two carriages of any description passing in opposite directions it is quite possible for 40 loaded carts to be upon it at one-time besides foot and horse passengers".

Although the final siting dispensed with the need for a free standing pier on the English bank, and produced an asymmetrical relationship between chains and platform, the final bridge was a considerable improvement in design and engineering principles. In all its essentials, the bridge looks much the same today as when first constructed, even though the design and construction of the platform has been changed four times, first in 1834, then in 1971,

Fig 80 - Detail: Plan attached to contractual engrossment

1902 and 1974. The steel wire rope cables that were added in 1903 are visually acceptable, but it is extremely unfortunate that the Toll House which originally formed part of the English pier was taken down in 1955.

No final bridge design or record drawings made by Brown or his associated engineers have been found. Nevertheless, evidence about the complete structure, particularly detail describing the original platform, is contained in an account by Robert Stevenson published in the *Edinburgh Philosophical Journal*, No. X., which was partly quoted in the *'Monthly Magazine'*, August 1st 1822, also abridged in *'Marshall's Naval Biography No. VII'*, and edited by the Civil Engineer C S Drewry in *'A Memoir on Suspension Bridges'*, published in 1832. Drewry's account also contains the earliest discovered detail record drawing, which confirms the relative accuracy of the Stevenson account. One other drawing exists that explains the design of platform between 1837 and 1871, which was made by the Trustees surveyor after survey in 1871, following his critical assessment of the structure, when an order by the Trustees for the platform reconstruction included a design change. In appearance, the bridge design shown in the survey drawing identifies in detail almost exactly with Nasmyth's painting of the project, particularly the elaborately moulded cornice that was planted over the ends of platform transoms. This cornice feature disguised the structure and although alien to the general concept was nevertheless decorative, and emphasised the platform line. The various contemporary published accounts generally give similar information. except for the dimensions of the platform length and overall chord length between the centres of suspension which now measure 361'6" and 437'0" respectively, and as is to be seen in his letter to Stevenson, Brown stated the span to be 440 feet 'without any support in the centre'. The following description is quoted from 'Art.I - Description of Bridges of Suspension by Robert Stevenson, Esq. F.R .S.E. Civil Engineer' that was published in 'The Edinburgh Philosophical Journal. Vol. No. 10 '...The road-way of this bold design is made of timber, on which iron cart tracks are laid for the carriage wheels. It is 18 feet in width, and is no less than 361 feet in length. The main beams or joisting measures 15 inches in depth, and 7 inches in thickness. The timber cleading or planks are 12 inches in breadth, and 3 inches in thickness. This great platform is suspended at the height of 27 feet above the surface of the summer water of the river. It is also made to rise about 2 feet in the centre, and is finished on each side with a cornice of 15 inches in depth which adds to its ornament, and gives it an additional appearance of strength.' Drewry states that the '...carriageway is protected by cast iron guards, 4½in. high, and is covered by iron straps, about ¾ of an inch thick, placed lengthwise on like a rail road, in the track of the wheels, and crosswise in the track of the horses' feet...' This detail information is shown in Drewry's drawing, but because increased costs became a subject of argument between Brown and the Trustees near to the completion of contract the refinement of iron guards and strapping may well have been excluded. However, it was a sensible idea, and its development into a raised curb and footpath after 1837 may have resulted from need or experience.

The description continues:
'...The roadway is suspended from the catenarian or main chains by circular rods of iron, which measure 1 inch in diameter. These perpendicular rods are wedged into caps or pieces of cast-iron, called Saddles, which are placed at the distance of 5 feet apart, and made to rest upon the shackles or joints of the catenarian chains...' The attachment of the lower ends of these rods to the beams of the platform which they pass through, is by their embracing a bar of iron which runs along the whole extent of the bridge under the beams of the roadway, on each side. These bars measure 3 inches in depth, (Drewry - 3 inches deep by 7/8 in.thick) and they are connected with the suspending rods by a spear bolt which, in a very simple manner, completes the connection of the roadway with the perpendicular suspending rods and catenarian chains.' Drewry's illustration shows the tail ends of the suspension rods shaped into the-form of flattened forks, that carried the continuous 'run-bar', seated upon a dowel or bolt, and secured into position by iron wedges. This corresponds to the information shown in the survey drawing of c 1871, (see photographic reproduction from the original). Apparently, the main beams or transoms, were simply notched over the 'run - bar' for an inset depth of about 2 inches, there being no other engaging device.

Stevenson: "...The catenarian chains of this bridge are twelve in number, ranged in pairs; the one pair being placed over the other, between the points of suspension on each side of the bridge. These chains, and indeed the whole of the iron-work, is made of the very best Welch iron. The chains are worked into a circular form, and measure about 2 inches in diameter. The Links, as they may be termed, consist of rods of 15 feet in length, and have bolt-holes, which are strongly welded, and neatly finished at each end. These links or rods are connected together by strong shackles..." (Drewry: "...open coupling links 6¾ long centre and centre, made of iron 1⅛ square.") "...and a bolt is passed through them, which is of an oval form, measuring 2¼ by 2½ inches. At each joint of the three tiers of the catenarian chains respectively, one of the saddle pieces of cast-iron, formerly alluded to, are introduced. The first saddle piece, with its suspending rod, for example, on either side of the bridge may be conceived as resting on the upper pair of chains ... the next saddle piece in the longitudinal direction of the roadway, rests upon the middle pair of chains, and the third upon the lower pair, and so on alternatively, throughout the whole extent of the bridge. By this means all the chains bear an equal strain, and the joints are arranged in so precise and orderly a manner, that a saddle-piece and perpendicular suspension rod occurs at every 5 feet, so that the distance between each pair of suspension rods forms a space of 5 feet. By this beautiful and simple arrangement, the suspending-rods are made to rest upon the joints of the catenarian chains, so that the links or rods of which they are composed, are kept free of distortion, when loaded with the weight of the suspended road-way. The spaces of 5 feet between the suspending rods above alluded to are formed into meshes of 6 inches square, to the height of 5 feet on each side of the bridge, and answer the purposes of a parapet wall for the safety of passengers."

(Drewry: "...The parapets are 5 feet high; they are formed by several rows of horizontal rods, 1 inch diameter, which connect the vertical suspending rods together, and are fastened also to other vertical standards, placed between each pair of vertical suspending rods. The upper and lower rows of horizontal rods are flat iron, 1¾ by ½ thick; the suspending rods pass through holes in the horizontal tie rods, and the latter pass through openings in the vertical standards between the suspending rods. Hence the suspending rods are tied to the parapet.")

Drewry's description of the parapet ironwork corresponds to that which Brown provided, and still exists; there being five horizontal rails, with one vertical standard dividing the spaces between each of the suspension rods. Both Professor Sir John Leslie and Robert Stevenson were present at the bridge opening, and although they cast an eye over the structure, it is not difficult to understand reasons why differences in subsequently recorded description were made. They both had drawings, which may have shown lattice parapets, but it must be remembered that the great day of opening was 'spent with much conviviality and good humour'.

Stevenson: "Though the timber roadway is only about 361 feet in length, yet the chord line of the main-chains measures no less than 432 feet between the points of suspension, with which they make an angle of about 12°, and in forming the catenarian curve-drop, at the rate of 1 perpendicular to about 7 feet in the length of the chain, the versed sine of the middle pair of chains being about 26 feet."

Drewry gives different figures "... The chord line, or distance between the points of suspension, is 449 feet; and the deflection about 30 feet..." As already mentioned, the chord line is in fact 437 feet, and the versed sine, or deflection of the upper chain 32 feet 3 inches.

Stevenson: "The twelve main chains, with their apparatus, weigh about 5 tons each, and the weight of the whole bridge, between the points of suspension, has been estimated at 100 tons."

The description of catenarian chains, and their connections, corresponds to those existing; and probably because no work was done to them in the 1871 platform replacement, no detail survey record was made at the time.

Brown's link and saddle joints were ingenious and overcame the compound problems of jointing lengths of bar, keeping the pairs in parallel arrangement; also providing a saddle bearing that would secure a suspension rod in a vertical position relative to the varying angle of catenary chains. In order to maintain the location and position of each pair of chains at their respective joints with the cast iron saddles, downstanding projecting teeth form part of the semicircular shaped bearing casting that fits between the faces of the connecting links.

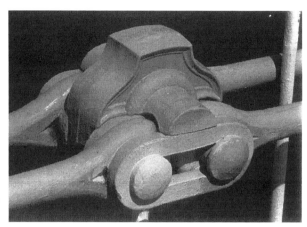

Fig 81 - Union Chain Bridge, saddle chain connection

Measured survey sketches made in 1974, are illustrated to show Brown's barlink device, whereby each section length of chain bar is connected with a pair of links or shackles and oval section shaped pins that have flanged dome heads on the outside, and secured by iron wedges through slots on the inner ends including large washers. The cast iron saddle provides the essential element that retains both the parallel lateral position of chains, and also provides the fixing for suspension rods. The fixing for rods is simply a wedge shaped rectangular hole through the saddle casting into which the splayed squared ends of the otherwise round rods are wedged, the size being adequate for rod fixing thereby providing sufficient tolerance for the difference in angle that suspension rods make with the catenary chains.

The saddle connection device provided for considerable joint movement, and in common with the practice of the time, it is reasonable to assume that boiled linseed oil was used as a coating before joint assembly and subsequent painting, a technique that would also have retarded oxidisation and eventual rusting. As the saddle is kept in position by the weight on the suspension rod, it was therefore important that nothing should happen to raise it off its seating, otherwise the respective pairs of chains could part. No provision against such an event was made though fortunately, oscillation of the platform has never been sufficient to prove the free joint a defect.

Mr. Stevenson continues the description:

> "On the Scotch side of the river, the catenarian chains pass over a pillar of aisler masonry, which measures 60 feet in height, is about 36 feet in its medium width, and 17½ feet in thickness. The sides of the lower 10 feet of the walls of this pillar are square, but at

this height the walls begin to slope at the rate of 1 perpendicular to 12 horizontal. The archway in the masonry of this pillar, which forms the immediate approach to the roadway, measures 12 feet in width, and 17 feet in height. Each pair of main chains, being suspended horizontally, pass through corresponding apertures in the masonry, at the distance of about 2 feet above one another, and go over rollers connected with the building. The links of the main chains at these points are made as short as the strength or thickness of the iron will permit of their being welded, in order that they may pass over the rollers, without distorting or unduly straining the iron. After going through the masonry of the pillar, the chains are continued in a sloping direction to the ground.... Here they are sunk to a depth of 24 feet, where they pass through great ballast-plates of cast-iron, into which they are stopped by a strong iron spear or bolt, of an oval form, measuring 3 inches by 3½ inches in thickness. The cast-iron ballast plates measure 6 feet in length, 5 feet in breadth, and 5 inches in thickness in the central parts, but towards the edge, they diminish in thickness to 2½ inches. The ends of the chain thus fixed, are loaded with mound-stones and earthy matters, to the level of the roadway of the bridge.

On the English side of the Tweed, the pillar or tower of masonry forming the abutment or point of suspension, is built upon a bench or foundation, excavated in the face of a precipitous sandstone rock, and is only about 20 feet in height, but its other dimensions correspond with the upper part of the masonry on the Scotch side. The chains on the English side are made to rest upon plates of cast-iron, included in the masonry, instead of rollers, as on the opposite side. Here the ballast-plates are of the same dimensions as those already described, but, instead of being sunk into the ground, as on the Scotch side, their position is rather above the foundation of the pillar where they are set nearly perpendicular, but are placed so as to correspond with the direction of the strain or weight of the bridge. For the greater security of the position of these ballast-plates on the English side, they are connected with a horizontal arch of masonry, which is dove-tailed into the rock.'

This account accurately describes the bridge piers as they are today, and also mentions the existence of roller bearings for the chains that pass over the Scottish side pier. A recent examination of these bearings by the County Surveyor's staff has revealed them to be a central single roller for each set of chains, mounted in tiers between cast iron cheeks. A triple set of links pass over the rollers, which provide for reasonable chain movement, but in leaving the rollers the chains are made to pass over cast iron bearing plates at the extreme edge of the pier, where they change directional angle. This really makes a nonsense of the roller bearing, and also introduces a high stress point at the bend in the chain bar, very close to the eye link.

On the English side, bearings are simply fixed cast iron beds rounded at the pier edge point of chain entry. They then pass through a small chamber and into the solid rock.

Although Brown did not record his methods of calculation, his approach to the general bridge design problem seemed simply to revolve around the capability of the main chains to carry the dead and live loads. No consideration was given to the effects of other forces, except for the tension factor at the points of suspension, which thereby increased the 'real weight' of the load suspended.

Stevenson recorded:

"....a remarkable instance occurred at the opening... when it was intended to keep the roadway clear for the ceremony of the day; but this proved quite impracticable, and a crowd of people broke through every obstruction, and forced their way upon the bridge; and it was estimated that at one time there were about 700 people upon the roadway, Now, taking each person and this number at 150lb., it would give about 47 tons, besides its own weight which is sustained, without any apparent derangement."

The incident must have caused Stevenson some concern, for having witnessed the chaos and carefully examined the structure, he wrote to Brown two days after the opening.

"28 July 1820. There was so much trouble on the 26th at the opening of the Union Bridge that we had little opportunity for conversation on the subject of that work which does you so much credit. I was also obliged to set off without having had an opportunity of taking leave of you at the moment. But I now think it right to call your attention particularly to what I only talked of generally when with you and Mr. Thomas on the 26th. On the Scotch side of the river I noticed that the pier of Masonry had evident marks of a shake or fissure throughout the upper part on the eastern side of the archway which should be carefully watched for a time to ascertain if it is upon the increase. This in all probability arises from the shaking of the arch and may perhaps go no further but ought to be attended to least the motion of the Chains and bridge extending a weight equal to about 160 tons may affect it further. On the English side I am of opinion that you have still more to guard against. The mass of rock where your fixtures are made is so full of shakes or fissures that it is impossible for one to form a correct judgement of things who have not seen the progress of the works. I examined this part in the forenoon of the 26th Inst, with yourself - but in the evening I went down into the chain plate pits and particularly noticed the appearance of the whole. From the last inspection I am decidedly of opinion that the chain plates have shifted about half an inch inwards toward the Bridge.

These appearances on both sides of the Bridge now alluded to might not be considered much in the way of creating alarm in the ordinary operations of the engineer where the pressure or strain is equal and uniform, but in the structure of a chain bridge which is so intimately connected with the operation of the action and reaction of its parts the case seems to be widely different and therefore everything about the Masonry should be of such a construction and solidity as to be proof against the appearances. I am now taking the liberty of calling your attention to.

On the English side I am sorry to remark that the extension of the chains stops short of their best effects in resisting the strain as the chain plates are so near the top of the masonry where to speak generally a pound of back weight has not so much effect as an ounce would have when applied as on the Scotch side of the Bridge I am therefore to recommend that you should still penetrate the Bank & Rock 20 feet and there place an additional set of chain plates. The masonry should also be laid upon a sloping bed square to the direction of the strain and not to the horizon.

Although I approve highly of the design & execution of the whole of the iron work I think your perpendicular rods of suspension & the horizontal bars under the Roadway too slender for the effects of waste from oxydation. The beams of the Roadway are strong & perhaps might have been made lighter if the work had been trussed or formed into frames.

In thus delivering my opinion to yourself freely I hope you will receive it as from a friend. I wrote you in compliance & without having had an opportunity as yet of conversing with Professor Leslie on the subject.

His attention was chiefly directed to the effects of expansion on the metal & to the strain when the bridge was loaded. In an account of the matter it may be necessary to be somewhat guarded but nothing requires or shall be noticed which would have a tendency to create any doubt in the public mind upon a subject so delicate. All that I think necessary is to state to yourself what occurs to me and as I know you are partly aware of what I am stating I hope you will the more readily enter upon making provision against the possibility of an accident."

Brown was quick in replying to his friend Stevenson's letter, which he wrote from Berwick on July 30th 1820.

"I have perused yours of the 28th Inst. with attention and have to thank you for the information and advice contained and as you request me to consider your remarks as coming from a friend, rather than as from a critical judge I assure you that I take it in that light and will in as candid a manner make my observation on what you conceive to be insufficient. lst. with respect to the shake in the pier on the North side I have been up and observe that there is not the least appearance of crack or of the mortar being disturbed for 3 courses under the lower chains all the chains rest on broad saddles and in the centre they bear upon rollers so that if there should be any giving from the plates which are 40 feet under the road it would produce no drag on the Tower, there is a very slight appearance of shake under the cornice there and what had the worst appearance, a bad joint in the cornice proceeds from the interposition of scaffolding I am quite satisfied with the Tower it is all solid masonry being entire courses, headers & stretchers, from the foundations Which is 50 by 40 on the south side I perfectly agree with you that further precaution is necessary I say precaution rather than further strength because I did expect that the masonry would be somewhat disturbed from the very principle of the work it is intended to represent one side of the bank. Which is rock B is a tongue of Rock between B and C...C is the other side of the hill the dotted lines in front use part of the same rock considering the support of the rock insufficient I laid two courses of arched stones the abutments being one side of the quarry A the tongue of the centre rock B and the other side of the quarry C. therefore before the plates behind the work could draw forward the sides of the quarry must be positively thrust asunder which it is not possible to conceive altho it might be expected that the arch would draw tight by the drag and consequently cause an appearance of shake, but as I said before I do not mean to trust to this and I assume you will do me the justice to believe that I do not wish to reason myself into deceptive security. I intend to go into the rock 20 feet behind the plates and fix cast

Iron Lewis's with 4 bolts to pass through and bolt to the back of the plates those bolts are to be 23/8 Dia.. the strength of these agreeable to my experiments is 520 Tons but they will begin to stretch at 75 Tons each so that I shall only prove them up to that, which will give me an additional strength of 300 Tons and the Lewis's I think cannot draw because the rock on both sides must be thrust away before it can draw out. With regard to the perpendicular straps they are perhaps 36 times or 2,592 Tons stronger than necessary, and it was merely to avoid the appearance of slightness that I adopted bolts of this size, and with respect to corrosion with common care it is scarcely possible to calculate on their durability, but I can take them all out one by one and when the period does arrive however remote both those and the other component parts of the bridge can be renewed. The objection I have to trussing is that in a structure exposed to wet and dry it would infallibly rot, in the joints and mortices, no trussing laterally will ever stop the undulation or waving motion of the bridge and no wind that ever blew will bend it edge ways.

As we agree on the principal object of giving greater security to the south side which I am now about I mention these secondary considerations mainly as being adverted to in your letter. I shall soon be in Edinburgh and will be happy to dine with you as soon as it is convenient indeed I wish to have some conversation with you because I am of opinion that bridges of this description will be much in demand and I think we may be mutually serviceable to each other believe me to be my dear Sir. Yours truly Sam Brown"

Brown and Stevenson enjoyed a close friendship which excluded professional and business conflict, and it was in this sense of understanding that Stevenson set down his feelings after the formal bridge opening, to which Brown replied in like vein and leaving no doubt about his command of the matter. Brown refuted the suggestion that the Scotch side tower was in any way faulty through the effects of loading, but conceded the criticism of the English side anchorage.

Stevenson's recommendation that an additional 'set of chain plates' should be installed 20 feet further back into the rock was readily accepted, and the work was carried out. (The County of Northumberland survey drawing No. N/C2/TB/24 February 1903 records the position of the additional anchorage extension, which was approximately 16'0" in overall length, the anchor block being wedge shaped in the vertical plane 2'0" in length, 1'6" deep, and in plan width 1'3" at the front and 1'6" at the rear, with the cable bar passing through the block centre secured by iron bar wedge at the back.)

His sketch plan of the anchorage (page 3 of letter) shows the respective pairs of catanarian cables at the tower face entry, with dotted lines suggesting the tower head chambers, beyond which the hatched area indicates the solid rock against which the chain plates bear, and running away from these are indications of the proposed additional anchor cables. The sketch section (page 5 of letter) merely amplifies the sketch plan, showing the 'present pit' and a linked-bar anchor extension from the 'chain plate' to anchor block. The merits of the arithmetical reasoning are open to question, but it was rather a form of blind faith or simply a case of mind over matter that Brown was putting forward in explanation.

Stevenson's reference to 'oxydation' proved to be right, although in fairness, the iron run-bars did survive for fifty one years, and Brown's objection to 'trussing' the platform was sound in judgement.

In the course of his investigations into the strength of iron bar and related linkage, Stevenson had witnessed Messrs Brunton's experiments at their premises in Commercial Road, London, in which the ultimate strength of 2 inch diameter bar was found to be 92 tons. He noted:

"...when the strain had amounted to 60 tons, it was observable that small particles of oxide of iron began to separate on the surface, and when the hydraulic machine was wrought up to a pressure of 75 tons, the part which ultimately separated and gave way, became sensibly smaller, its temperature was also somewhat increased, and when the register of the machine indicated 92 tons, it suddenly parted and broke asunder."

As has been seen, Samuel Brown's tests upon a 2 inch diameter bar, 12 feet 6 inches long, broke under an axial load of 82¾ tons. In practical terms the relative loads, and findings at fracture were very similar, but as Thomas Telford was to point out in his 'Supplementary Report' for the Runcorn Bridge - July, 1817, the 'elastic limit' of a bar under load, was the crucial information that had to be known.

Telford describes his test experience:

".. it has been ascertained, that a Bar of good English malleable Iron, one inch square, will suspend from 27 to 30 tons before it breaks, and that it bears from 15 to 16 tons before it begins to be extended in length. By my experiments, it was ascertained, that with a curvature of 1/20 of the length, malleable iron besides its own weight sustained 1/3 of 15 tons, without deranging its parts...".

Stevenson had witnessed, and recorded, similar conditions in which the bar under test reached its limit of elasticity, yield point and moment of fracture, and in relation to the knowledge that 700 people (47 tons) had thronged onto the bridge "..as the greatest load which is likely to be ever brought upon it at once..", then the combined dead and live load was being considered as 147 tons. He had established that the ultimate aggregate strength of the twelve bars of the Union Bridge to be ".. 92 x 12 = 1104 tons", and summed up, by stating, "...assuming the angle of suspension at 12 degrees, we find that the real weight is increased to about 370 tons of tension on the catenarian chains. But as we find the strength of these chains to be equal to 1104 tons, there remains a surplus strength of about 734, or say 700 tons, to resist any emergency beyond a weight of 50 tons." These were optimistic remarks, but undoubtedly served to provide Brown, and all concerned with a degree of confidence in design procedure.

Before the deck improvements made in 1974, the weight of suspended chains and asphalted platform, amounted to about 112 tons, which also allowed 5% for water saturation of the timber. A dead weight of 100 tons would therefore be a realistic figure for the original structure, allowing for its single layer plank decking and decorative fascia.

By the time that Brown settled down to the design of Union Bridge, he had the benefit of his own bar testing apparatus, the comparative test information from Messrs Brunton's, and the views of Peter Barlow. He had also enjoyed the benefits of a 'full conference' with Thomas Telford, so, with this background, coupled with the years of practical experiences in the manufacture of iron-bar, and his model bridge behind him, Brown was able to confidently proceed with the bridge design. However, to have attained a uniformly distributed loading of 100 tons over the bridge platform with safety, would require a yield stress in the suspension chains of 12.5 tonf/in2 , which is a very high figure for wrought iron.

Barlow advocated a yield stress of about 10 tons per square inch, and Telford was thinking that 4 tons per square inch was more prudent; somewhere in between was therefore approaching the real stress limit, by present day standards. Without knowing the exact safe working stress for the wrought iron that was used, it is not possible to accurately assess the likely working load but stress conditions produced in the structure can be established. The worst state is in the back stay part of the suspension chain, where the stress due to dead weight alone, is of the order of 6.5 tonf/in^2 . Assuming a safe stress in the wrought iron to be 7.5 tonf/in^2 then the superload stress capacity is only 1 tonf/in^2, which represents a total uniformly distributed superload of 16.7 tonf/ft.

The following figures give comparative values of the total uniformity distributed superload for different stresses. It is unlikely that the yield stress of the wrought iron is greater than 12.5 tonf/in^2 ; so the load for this stress could be considered as an ultimate value.

Assumed yield stress in suspension chain	Total uniformly distributed superload on deck
Tonf/in^2	Tons
8.5	33
9.5	50
10.5	67
11.5	84
12.5	100

These figures ignore the ability, or otherwise of the anchorages to resist the forces produced. With a superload of 100 tons the total tensions on the anchorages would be of the order of 470 tons, which represents a unit soil pressure of 4.2 tonf/ft^2 , and this is a very high soil resistance figure, about which to be assured. Apart from the strength of catenary chains, and the ability of anchorages to resist the imposed load, other aspects of the design obviously influence the overall maximum loading condition. The suspension rods, of one inch diameter, could be subject to a maximum load of 4.25 tonf, but the end fixings at chain saddle and platform supporting run-bar would substantially reduce this figure. Strength of the chains connecting links are also questionable items, and if everything is considered, even the lower loading figure of 100 tons claimed for the bridge by contemporary sources, seems to be high, and the amount of 33 tons is and always has been the more realistic. In 1820 cart wheel axle loads in excess of one ton would have been exceptional and breaking up of the deck through the wear of iron wheel rims was the more serious matter than actual loading. In later years, both platform wear and increasing weight became a matter for serious concern, but deterioration of the ageing chains in the relatively inaccessible pier bearing chambers provided the real worries.

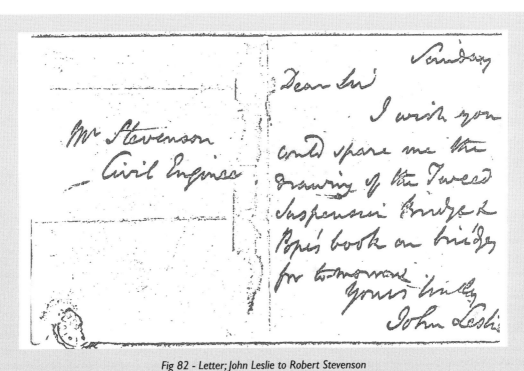

Fig 82 - Letter; John Leslie to Robert Stevenson
Copy of original letter from John Leslie, Professor of Natural Philosophy, Edinburgh University, to Mr. Stevenson of Messrs. Stevenson and Jardine - Civil Engineers. (Edinburgh University Library). Letter undated, but John Leslie is most likely referring to Samuel Brown's final design, and mention of 'Pope's book' relates to 'A Treatise on Bridge Architechture with an historical account of Different Bridges - T. Pope - New York 1811'

Robert Stevenson well summarised the problems and conditions that related specifically to suspension bridge design, the principles of which both Thomas Pope and James Finley had earlier identified albeit, beyond technical realisation.

Stevenson : "...But the effect we have to provide against in bridges of suspension, is not merely what is technically termed dead-weight. A more powerful agent exists in the sudden impulses, or jerking motion of the load, which we have partly noticed in the description of Dryburgh bridge.... Hence also the effects of gusts of wind, often and violently repeated, which destroy the equilibrium of the parts of a bridge of suspension; and the importance of having the whole roadway and side-rails framed in the strongest possible manner." Although Stevenson said that the "fastidious, upon examining this work, may perhaps find some parts of the general design capable of improvement....". he accepted that the work "..does the highest credit to Captain Brown," and made these complimentary remarks:

"The general effect of the Union Bridge, which we have now endeavoured to describe, is interesting and curious; and such is the extent, and its light and elegant appearance, that it has not inaptly been compared to an inverted rainbow, Those who visit this undertaking, as affording much novelty, to the scenery of this part of the banks of the Tweed, will not be disappointed in their expectations; while, in a national point of view, as a great improvement, it deserves the most particular consideration of the country at large."

SAMUEL BROWN AND UNION CHAIN BRIDGE

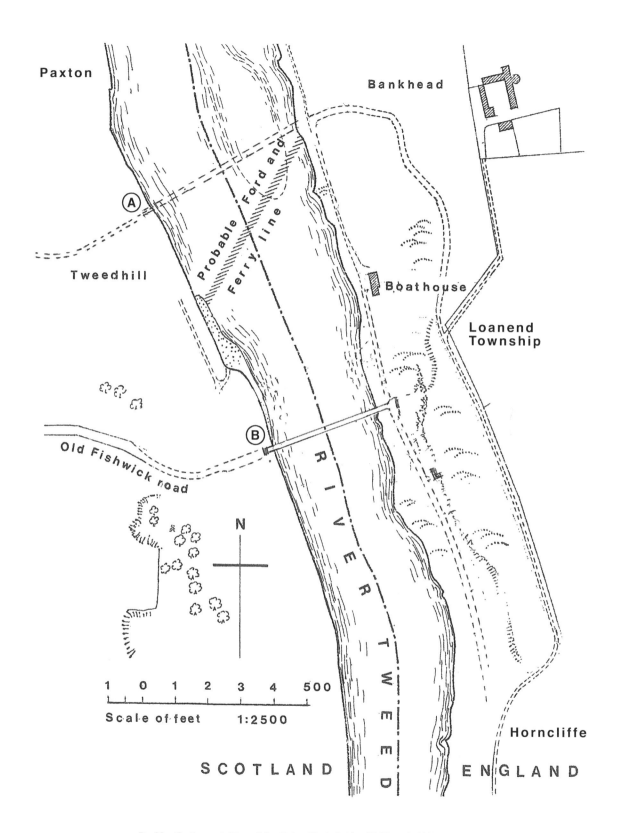

Paxton

Bankhead

Tweedhill

Probable Ford and Ferry line

(A)

Boathouse

Loanend
Township

(B)

Old Fishwick road

N

R I V E R   T W E E D

1   0   1   2   3   4   500

Scale of feet   1:2500

SCOTLAND

ENGLAND

Horncliffe

Fig 83 - Conjectural siting of the Union Chain Bridge 1818 at A; 1820 siting at B

5

From Contract to Completion

Under the Authority of an Act of Parliament, a body of Trustees was formed at an inaugural meeting at "The Hen and Chickens", Berwick, on July 3rd 1819. Invited members "severally took and subscribed the oath of Qualification prescribed by the Act, before they proceeded to act." They were fourteen in number, as follows:

William Grieve Esq   Thomas Boswall Esq
John Grey Esq of West Ord   Robert Johnston Esq
Thomas Grey Alder Esq   James Forster Esq
Matthew Forster Esq   Reverend Joseph Barnes
John Sibbit Esq   Anthony Gregson Esq
John Strangeways Donaldson Esq   George Dickson Esq
Henry Dinning Esq   William Pattison Esq

William Grieve Esq was elected Chairman. Mr. William Willoby was appointed Clerk to the Trustees, Mr. William Lowrey, Surveyor of the Roads and Mr. John Longhorn appointed Treasurer.

The Meeting also 'Resolved that Anthy. Gregson, John S. Donaldson, John Sibbit, Robert Johnston, Thomas G. Alder, Thomas Boswall, William Pattison, John Swinton and William Molle Esquire, to be a Committee to consider the proper places for the new Gates on the Roads in North Durham'

It was also 'Resolved that the Trustees consult with Captain Brown for the proposed Bridge at New Water for the sum of Four Thousand, Nine Hundred Pounds, as proposed by him, and that the above Gentlemen be also a Committee to revise and settle the Contract.'

Captain Brown's original drawing for the Bridge was signed by him and dated 'London, 7th September, 1818'; this drawing formed part of the contract agreement between the Trustees and Captain Brown, dated 21st August, 1819 and it was accordingly signed by the respective parties.

The proposal was almost one year old before Brown's scheme was finally accepted at a cost of £4,900: the original signing of agreement of intent (September 1818) rather in the nature of a sketch scheme and estimate, which would have given the necessary time for detailed development.

Because the bridge design proposal was a symmetrical arrangement its siting was obviously intended to be in close vicinity of New Water Ford, where the banks on both sides of the river are relatively less steep than up river. Such a situation also offered the advantages of existing approach roads, but with a suspension bridge, whose road deck needed to be a certain minimum distance above water level, and good cable anchorages had to be provided, the Ford position was not entirely satisfactory.

At a Trustee Meeting held on July 16th, 1819, suggestions about the location of 'Tollgates on the Road leading southward from the Tweed' were made. Captain Brown's draft contract for the bridge was produced at the Meeting and approved. No descriptive or detailed account of costs were minuted, but the overall cost of 'Bridge and Road of Communications will cost at least £6,000', and only £4,900 was available through revenue derived from existing road tax and loans. The required balance was to be sought from 'several Noblemen and Gentlemen - much interested in the improvement who have not subscribed to the loan'. The Meeting decided that the Chairman 'should write to a number of Noblemen and Gentlemen and request their aid for the carrying out of the works'.

Twenty two people were named in the minutes, viz:
Right Honble Lord Douglass
Right Honble Lord Bredalbane
Lumsdane Esq of Blanerne
Right Honble Lord Sinclair
Pat Murray Esq of Simprim
- Seymour Esq of Kersfield
Revnd. W Stow Lundie
Wm. Jeffreys Esq Sunnick
Sir Jas. Hecart of Allanbank
Geo Baillie Esq of Mellerstain for Foulden West Mains
Sir Jas Hall Bart for Chirnside
Sir Alex Don Bart for Whitsom Newton
Alex Christie Esq of Grueldykes
Genl. Maitland
Wm. Grieve Esq Ord House
Lord Grieve's Trustees
Shafto Craster, Esq.
Nich's Fenwick Esq for Felkington
P.J.Selby Esq of Twisel House
His Grace the Duke of Northumberland
A Allan Esq M.P. Baker Street London
H.H. St. Paul Esq M.P. Ewart Park Wooler

On July 26th 1819 William Molle Esq., Chairman of the Trustees laid the Foundation Stone. William Molle was a local land agent and respected member of the community who acted for William Foreman Home of Paxton House, the estate adjoining the north boundary of Tweedhill House owned by Mr. Joseph Macbraire.

A family relationship developed between W. Foreman Home and Admiral Sir David Milne, when his eldest daughter married the eldest son of the Admiral and the interest here simply lies in the author's belief that, through the influence of the Admiral, Samuel Brown secured an introduction for the Bridge contract. Both men eventually became Trustees, W. F. Home on 21st October 1820 and the Admiral on 4th June 1821.

A record of the Foundation Stone laying was published in The Berwick Advertiser' on July 31st 1819:

"...........UNION BRIDGE

On Monday last, the Commissioners of the Berwick Road Trust met at Tweedhill where the foundation stone of the Iron Bar Bridge of Suspension over the Tweed was laid by the Preses of the Meeting, in presence of the Commissioners and other Gentlemen, and of a vast concourse of people from both sides of the Tweed, who were anxious to behold the commencement of this interesting work. A bottle, including the coins of the present reign, and a Berwick newspaper, with the following inscription, on a copper plate, were put into the foundation stone:

'This foundation stone of an Iron Bar Bridge of Suspension over the Tweed was laid by Wm. Molle, Esq. of Maines, on Monday, 26th day of July, in the year of our Lord 1819, and in the 59th year of the reign of our Sovereign, George the Third.

'In the presence of the Trustees of the Berwick Roads, who are to erect the same under the authority of Parliament.

'Captain SAMUEL BROWN, R.N. Inventor and Contractor.

'May God prosper the undertaking"

After which, corn, wine, and oil were successively poured upon the stone, according to ancient custom, and the blessing of God invoked on the work.

- The Preses then addressed the meeting, so far as could be collected, nearly as follows:

"GENTLEMEN - I feel highly sensible of the honour you have done me, in intrusting me with the laying of the foundation stone of the iron bar bridge of suspension over the Tweed, an honour which I can attribute only to the good opinion which you entertain of my intentions, and of my zeal for the success of the measure; for there were many others who, from their abilities, and their rank and station in the commonwealth, were more justly entitled to this distinction - I consider this species of bridge to be the commencement of a new era in the progress and improvement of the arts. The substitution of iron in place of wood, in various arts, has been deemed a capital improvement, but it was reserved to the present ingenious inventor of the iron bar bridge of suspension, to be the first to apply iron to the construction of works of this nature; and if the present attempt should succeed, I may venture to predict that bridges of this kind will become general throughout the kingdom, for they can be erected in a shorter time, and at a much less expense than a stone bridge. A stone bridge would have cost at this place, near twenty thousand pounds; whereas our present bridge, the span of which will be about 430 feet, is only to cost £4,900 not a fourth of the expense of the other; and it will even possess a superiority above a stone bridge, as iron having no pillars in the middle of the water, it will not be liable to be swept away by the floods of the river; and as to the time of construction, our contractor has given us to understand, that in the course of five or six months, he will be able to complete the present bridge. It is, therefore, I submit, not going too far, to anticipate the pleasing hope, that bridges of this nature will be adopted generally throughout the island; and I need not say how much this will promote and facilitate the internal trade and commerce of the nation. To this district, in particular, the advantages of the present bridge are almost incalculable. It will abridge distance; it will save the lives of men, a paramount consideration in all under-takings; it will improve our agriculture and internal trade in these parts, and it will contribute to the comforts and convenience of life, by rendering our access to those essential articles of human consumption, coal and lime, perfectly safe, and more easy and expeditious in all weathers, and all times and seasons. It will further be the means of augmenting and promoting still more, the social intercourse and mutual friendship and esteem, between the two ancient nations, now happily united together.

Fig 84 - Engraving Union Chain Bridge, T Sutherland

'Now Gentlemen, as to the success of the present experiment,(for still it is an experiment,) I think that we cannot reasonably entertain much doubt; for the plan has not only been submitted to, and approved of by the most eminent engineer in the Kingdom (Mr. John Rennie,) after the most deliberate consideration; upon two several occasions, but we ought also to repose great confidence in our present contractor, who is no stranger to the strength and quality of iron; for from his being the ingenious inventor of the iron cables, an invention now universally used in the navy, and very generally in the merchant service, he has had repeated opportunities, for years past of trying the strength and properties of iron in all situations, and we all know that he entertains the most perfect confidence in the stability and durability of the plan of the present iron bridge, which he has presented for our adoption. Let me add, too, that this is the first bridge of the kind which will be completed in the island; and allow me to say, that it is highly creditable to this part of the United Kingdom, to have led the way in so capital an-improvement in the arts. It confers a benefit on mankind; it renders the use of iron still more general; and in fact, causes the bowels of the earth to contribute more to the improvement of the arts than the productions of its surface.

'Let us therefore pray that Almighty God pour down his blessings, and vouchsafe to prosper the present undertaking.'

The bridge was then named 'The Union Bridge' in commemoration of the union between the two kingdoms which it is calculated to cement.

The ceremony was concluded by the band of the Northumberland Local Militia playing 'God save the King' 'Rule Britannia', and other national tunes.

Afterwards the Commissioners, with a number of Gentlemen from both sides of the Tweed, dined in a tent which had been pitched on the side of the river. The dinner and wines, which were of the best quality, were provided by Mr. Dods of Norham, and gave great satisfaction. Many loyal and appropriate toasts were given, to which the band played suitable tunes, and the evening was spent with much conviviality and good humour."

On August, 7th 1819, the Berwick Advertiser carried an account of the party following the laying of the Foundation Stone:

"Capt. Brown, R.N., the architect of the New Bridge, gave a SALMON KETTLE to a respectable party, whereof fifty five sat down to a most excellent dinner, in a tent pitched for that purpose near the spot. This tent was constructed in such a manner, with an awning over the top, so as easily to be converted into a ball-room. After dinner the cheerful glass went briskly round and dancing commenced in the ball-room thus contrived, and kept up till a late hour, when the company retired highly gratified with the entertainment they had received.

On Friday night the bottle containing the coins now current, and which had been cemented into the foundation-stone of the Union Bridge, was taken away with its contents. The robbers have not yet been detected."

William Molle's poetry reading was also recorded, tinged with vivid descriptions of the Tweed in history, which attracted a witty response. While the whole key of Molle's verse was one of Union, it is important to remember that the effect of the Jacobite rebellion lingered on until 1807 with the death of the Cardinal of York; well within the memory of people present at the ceremony, which was on Scottish soil. In Scotland the dreams of the Jacobite party found expression in beautiful songs, and Molle was doubtless moved to launch the bridge in like spirit, and recited:

THE UNION BRIDGE

When the red roaring cataract rushes down from the Cheviot,
And fills the vast plains with a deluge below;
When great mountains of ice tumble down in the Teviot,
And the Ettrick and Yarrow are swoln by the snow:

Then the grand River Tweed, in her mantle of scarlet,
Sweeps all things before her proud waves to the main;
When a bold British tar comes from the Royal Charlotte,
And high o'er her surface he stretches his chain.

Now England and Scotland are connected together;
We visit each other when ever we please;
In summer and winter, and all kinds of weather,
We'll pass the Chain Bridge with safety and ease.

The rose and the thistle in love and affection,
Are walking like sisters in beauty arrayed;
The rose, in her mantle of varied complexion,
And the thistle, rapt up in her fine tartan plaid.

No Marmion now views Norham Castle's steep glory,
No war sounding bugle hails Flodden's high hill;
No hordes of marauders are riding the foray
Nor fording the Tweed at the mouth of the Till.

No gallant Earl Percy, with hound and with horn,
Three long summer days is hunting our land;
No bold Borderers now, with undaunted scorn,
Are guarding the Marches, with broad sword in hand.

These days are all gone, never more to return;
For now, when we meet, 'tis the plough to bid speed;
With love and with friendship our bosoms do burn
In fine social glee, on the haughs of the Tweed.

Our modern contention's to win the proud laurels,
As ploughman as shepherd, or as artisan;
Who longest makes the service, in peace without quarrels,
And who soothes the last days of the grey headed man;

Who makes the best roads and throws the best bridges;
Who rears the best mutton and feeds the best beef;
Who breeds the best horses to till our long ridges,
And to cart home in harvest; the golden wheat sheaf.

Success to the Tweed, with her rich salmon treasure;
Success to the people who live on her side;
Success to the man who concerted the measure
Of throwing a Chain Bridge over her tide.

The following lines were spoken, extempore, by 'W............y', on his health being drunk, by the company at the laying of the foundation stone of the Union Bridge, after the preceding poem had been read by William Molle, Esq. of Mains:

"Success to the Bridge, to the Molle and the Stone!
May they aye be preserved from mishap:
May the Bridge never fall till the world be gone,
And the Molle ne'er be caught in a trap!...."

Sometime before bridge work started, Alexander Nasmyth (1758 - 1840) had been commissioned to illustrate the intended structure in its setting. At what date, and by whom he was appointed is not known, but the painting he produced is a fine topographical landscape, and an accurate statement of the eventual bridge. In comparison with the bridge now, the proportions given in the drawing are remarkably correct, including the details and features - the triple banks of catenary chains, the alternatively arranged suspension bars and the Toll House, which forms an integral part of the English pier. However, an obvious error in the painting is the continuation of the suspension bars that are shown beyond the bridge deck end up to the pier face on the English side. This is a strange mistake to have made, for although Nasmyth was trained as a portrait painter and devoted himself to landscape in his later years, many of his youthful years had been spent as an engineering draughtsman assistant to a Mr. Miller of Dalwinton, "who was making mechanical researches and experiments."

Nasmyth was also employed in the beautifying of estates, and designed the Circular Temple over Bernard's Well near Telford's Dean Bridge Edinburgh. Because of his breadth of activity, Nasmyth was also respected as an architect, and it was unfortunate that owing to his liberal political attitude he was overlooked by his original aristocratic benefactors. However, Nasmyth was a Scotsman of outstanding merit in the field of fine arts, and doubtless the Border people chose the best, as their bridge illustrates.

It must be assumed that Nasmyth received his instructions and information according to Brown's contract drawing of August 21st, 1819, probably with notes and sketches about the bridge location and other required differences. This being the case, it is quite likely that Nasmyth built into his painting certain architectural refinements, apart from amendments that were given. The painting shows a false fascia applied as a continuous embellishment to the ends of the road deck transoms,

Fig 85 - Union Chain Bridge over the River Tweed; Alexander Nasmyth (The Paxton Trust)

moulded and dentil coursed, (details of this feature are shown on the survey drawings made of the bridge in 1871-72 at the time of the extensive reparations to the road platform, after which time it was removed). The drawing also illustrates the upper part of the English pier rising out of and above the level of the natural rock face, which would have been the case if the pier had been set forward as intended, but foundation problems emerged, the outcome of which was given in Brown's post justifications for additional progress claims given in his letter of September 30th 1820.

Although Nasmyth made the error of showing the suspension bars continuing beyond their necessary position, a similar mistake was also made on a contemporary drawing that was produced soon after the bridge was opened, which suggests that there was both lack of observation and technical knowledge. Assuming this drawing was a reasonably accurate record, it at least confirms the possible original absence of the stone blocks that now protect the back chains at their junction with the ground on the Scottish side, although this again may have been an oversight.

Many detail errors about the statistics of the bridge have been recorded in various works over the years, particularly in relation to span, load carrying capacity and actual location.

As Brown's contract drawing showed a clear span of about 392 feet,(scaled) then *'The Times'* of July 20th, 1820 must be forgiven for reporting the river width at '...437 feet from bank to bank', for at that time the river width at New Water Ford would have been about that distance, which suggests that the eventual bridge position information never filtered through to *'The Times'* in London.

The location of the bridge has also been inaccurately recorded; Kelso is given by S.B.Hamilton in his 'History of Technology' and the same author maintains the collapse of the bridge within six years. Likewise, Eric de Mare in his 'Bridges of Britain' and H. Shirley Smith in 'The World's Greatest Bridges' gave its life span as six months. In fact, the bridge never collapsed, but confusion about the matter probably arose from the Dryburgh Abbey Footbridge over the Tweed, that was built by John and William Smith in 1817 and was blown down in January, 1818. The replacement bridge is attributed to Samuel Brown but there is no real evidence to support this.

A small sub-committee set out upon a form of inspection of the Road some time during December 1819, and their report was presented to the Committee at their meeting on December 28th, 1819. Their descriptions included a reference to the New Water Ford "..., where preparations are making for the construction of the intended Iron Bridge, for the purpose of examining the access to that Ford,....." It is not clear from this description whether any real earthwork or other physical activity was being done, or whether the actual proposed bridge line was coincident with the Ford. Whatever the situation at that time, the proposed height of the bridge deck above average high water level was a matter of great concern to the Committee of the Trustees and their Clerk wrote to Captain Brown:

"Berwick, 4th March, 1820

Dear Sir,

The Statutory Committee of the Trustees under our Road Act met here this day - Among other matters which came under their consideration was the proposed height of your intended Bridge above the River. They understand that at the breaking up of the late Storm the Water and Ice rose to such a height that the Bridge, if it had been previously completed, must have been destroyed, and it is suggested by some persons of respectability who have for many years been in the habit of paying much attention to the Tweed that it has been known to rise from two to three feet higher than on this occasion.

The Committee understand from Mr. Redpath that he has made a communication on this subject to you but it appears to them a matter of such importance both to you and the County, that they have directed me to draw your attention to the information they have received, with the view of your adopting such alterations as may insure the future safety of the Bridge.

I am Sir
William Willoby

To Captn. Brown"

The Captain replied in a week:

"Billeter Square 12 March 1820 Sir

I was duly favoured with Yours acquainting me that a Meeting of the Trustees of the Union Bridge had been held and they were desirous to know whether I intended to adopt any measures to avert the danger which the Bridge would be subject to from the recurrence of such a flood as took place on the...last. I have to request you will inform the Trustees on the Committee that I was advised of that event by Mr. Redpath and from his description I immediately decided on raising the Pier on the North side and erecting a corresponding height of Masonry on the Rock on the South side - The original height intended was 20 feet above the ordinary surface of the River, being about 6 feet higher than the Haugh land behind the pier, and from all the information I could collect in the neighbourhood that was considered sufficient, and I made my Estimate accordingly. Mr. Redpath is of the opinion that 3½ or 4 feet would raise the Bridge above the reach of such a flood and accumulation of Ice. But in order to prevent the possibility of danger from even a greater inundation I propose to raise both sides of the building 7 feet so that the Bridge will hang 27 feet above the Water in its ordinary state. This will increase the expense of the work, including alterations in the Iron materials about £300.

With this additional elevation, the Bridge may be considered as perfectly secure for ages; the durability of the materials becomes a matter of the next importance.

The chief expense in maintaining the Bridge will be the renewal and repair of the wearing surface - I have therefore directed Iron Rail roads to be made for carriages passing in opposite directions, which will prove a most essential saving to the County for Years after the termination of my guarantee.

The first expense of this Iron work will be considerable but as it will ultimately be a saving to me in keeping the Bridge in repair I do not intend to solicit the Trustees to defray any part of the expense. I have however to submit to their consideration the propriety of their paying the difference of the expense of an iron railing on each side of the bridge in lieu of a wooden railing - The cost of the former will be £300, the latter, £100 - The iron railing would last as long as the Bridge and the expense of preserving it from rust will be so trifling that it scarcely need be named -
The wooden rail would no doubt last for 10 years - after which it must be repaired or renewed at the expense of the Trust - I have to beg you will take the sense of the Trustees to the expediency of their allowing me £300 for the additional expense of elevating the bridge and £200 for the Railing as above in addition to my loan of £500 to be redeemed from the first proceeds of the Bridge as stated in the agreement - I beg leave to add this from the information I have received from Mr. Redpath that I shall begin to erect the Bridge about the beginning of April, and will have it finished considerably within the period contracted for.

I am Sir

To W. Willoby   Sam Brown'

From this letter it is evident that Brown had already acted upon information received through Mr. Redpath and planned to raise the Bridge level. The letter of March 4th from William Willoby to Brown was worded in terms of an expressed instruction to amend the design, which clearly involved additional expense, but the Trustees were not all of the same mind about paying, as the Minutes of their April meeting recorded:

> "The Trustees having taken into consideration Captn. Brown's letter, are of the opinion that any deviation from the terms of the Contract would at present be liable to objections - If however it shall be hereafter found that the success of the iron Bridge accords with the expectations formed of it, the Trustees will feel disposed to take a liberal view of Captn. Brown's claims to be indemnified in the additional outlay of £300 incurred by him in raising the line work of the Bridge - The Trustees are also of opinion that it will not be advisable at present to incur any additional expense in respect of the railings of the Bridge…………:
> Ordered that the Statutory Committee do ascertain the amount of the Subscriptions for the Union Bridge and if they find it sufficient for that work and for the new Road on the South side that they then get a proper specification of that Road prepared - If the subscription be found insufficient then the Committee are requested to consider what are the best means of procuring funds for accomplishing that work …."

Both sides were trying to get the best of the bargain. Brown merely wanted to obtain the cost for works that he had not reckoned with, and the Trustees were leaning upon the terms of an Agreement, that presumably tied their contractor to provide a completely satisfactory structure according to conditions to which it would be subjected. No record of the Agreement exists, but without doubt the terms would have been demanding upon Brown. In any event the Trustees were being extremely adventurous, and to a greater extent taking risks, for the very idea of a suspension bridge spanning the Tweed that was capable of supporting carts and wagons loaded with coal and limestone, was to most people of the time a romantic dream. However, in financial terms, Brown was making a great offer and he also gave guarantees favourable to the Trustees, backed by a reputation for skill and competence. The cost of the proposed bridge was a small fraction of any alternative bridge type, which brought the whole venture within the financial scope of the Trustees.

Nevertheless, for the Trustees it was a game of chance, as they carried the responsibility to provide and maintain the bridge. A suspension bridge was considered to be a very worthwhile experiment, and faith and trust existed on both sides. For Brown, the Bridge offered great opportunity to prove himself and his ideas, which until now had only been partially realised in an experimental model footbridge of 100ft. span erected near his works on the Isle of Dogs in 1818, which John Rennie had inspected. A most valuable encounter was the exchange of ideas and knowledge between Brown and Thomas Telford over the abortive Runcorn Bridge proposal; this was to Telford's benefit, and contributed to that engineer's Menai masterpiece, but undoubtedly Brown's influence must have been considerable, for he had already developed and received Letters Patent in 1817 for flat eye bar chain links; the principle that Telford employed.

The description given by Brown in his letter of 12th March, 1820 concerning the raising of the north side pier and masonry against the rock of the south side, leaves no doubt that the bridge was destined for its ultimate position, and that the 'contract drawing' which bears no relation to the eventual site must have been prepared, and accepted, as an example of intention. Nevertheless, if design and costs were agreed in August 1818 for a bridge with two free-standing piers and side railings for the roadway, for what reason exchanges were taking place about errors in March 1820, just before serious site work was to start, is difficult to understand. It can only be presumed that the final bridge siting that provided one free-standing pier, with the south end taking advantage of the existing rock face, would merit equal material and effort, and therefore balance the books, but in fact such changes may have been cheaper for Brown, and no comment appeared to be raised, or recorded in the Minutes of meetings. From an overall point of view the cost of the actual project was undoubtedly more expensive than the scheme contained in the contract drawing, for the catenary chains were to span 425 feet clear, instead of 392 feet; and became 3 sets instead of single bank, and the suspension rods were increased from 10ft to 5ft spacing.

The construction of the Union Bridge was only part of the Trustees' responsibilities; it had to be paid for, together with approach roads and improvements to existing roads, and such money had to be derived from tolls levied at the Turnpikes. Decisions were taken about their most advantageous positioning, and the Trustees' objective was to let the respective Toll Gates to the highest bidders, and they were accordingly advertised. The Trustees considered the outcome at a meeting on May 3rd, 1820:

"Sir John Marjoribanks Bart, took and subscribed the Oath of Qualification prescribed by the Act before he proceeded to act.

Whereas the Tolls to be collected at the several Toll Gates herein before mentioned were set up at this Meeting, to be let to the highest bidders, pursuant to Act of Parliament, and the several persons herein after mentioned were the highest Bidders for the same, at the Rents respectively herein after mentioned (that is to say) :

		£	s	d
Tweedmouth Low Gate	George Brown	634	0	0
Tweedmouth High Gate	George Brown	538	0	0
Twisel Gate	William Short	505	0	0
Castlegate Gate	William Paton	300	0	0

It is ordered that leases of the said Tolls be granted to the said several persons respectively from the twelfth day of May instant, for one year, under the said several Yearly Rents; such Leases to be drawn and prepared according to the tenet and effect of certain Rules for letting the Tolls bearing date this day.

The Standing Committee presents this Report relating to the southern approaches to the Union Bridge of which the following is a copy:

'After a careful and minute examination of the ground your Committee instructed Mr. John Blackadder, surveyor, to prepare a plan and Report on the proposed road on the principles approved of and agreed on by your Committee on the Spot - The Plan and Report alluded to are herewith presented, on which your Committee have to offer the following observations:

1st: The Bridge being in a state of great forwardness, it becomes a matter of extreme Importance, that no time should be lost in executing the southern approach without which the Bridge is totally useless - Your Committee therefore recommend that Instructions should be given to them by the General Meeting of this day, to proceed with the utmost possible despatch in carrying the Plan into effect.

2nd: As it appears that a considerable sum of money is still wanted to enable the Trust to carry the above operation into effect, Your Committee have to suggest that a strong application should be made by the Chairman of the Meeting in the name of the Trustees to those proprietors who have not yet contributed to the loan, and whose properties are benefited by the Improvements, and also that measures be used to interest the Members of Parliament for the Counties of Durham, Northumberland and Berwick, and for the Borough of Berwick, so as to induce them to endeavour to obtain the aid of Government in the way of loan for the advancement of an object so greatly and evidently beneficial to the Public.

3rd: With regard to the Plan and Estimate, your Committee
have to observe that it is impossible to ascertain whether great part of the solid substance to be cut thro' in forming the Roadway may not turn out to be Rock, the sum estimated for cutting must by no means be considered as the utmost of what will be required, and under that uncertainty your; Committee foresee considerable difficulties in finding Compositors willing to undertake it for a specific sum.

4th: Your Committee also apprehend from Information they have been at some pains to obtain from professional men, that the sum estimated for metalling the Road will be very insufficient, from the Distance from whence proper Metal must probably be got.

John Sinton, Jos. Marshall, John Grey'

The said Report is approved of, except as to the mode of application which is ordered to be by letter from the Clerk, instead of the Chairman of the Meeting. Resolved that the Committee be and they are hereby authorised to advertise for Estimates and contract for doing the work necessary for the south approach and the Toll House, and that any deficiency to the extent of £400 shall be provided for by raising money on the individual Security of the following Gentlemen present who have consented hereto,
viz: John Marjoribanks, Bart, John Sibbit, Joseph Marshall, Daniel Ord, John Grey, John Swinton, William Molle and James Forster, Esquires.

The Meeting resumed the consideration of the representatives at last Meeting about the Tillmouth and Twisel Road - Resolved that the Road shall be changed and improved under the authority and Powers vested in the Trustees by the Act, according to the Plan."

The Trustees were becoming necessarily concerned about the timing of the overall work programme. Captain Brown had promised his Bridge complete within the period contracted for, the south end of which was to terminate below the sheer rock bank, and for continuing the road an inclined cut some 250 yards long parallel with the river had to be made, and the Trustees were not sure if the ground was solid rock, or more easily removable sub-soil. An air of panic seemed to temper proceedings; all of a sudden everything was happening and there was not much time to tie up the ends. The Surveyor was authorised and 'directed to apply to two Justices of the County of Durham for an order to get materials at the Heaton Quarry - provided always that it is distinctly understood that this Trust is not to be subjected in any event to any Charge or Expense beyond the sum of £400 already subscribed by the Trustees.'

At a Trustees Meeting on June 12th, 1820, their ranks had swollen to twenty three in number, and Daniel Ord chaired the meeting, which started by ratifying the recommendations of the Committee Meeting held on July 16th 1819 about positions for the Tollgates on the Road leading southward from the Tweed, and a committee of five Trustees was appointed to 'get a Plan and Specification prepared for the Tollhouses, and to contract for the same, and to get the Gates set up as soon as practicable, and to appoint Persons to collect the Tolls at these Gates till they shall be let -'

The Standing Committee reported to the meeting that the contractor making the road down to the bridge had discovered a Quarry and he was proposing that the material should be used as Metal for the Roadway. The Committee reported inspecting the discovery and in an ambiguous way recommended the use of certain material:

> "It appears to them that of various strata of which the Quarry is composed, a very small part is in any degree admissable as Road Metal, and the Committee recommend it to the Trustees to direct their Overseer to pay the strictest attention that none be applied that is not perfectly safe - The Committee has directed the Overseer to lay before the Meeting specimens of the Strata which appear to them to be admissible - the committee have taken into attentive consideration the proposed situation of the Portage House, and upon the whole have no hesitation in recommending that it be placed as represented on a Plan to be laid before the Meeting by Mr. Redpath - It was certainly to be wished that there had been a little more space between the front of the Tollhouse and the Bridge, but under all circumstances it appears to the Committee that to place the Tollhouse in any other situation would be attended with still greater disadvantages, and that the proposed Position of it will remedy a very offensive Deformity which otherwise the Trustees would find themselves under the necessity of doing at considerable expense.
>
> John Swinton
> Jos. Marshall......"

The Meeting approved the use of certain stone for road metalling and the site of the Portage House. This is the first reference to the Tollhouse, and its description identifies it with that shown in Nasmyth's painting.

At the same meeting, the Clerk was ordered to seek permission from Henry Collingwood Selby to get materials for the Roads from Holy Island, the Trust agreeing to pay reasonable damages, and at the same time, the Standing Committee and Surveyor were required to 'make inquiries as to the expense of bringing such materials by Sea for the use of the Trust.' It was further 'ordered that the Clerk do write Mr. Bailey, Agent for the estate of Tankerville, for leave to get stones from Heaton Quarry and if refused that the measures directed by the Act be adopted for obtaining an Order of Justices for that purpose.'

Evidence of some considerable activity by Captain Brown's workmen across the River was brought home to the Committee by a claim for compensation by men whose fishing for salmon had been seriously affected. At the termination of a long meeting, the complaint received scant regard; it was mentioned as follows:

"The following Notice was laid before the Meeting:
We do hereby give you Notice that we have sustained considerable loss in the Fishing Water called 'Scotch New Water' of which we are tenants by the Erection of the new Bridge at New Water Ford, and we shall be glad to meet such of the Trustees as may be named to agree for the damages so sustained by us and we are

	Gentlemen
Berwick 12th	Your most Obedient Servants
June 1820	John and George Bell

To the Trustees, named and appointed in and by an Act of Parliament for making certain Roads and Bridges for the Counties of Durham and Berwick.

The consideration thereof is referred to another meeting.

Ordered that the next Meeting be held at the same House on the Tenth day of July next.

Dan Ord Chairman"

Although the great moment of the Bridge opening was little more than days away, insufficient Trustees were present at the July 10th 1820 Meeting for any business to be conducted, and for the same reason neither did the Meeting convened for August 7th take place. For all the pomp and splendour of the official opening, no mention of the eventful day was recorded at the meeting of October 2nd 1820.

Now that Captain Brown had fulfilled his contract he was eager that his accounts be settled, properly and in a gentlemanly manner. Typical of the time, business houses had almost to beg for remuneration, and Brown was no exception. His London based business was expanding and his services were being sought for new engineering adventures, and money was an obvious necessity. At a Meeting of Trustees at the 'Hen and Chickens' on 2nd October 1820, Brown's plea in writing was presented:

"William Willoby, Esq. Berwick, 30th September 1820 Sir,

I take this opportunity of the General Meeting of the Trustees for the Union Bridge of Suspension, of laying before them the accounts which are all collected which I have stated in one general account No. 1 - I have greatly to regret that the expense of erecting the Bridge should have so far exceeded the Sum contracted for and if I were not sensible that must be attributed to unforeseen and unavoidable causes, I would not presume to make application to the Trustees for remuneration.

It generally occurs that in all great works that the expenses greatly excccd the estimates, in some recent instances, more than double -

The Union Bridge has cost about one fourth more, principally from the following circumstances, viz:

Unsuccessful attempts to get foundations on the south side where it was first intended - The greater span of the present situation - additional height of Towers and many contingent expenses inseparable from new undertakings.

I am however perfectly aware of the obligatory nature of the contract and if the Trustees are pleased to defray the actual cost of the Bridge (which from the extensive means and advantages I possess is less than would have been incurred thro' any other means) I must ascribe it entirely to their liberality. In the limited state of the funds for carrying on the other operations connected with the work perhaps it may be inexpedient or even impracticable to accomplish this object at present I would therefore willingly allow the surplus to remain as the security of the Trust on the same conditions as my first loan of £500.

I beg leave to conclude by assuring the Trustees that I have the most perfect confidence of the present and future strength and security of the Bridge and it will always afford me the most agreeable reflections and I shall consider my own exertions and the time I have employed in the execution of the design well bestowed if they tend to promote men individual advantage and the good of the Country in general.

Sam Brown"

Here is evidence of an open-ended contract shrouded with hard and fast rules. Brown had obviously been required to present a detailed account in his claim for payment, which would have set out quantities of materials and labour involved. In his original make-up of costs, a similar Bill 'of

Quantities may have been prepared related to an agreed contract sum, and we can only presume that variations for unforeseen works were to be reasonably admitted. Brown was nevertheless cautious, yet candid, in the case he presents; he regretted the extra expense, almost pompously points out that 'all great works' cost more anyway. Having fired the salvo Brown was quick to review the situation, and admitting to the 'obligatory' condition of the contract, humbly sought the Trustees' 'liberality'. Not only was Brown seeking agreement for the additional payment – but prescribing a tidy and beneficial way for him to collect money he considered due. It must not be forgotten that the bridge was an admitted experiment about which Brown had given guarantees, and that if it failed, or did not see out its expected life span, what real lever did the Trustees have upon Brown other than his 10% stake? This aspect undoubtedly troubled the minds of some Trustees.

The Minutes of the October 2nd 1820 Meeting continued:

"And the several accounts referred to in his letter were all laid before the Meeting, the total amount of which appeared to be £6449. 18. 8.
Resolved that it is the opinion of this Meeting (By a majority of 9 to 2) that Captain Brown should be remunerated the actual Cost of the Bridge as it shall be ascertained, the same to be secured by Mortgage on the Tolls and Pontage, and on condition that Captain Brown be put on the same footing for that sum and the £500 before agreed to be lent, as other Creditors of the Trust and that William Pattison, John S Donaldson, Thomas J Steel, John Robertson, and John Sibbit Esquires be a Committee to inspect the accounts and report to the next meeting what Capt. Brown's actual expenditure has been.

Ordered that the same Committee do report their opinions about claims for damages for land fisheries at the Union Bridge.

Ordered that the Committee for the new Toll Houses do take steps for the purpose of collecting the Tolls and Pontage on the Union Bridge and for planning a Schedule of the Tolls on the Bridge. The Meeting took into consideration the Tolls to be taken by way of Pontage on the Union Bridge and resolved and ordered that the whole Tolls acquired by the Act be collected except as to the following articles:

For every Horse, Mule, Ox, or other Beast whatsoever drawing any Waggon, Wain, Cart, or other Carriage which shall be threepence instead of sixpence.

Ordered that the next Meeting be held at the same House on the twenty first October.

Willm. Molle, E….."

So it was, that by a majority vote of 9-2, Captain Brown secured agreement to his claim for 'Actual cost' payment on the basis of his own loan suggestions. This still meant that his accounts were to be the subject of scrutiny and verification, as in the Committee's words, the 'actual cost as it shall be ascertained.' So, alas, Brown was not entirely off the hook.

The Meeting of Trustees duly took place on 21st October 1820, at which meeting 'William Foreman Home Esquire, took and subscribed the Oath of Qualification . . .'

"The Committee appointed to investigate the actual expenditure on the Union Bridge reported as follows:

The Committee appointed to ascertain the actual expenditure on the Union Bridge beg to report that they have investigated the several Accounts mentioned in Captain Brown's Abstract except the account for Wrought Iron and they find that the whole is satisfactory.

With respect to the Bill for the Iron Work they found that they were not competent Judges and that besides they could not obtain the necessary information in this neighbourhood.

They therefore made application to respectable Houses in Newcastle London and Wales and have received some communications in answer but not such as to enable them to make a report. They have received their Correspondence and are in Expectation of receiving such Information as will enable them to make a satisfactory report to the Trustees by the next Meeting on 7th November, which time they request to be allowed for that purpose.

Ordered that they have the time requested to make their report.........."

That concluded the relevant matters of interest, the only stumbling block, as far as Brown was concerned, being his charge for the ironwork, and about this the Committee were going to a lot of trouble in seeking expert advice. There was a big turn-out of Trustees for the November 7th meeting; fifteen in number; they started their proceedings at the Hen and Chickens and subsequently adjourned to the Kings Arms. This change of venue may have been for security as their main topic for decision was letting the Toll Gates.

The Minutes of the Meeting were recorded as follows:

"Whereas the Tolls to be collected at the several Toll Gates hereafter mentioned were set up at this Meeting, to be let to the highest Bidders for the sum, at the Rents respectively hereafter mentioned (that is to say):

		£	s	d
Union Bridge Gate	David Liddle	100	0	0
Thornton Gate	Matthew Thompson	48	0	0
Shoreswood Gate	Joseph Scott	84	0	0
Sandybank and Grindon Ridge Gates	Murdoch Stewart	20	0	0

It is ordered that Leases of the said Tolls be granted to the said several persons respectively from the eleventh day of November Instant - to the twelfth day of May, 1821 under the said several Rents;such Leases to be drawn and prepared according to the tenet and effect of certain Rules for letting the Tolls bearing date this day."

The Committee appointed to report on the actual expenditure on the Union Bridge delivered their report to the Meeting, a Copy of which follows:

"The Committee appointed to enquire into the actual expenditure on the Union Bridge beg to report that, after having investigated the whole of the Accounts, they are perfectly satisfied with those for all the works, with the exception of that of Brown & Co. for the wrought iron. With respect to that part of the material they have resorted to some proprietors of Iron Works of respectability for information as to the prices and the result of the amounts of such of them as have given answers is as follows:

'One House (Hawks House) states that the iron could have been furnished at the Rate of 28.00 per ton and another (W. Flyn) states it at £30.00 to be delivered at Berwick - the average therefore is £29.00 - the average price charged by Brown & Co. being at least £39.00 - it results that according to the reports of the above two Houses, the price ought not to be so much as is charged by £10 per Ton.'

Ordered that a Copy of the above report be sent to Captain Brown to give him an opportunity of making any comments he may think proper on it - and that a remittance be made to him so as to make the whole sum, with what he has already received, amount to £4000."

On the face of it Brown was charging 25% more for his ironwork than other suppliers considered it was worth, but fortunately the Committee did not over-react and gave him the opportunity to reply.

It must be remembered that during the years 1819-20 and before, the quality of maleable (wrought) iron was extremely variable; its conversion from cast iron required the removal of certain base chemical elements and the retention of a very small carbon percentage. This involved an understanding of the chemistry, skill and very hard work. The skill and physical effort was in the mind and hands of the 'puddler' whose task it was to churn some hundredweights of iron, mixed with hammer scale or black oxide of iron, in a furnace with a long rake until certain physical and chemical changes occurred, when the metal was worked into balls or 'blooms' of about 60lbs. weight. After this the furnace temperature was raised to full welding heat and the blooms were transferred on the ends of bars and committed to a hammering process to remove the slag, then finally run through puddling rolls to produce puddled-bar. It was then usual for a number of bars to be bound together with wire and subjected to re-heating and rolling, which provided larger units of material. This additional working of the material improved the fibrous and tenacious properties and it was known as 'best-bar-iron.' Brown & Co. excelled in the knowledge and ability to manufacture best-bar-iron, the ore for which was mainly from the Rhondda and Cynon Valleys of South Wales, which was relatively free from the unwanted adulterants and smelted in works at Pontypridd.

The puddling part of the manufacturing process was the real determining factor as to quality, but expensive, particularly in human life. Neither Trustees nor Committee members could have had any idea as to criteria or what was involved in the making of wrought iron, but it was a matter which they admitted. They at least made efforts to seek the truth, and the controversial issue was soon to turn in Captain Brown's favour after a visit to the Bridge by 'Foreman Golightly' of Messrs. Hawks Stanley & Co. who pronounced the work in question to be 'worth £50 per Ton'. Nevertheless, Brown had to battle for an agreed final amount and payment settlement, and the Trustees decided that he should receive an amount of money making the total payment on account to-date of £4000.

There was a Meeting of Trustees at the Hen and Chickens, Berwick 29th December 1820. Only six members attended including William Molle, Chairman. Now the fun was over and interest was dwindling.

"A letter from Messrs. Hawks & Co. of Gateshcad was laid before the meeting, a Copy of which follows.

'Gateshead 30th Nov 1820

Messrs Hawks Stanley & Co.

Gentlemen - To Messrs Sam Brown & Co

Our Foreman Golightly has paid his visit of suspension* on "both sides of the Tweed" from which visit, we have much to regret that our sentiments thereon were not entirely suspended; indeed had we entertained the least idea of the true nature of Mr. Willoby 's correspondence, he would have had a very different opinion from us however to treat the subject as it really deserved.

Golightly arrived at Berwick on Friday, where he had every attention shewn him and was accompanied by a proper person to examine and answer all such questions as he wished, from which he pronounced in his own mind, the work in question to be worth £50 per Ton, and yet thinks, taking all circumstances into consideration, not many would like to do it much under that price. He was highly gratified by the sight of it, and still if possible more by the Workmanship. He cannot say more, but will wait Captain Browns_ Sentiments as to the manner in which he thinks our Formans further observations should be communicated.

Signed   R.S. Hawks'

(*The minuted record of letter from Messrs. Hawks Stanley & Co. is as shown, but obviously the word 'suspension' should be 'inspection')

Resolved that this matter be referred to a future Meeting - and that the Committee before appointed to make further inquiry on the subject and report the result to a General Meeting of the Trustees: Ordered that two Constables be sent to Shoreswood Gate to assist the

Tenant in collecting the Tolls - and Notice given by Handbills that any persons refusing to pay Tolls will be punished according to the Act - and that the same be done respecting the other Gates when necessary."

Needless to say, Roads and Bridges subject to Tolls have never been liked. For some reason charges for other public services have always been accepted but the right to wander and haul ones goods about caused anger from the very beginning and North Durham was no exception. The Committee appointed by Trustees also found trouble with their falling membership and became concerned about their ability to act. The Minutes of Trustees Meeting on 2nd April 1821, were reported as follows:

"The Committee appointed to ascertain the expenditure on the Union Bridge reported as follows:

January 9th 1821

At a Committee appointed to enquire into the actual Expenditure of the Union Bridge

Present
Thos J Steel Esq; John Sibbit Esq; John Robertson Esq

The Members of the Committee now present taking into consideration that the Committee is now reduced to three effective members and that the matters referred to them are of great importance to the Trust beg to request of the General Meeting of Trustees either to appoint some additional Members of the Committee or to take on themselves to dispose of the business in such way as to them may seem best."

This resulted in two more Trustees being added to the Committee. For some, the Bridge had brought a great change in financial circumstances, and the Ferryman was suffering as reported to the Meeting:

"Robert Robertson made a claim to the Meeting for compensation for damages sustained by the discontinuance of the ferry which is referred to a future Meeting."

Time passed by, and Trustees' pre-occupation was the failure of the Tollgate Keeper to collect toll dues equal to their respective lease bids which resulted in claims for compensations. More serious was the lack of any bidders for Twisel and Castlegate gates, reported at the April 30th 1821 Meeting - Captain Brown was also waiting for his balance of payment and the matter was dealt with at the Trustees' Meeting on June 4th 1821.

The question of compensation to Captain Brown for his expenditure on the Union Bridge being taken into consideration, it was resolved by a majority of 7 to 5 that Captain Brown be allowed the sum of £1009. 18. 8 for his loan on the work.' On the same day after the meeting of June 4th,

Brown wrote to Stevenson from Berwick about a pair of carrier pigeons that he was in the process of obtaining

> '.. which will be sent you I expect soon. The breeder warrants them the Moorish breeds and could have supplied me with a pair of old ones but he was minded (to) the young upon the scriptural proverb of train up a child in the way he should go etc etc..'

After that philosophical thought, Brown concluded his letter

> '.. I have got a settlement at last with the Trustees of our Bridge Iron they have awarded me £1000 more than the contract leaving me minus £500. I am glad however that the thing is settled even in this way. I shall be in Edinburgh to finish my other concern on Thursday with the best regards to Ms Stevenson, I am and sincerely remain
>
> yours truly Sam Brown'

So far, so good, but Brown was not entirely satisfied with this simplification of the financial situation and a letter setting out the facts was accordingly sent to William Willoby and laid before the Meeting on November 6th 1821.

> 'London, 27th October 1821
>
> Dear Sir
>
> By last accounts received from Messrs Batson & Co. there appears a balance due to me of £586. 5 6 for the Union Bridge. You must clearly perceive that I have not anything to do with the Collection of this money, and it is extremely inconvenient to have it unsettled in this way. I shall feel much obliged if you will get the Trustees to order the payment of the above sum with interest, from the 5th September, or if they have not yet got in all the Subscriptions, request them to give me a Bill bearing Interest at three months or even a longer date if it is more convenient and then this long protracted settlement will be brought to a close and my account will then be simply the receipt of the Interest and the payment of the following items, viz:
>
> Interest on £500 from 12th May to 11th Nov. 1821:   £1009.18.8
> Sum awarded on 4th June 1821 to 11th Nov 1821
> No allowance for upholding the Bridge from 26th July 1821
>
> It should be paid up to the term when the whole will come under the half yearly Payment afterwards.
>
> Requesting you to see into this matter with all convenient dispatch
>
> I remain Dear Sir
> Yours Truly
> Sam Brown'

This letter was an embarrassment to the Trustees and the Clerk was duly 'ordered' to 'write those Gentlemen who have not paid up their subscriptions, urging them to pay them up and that he inform Mr. Brown thereof'

Brown was eventually paid up for the amount claimed and then drifted from the scene of operation to embark upon other works including the re-building of Netherbyers in Berwickshire, where he lived for some years before finally moving to London.

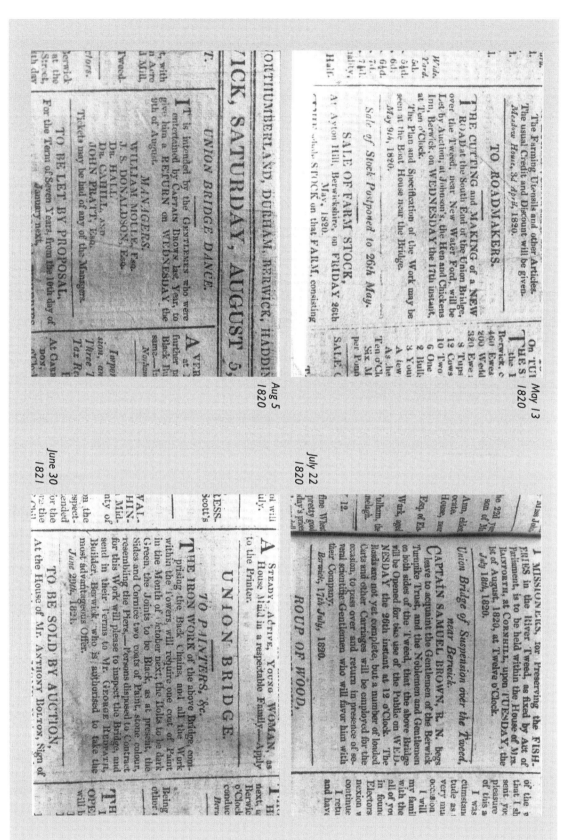

Fig 86 - Four public advertisements from the Berwick Advertiser relating to the Bridge (TheTweeddale Press Group)

May 13
1820

July 22
1820

Aug 5
1820

June 30
1821

6

The Grand Opening

Samuel Brown's great day was on Wednesday July 26th 1820, when at 12 noon, his Chain Bridge of Suspension was formally opened, exactly one year after the foundation stone was laid. *The Times* characteristically reported the forthcoming event on July 20th, sandwiched between Crown Court cases of High Treason and malicious wounding. So much for the romantic and remarkable achievement; the announcement simply stated:

> "The first Chain Bridge in Great Britain - the river is 437 feet from bank to bank, and the bridge across it is without any central support, to the astonishment of the beholder. Its appearance is at once extraordinary and magnificent; and if found to answer the purpose, as it is confidently expected to do, its application to the other rivers must be productive of great benefit to the country at large... We mention the work as the first of the kind in this or any other country, and the magnitude of the length and access will render it worthy of being recorded as unexampled...."

It was also William Molle's great day, for he had laid the foundation stone, and thereby became closely associated with Samuel Brown and the project. He revelled in every moment, and as agent to William Foreman Home, Esq., of Paxton House, he addressed a letter of explanation about the event:

"My Dear Sir

The Union Bridge is to be opened by Capt. Brown on Wednesday the 26th at 12 o'clock - when Capt. Brown will put a greater weight upon it than in all probability it will ever have to sustain.

I am happy to acquaint you that Capt. Brown and I have prevailed on Professor John Leslie of the Natural Philosophy in this University, and one of the greatest mathematicians in the Island, and Messrs. Stevenson and Jardine, two eminent Engineers to come out and inspect the Bridge on that day. They seem to consider it as a matter of great curiosity in the Arts, and an object of national importance; as I shall have the honour of introducing them to you on Wednesday they are to come out in a Post chaise, at Capt. Brown's expense.

Mrs. Molle and I alongside with one of the young people propose to do ourselves the honour of taking a Family Dinner with you and Mrs. Smith on that day, if it be convenient - Mrs. Molle will call on Mrs. Smith about 11, in order to go alongst with her to the Bridge, if it be agreeable -

Fig 87 - Letter from Wm Molle to W F Home 20th July 1820

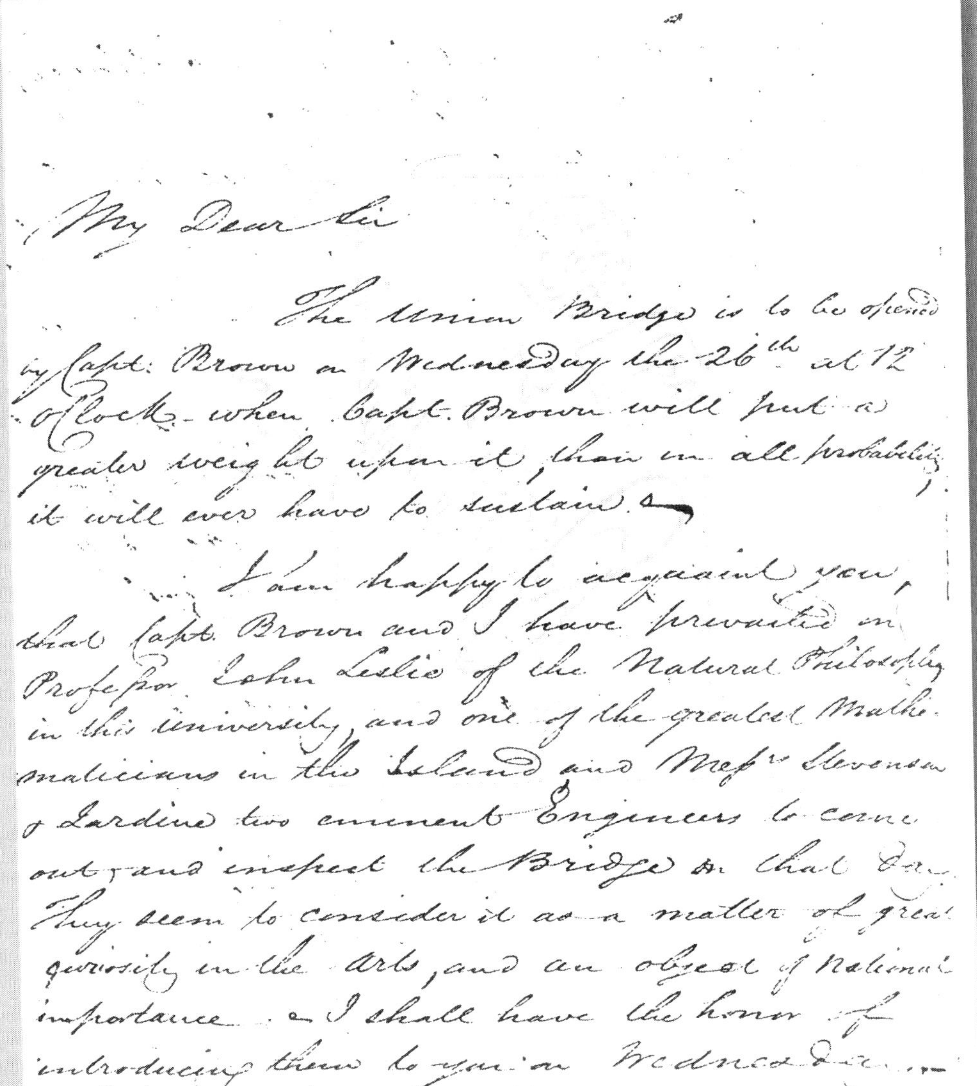

My Dear Sir

The Union Bridge is to be opened by Capt: Brown on Wednesday the 26th at 12 oClock — when Capt. Brown will put a greater weight upon it, than in all probability it will ever have to sustain.

I am happy to acquaint you, that Capt. Brown and I have prevailed on Professor John Leslie of the Natural Philosophy in this University, and one of the greatest Mathematicians in the Island and Messrs Stevenson & Jardine two eminent Engineers to come out, and inspect the Bridge on that Day. They seem to consider it as a matter of great curiosity in the Arts, and an object of National importance. I shall have the honor of introducing them to you on Wednesday. They —

They are to come out in a Post Chaise, at Capt. Brown's expence.

Mrs Mollo & I alongst with one of the young people propose to do ourselves the honor of taking a Family Dinner with you & Mrs Smith on that day, if it be convenient; Mrs Mollo will call on Mrs Smith about 11, in order to go alongst with her to the Bridge, if it be agreeable:

I shall be at Netherbyres to-morrow Evening alongst with Capt. Brown who is my fellow traveller.

I beg to offer my best regards to you & Mrs Smith and am

My Dear Sir
Yours Sincerely
Willm Mollo

12 Northumbd Street
Edinr 20 July 1826

I shall be at Netherbyres tomorrow Evening alongst with Capt. Brown, who is my fellow traveller.

I beg to offer my best regards to you and Mrs. Smith and all.

My Dear Sir
Yours sincerely,
William Molle

12 Northumberland Street, Edinburgh. 20 July 1820...'

The awe and splendour of the occasion can be imagined, for nothing like this frail structure stretched across the river as a filmy substance could really have been believed. Arched iron bridges were barely forty years old, which in general scale and form resembled their stone counterparts, and for Border people, Union Bridge was tantalisingly supernatural. Hordes of people gathered on both banks of the river, and upon it in boats, gay and colourful with bands, tents and bunting, and a bright sky to enhance the wonder.

Although Samuel Brown was full of confidence, the magnitude of the moment must surely have caused a twitch of mind to drift over -innumerable points. It was a test of courage, apart from skill, for imagination had little technology as reinforcement, but Brown abounded in determination and a will to experiment.

The *Berwick Advertiser* recorded the event on July 29th 1820:

UNION BRIDGE OF SUSPENSION OVER THE TWEED, NEAR BERWICK

The opening of this curious and elegant structure the first of the kind in The Island, took place on Wednesday. At an early hour of the day various groups were observed hastening to witness the interesting aspect. The River itself was covered with different parties in boats, its northern banks exhibited lines of carriages, horsemen and pedestrians, booths, and other places of refreshment, while the precipitous declivity on the south occupied by numerous groups picturesquely scattered on its surface, produced the most delightful effect. A little after noon Capt. Brown, the inventor crossed and recrossed the bridge in a tandem, followed by a number of loaded carts, amidst the loud cheers of the multitudes assembled, while the bands of the Berwickshire Militia, and the Northumberland local Militia, played "God save the King"; soon afterwards the Trustees of the Berwick roads, and a large party of gentlemen with the Earl of Home at their head, preceded by the bands playing the King's Anthem, crossed from the northern to the southern end of the bridge, and returned, giving three cheers at each side of the Tweed. The ceremony here ended, and the strength and fitness of the beautiful structure being thus ascertained, the barriers were removed, and the public permitted to pass.

All the rank, beauty and fashion of the Borders were assembled on this occasion. A numerous company (eighty four) amongst whom we observed Lord Home, and many other persons of distinction, dined in a huge tent, which had been erected near the bridge, many loyal and suitable toasts were given, to which the bands played appropriate tunes, and the evening was spent with much conviviality and good humour.

Amongst the gentlemen present we observed Professor Leslie of Edinburgh and several other gentlemen of science, who admired very much this curious specimen of the arts, so nicely adjusted in all its parts, while at the same time, they considered it in a national point of view of much importance. This bridge is only to cost £5,000; a stone bridge at the same place would have cost upwards of £20,000, and it possesses this superiority over a stone bridge that from having no pillars or support in the middle of the water, it will not be liable to be swept away by the floods of the river. It is obvious therefore that bridges of this nature will become general throughout the Island, and it is hardly necessary to remark how much they must facilitate the internal trade and commerce of the country. To this quarter the advantages of the present bridge are incalculable; in particular it will save to an extensive district of country seven or eight miles in going for their cost and time, and will render these articles accessible to them at all times of the year, and in all states of the river.

The extreme length of the suspending chains from the point of junction, on each side of the Tweed is 590 feet, from the stone abutments, or towers 432. The platform, or roadway is 360. The height of the bridge above the surface of the river is 27 feet. The weight of the chains, platform, etc, is about 160 tons, but the bridge is calculated to support 360 tons, a greater weight than ever, in any probability, it can be subjected to. Although twelve months have elapsed since the work commenced, we can state on good authority that the workmen have not been employed above one half of that time; and with pleasure we add that during its progress, and on Wednesday when the crowd was excessive, and anxious to see so great a novelty, no serious accident occurred. In the centre of the bridge on each side is the following inscription:

VIS UNITA FORTIOR"

Public recognition had at long last come to Samuel Brown as his ambitions became a reality. His earlier years in proving the value of iron chains for the Royal Navy were successful, and he founded the Isle of Dogs manufacturing works, where in 1813 he constructed an experimental suspension footbridge using plate and bolt connected wrought iron bars. In July, 1817 Brown was granted letters patent for the design and manufacture of 'iron bridges of suspension', and now, with the acclaimed Union Bridge, his professional standing was established.

Fig 88 - "Vis Unita Fortior" cast plaque

SAMUEL BROWN AND UNION CHAIN BRIDGE

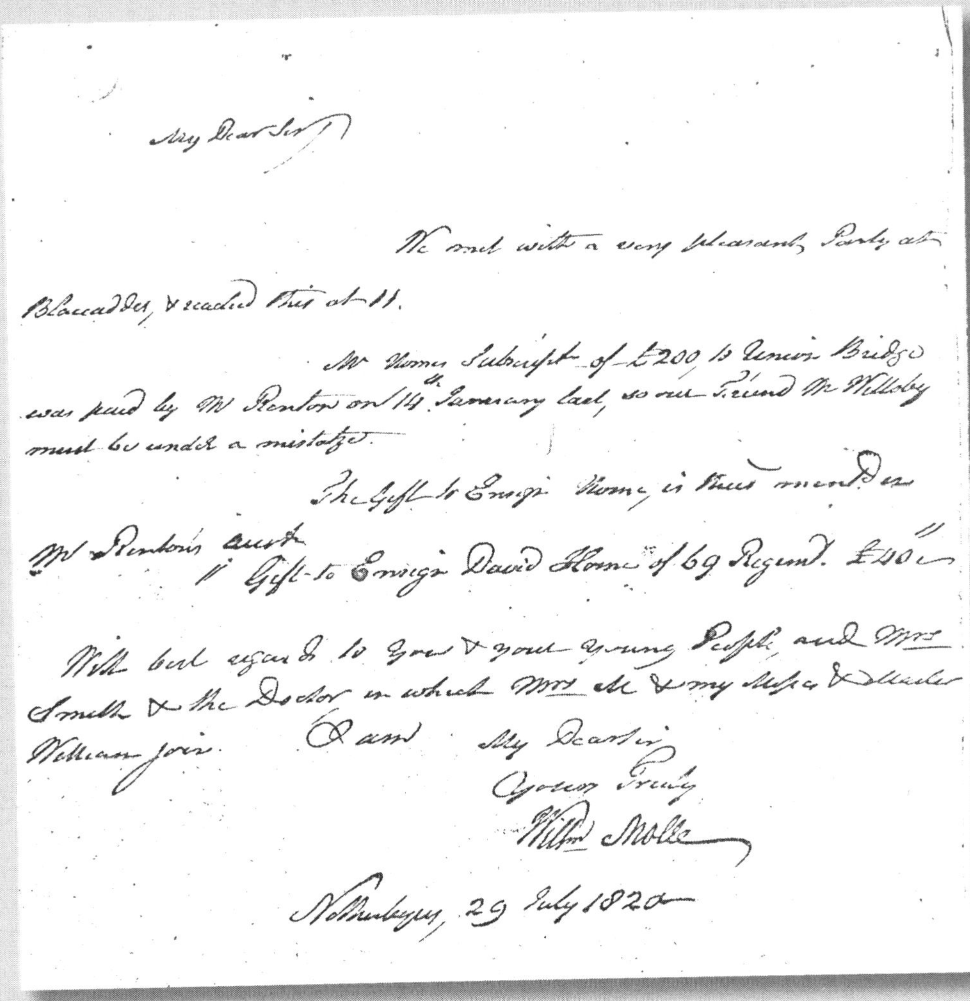
My Dear Sir,

We met with a very pleasant Party at Blackadder, & reached this at 11.

Mr Homes Subscript. of £200 to Union Bridge was paid by Mr Renton on 14th January last, so our Friend Mr Willoby must be under a mistake.

The Gift to Ensign Home, is thus mentd. in Mr Renton's acct.
" Gift to Ensign David Home of 69 Regimt. £40 "

With best regards to you & your young People, and Mrs Smith & the Doctor in which Mrs M & my Misses & Master William join.

I am My Dear Sir
Yours Truly
Willm. Molle

Netherbyres, 29 July 1820

Fig 89 - Letter from Wm Molle to W F Home 29th July 1820

My Dear Sir,

We met with a very pleasant Party at Blackadder and reached this at 11.

Mr Homes Subscript. of £200 to Union Bridge was paid by Mr Renton on 14th January last so our Friend Mr Willoby must be under a mistake

The gift of Ensign Home is thus mentd. in Mr Renton's acct.

"Gift to Ensign David Home of 69 Regimt. £40"

With best regards to you and your young People and Mrs Smith & the Doctor in which Mrs M and my Misses & Master William join.

I am My Dear Sir
Yours Truly
Willm. Molle
Netherbyres, 29 July 1820

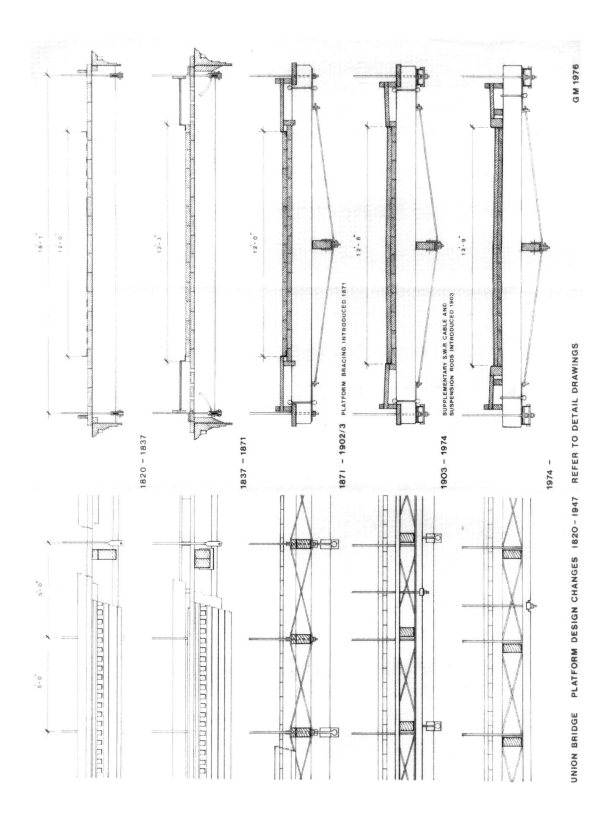

Fig 90 - Union Chain Bridge Platform Design Changes 1820-1974

SAMUEL BROWN AND UNION CHAIN BRIDGE

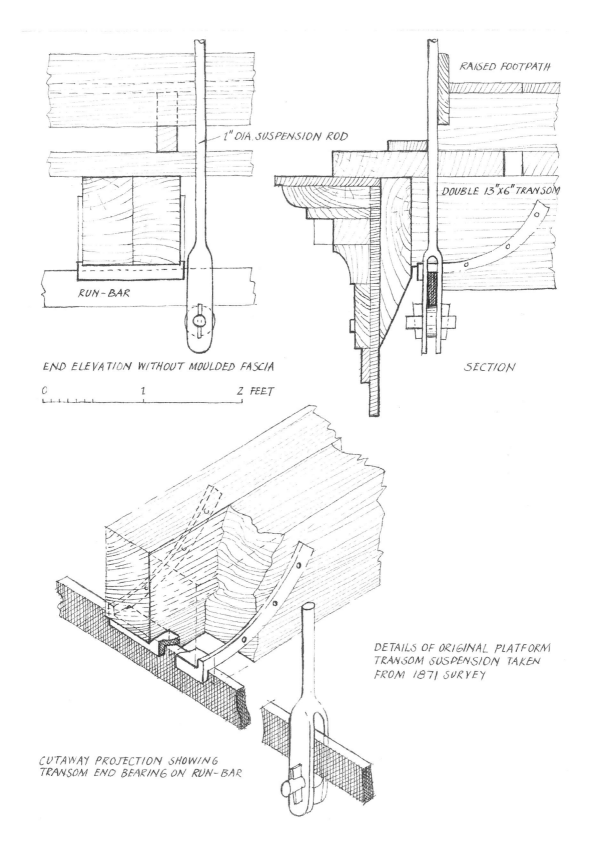

1" DIA. SUSPENSION ROD

RAISED FOOTPATH

DOUBLE 13"x6" TRANSOM

RUN-BAR

END ELEVATION WITHOUT MOULDED FASCIA

SECTION

0   1   2 FEET

DETAILS OF ORIGINAL PLATFORM
TRANSOM SUSPENSION TAKEN
FROM 1871 SURVEY

CUTAWAY PROJECTION SHOWING
TRANSOM END BEARING ON RUN-BAR

Fig 91 - Detail: Union Chain Bridge original platform from 1871 survey

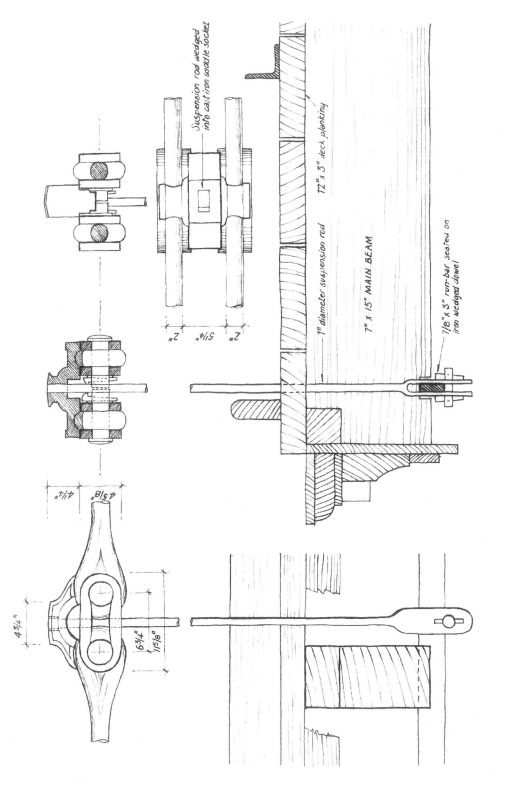

Suspension rod wedged into cast iron saddle socket

12" x 3" deck planking

1" diameter suspension rod

7" x 15" MAIN BEAM

7/8" x 3" run-bar seated on iron wedged dowel

2" 5¼" 2"

4 5/8" 4¼"

4 5/8"

4¾"

6¾" 1/5/8"

DETAILS - CHAIN BAR LINKS AND SUSPENSION SADDLE - PLATFORM DESIGN 1820-37

GM 1976

Fig 92 - Detail: Union Chain Bridge chain bar links and suspension saddle 1820-37

219   SAMUEL BROWN AND UNION CHAIN BRIDGE

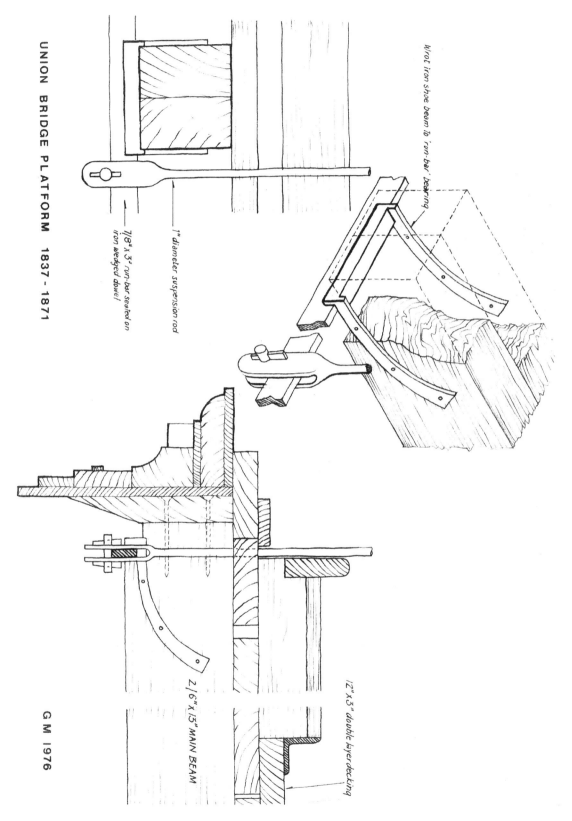

Wrot iron shoe beam to 'run-bar' bearing

7/8" x 3" run-bar seated on iron wedged dowel

1" diameter suspension rod

2/6" x 15" MAIN BEAM

12" x 3" double layer decking

G M 1976

Fig 93 - Detail: Union Chain Bridge platform 1837-1871

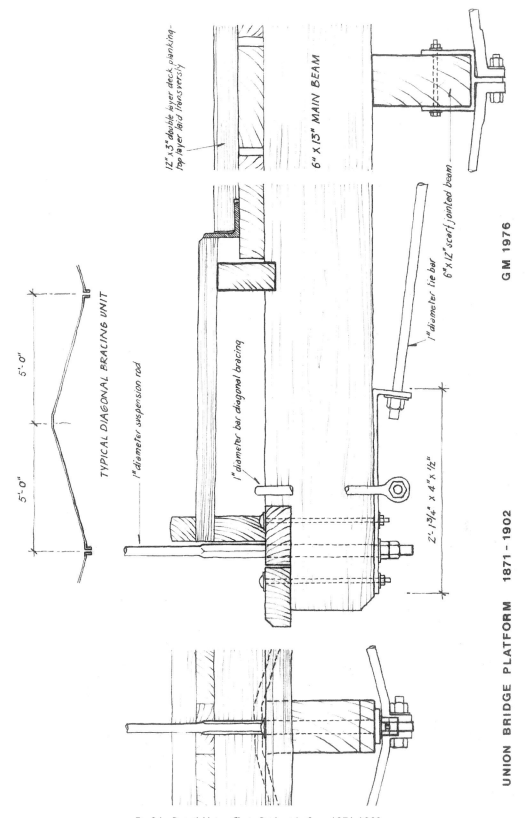

Fig 94 - Detail: Union Chain Bridge platform 1871-1902

7

The Years 1820 - 1904

The continuous care and attention given to Union Bridge by successive Trustees, and their advisers, is the main reason for its survival; a contributory factor is the variable conditions of use to which it has been subjected. Initially, the cartage of lime and coal made its impression, but this use declined until the last decade of the century, when great numbers of cattle were herded across the bridge for transport south from Velvet Hall station, and caused severe deck decay through the accumulation of mud and dung. In this last decade it is said by descendants of witnesses, that a travelling fair was hauled over the bridge by a showmen's steam traction engine. If true, the fair people had really chanced their luck, but the news did lead to the roadman who occupied the bridge cottage being instructed to prevent and report any further such incidents.

A notice of weight restriction was soon to follow.

From its beginning to the present day the bridge has been the subject of local attraction and interest, and through this influence, and because of its natural seclusion, it has found security.

Over the years there was a continuous process of structural damage and decay caused by wind, wet and frost which allowed no let up in the need for continual maintenance. Apart from regular attention to paintwork, wood deckwork and surfacing, the first recorded need for more extensive works was presented to a meeting of the Trustees of the Berwick Turnpikes on June 8th 1837 in the form of a Report by Mr. W. Smith, Architect, with a plan of the repairs necessary at the Union Bridge.

> '. . .on considering the same it is resolved that it appears to this meeting to he absolutely necessary that repairs recommended by Mr. Smith be done as soon as possible; and that it be referred to the Standing Committee to carry the -work into effect, with this recommendation that they take Tenders for the Timber, Iron and Tar which may be wanted.'

Mr Smith's recommendations of improvement may be accepted as that shown on the record drawing made in 1871. After seventeen years of existence the decking must have been badly worn and decayed, and the relatively small bearing area between the main beams and the 7/8" width of 'Run-bar' was an undoubted weakness. Whether or not the iron guards, for restricting carts to within the intended twelve foot carriageways, were provided is not known, but the inevitable fouling of the deck must have been very unpleasant for people walking. Although the changes in platform and deck design, made by Mr Smith in 1837, were not radical, they significantly dealt with the obvious problems, The original 15" x 7" main beams were replaced by 13" x 6" members, arranged in pairs and bearing upon the original 3"x $^7/_8$" 'run-bars', reinforced by a form of iron shoe that embraced the main beam cheeks, with a tail fashioned to provide an iron to iron bearing in the form of a hook that gave a more positive engagement with the 'run-bar'.

The decorative fascia was retained, and possibly enlarged in its girth, but was now to be planted against a substantial three inch thick continuous backing plank, all securely spiked together.

Raising the footwalks at each side, and above the level of carriageway, became a distinctive new feature, blocked-up with transverse timbering decked with planks arranged longitudinally. Platform decking was now to be laid double, with 3" thick planks, all arranged longitudinally, including an iron angle at the junctions with the footwalk.

Mr Smith's recognition of accrued damage was timely and his ideas for design changes reflected faults that had become obvious to all concerned. However, by doubling the deck planking and proposing raised level footwalks, new conditions were being introduced. From the aspects of physical wear and niceties of use, both changes were sensible, but the numerous passages of escape for surface water which formerly existed were now being eliminated. Drainage was now to become reliant upon the lengthwise falls of the bridge camber; a mere 1 in 90 each way from the bridge centre.

More extensive works became necessary during the years 1871-72, by which time the Trust had become The Berwick and Norham and Islandshires Turnpike Trust.

No record drawings of work actually carried out at this time have been found, but at the time of the 1902-3 restoration reasonable drawings were made of the existing structure in relation to new propositions. This information may therefore be taken as an accurate clue to the work completed in the 1871-2 period. The most important design change was the method introduced for supporting the main platform beams. The original iron 'run--bar' was freely connected to the suspension rods for engagement with the beam ends, this was now to be dispensed with, and the double 13" x 6" beams reverted to single members, 13" x 6", but drilled at their ends to allow the suspension rods to pass through the beam. The ends of suspension rods were screwed with Whitworth threads, and double nuts and a large washer completed the termination. Had the original suspension rods been sufficiently long, the forked end could simply have been cut off and the tail threaded, but they were not. One of two methods may have been resorted to, the most obvious being new rods, but that would have been unnecessary and expensive. Working from the ends of the bridge, it is most likely that sets of rods were disengaged from their respective saddles and run-bars, and their tail ends re-formed. This would have involved a forging operation, in which the forked ends were worked into a hexagonal section shape of about 17" length and swollen out by the possible welded addition of more iron to provide: a tail end screw thread of 1¼" diameter. It is possible that this work was done by a local smith, but the accuracy of their section suggests that a shaping tool and press was used in the forging.

Stiffening of the platform was now introduced by the provision of a 12" x 4" timber scantling placed centrally under the whole length of platform. The scantling was secured in position only to alternate main beams by one inch diameter sets of bracing rods, bolted at the underside, in combination with 'U' shaped iron clamps around the scantling. The bracing rods were carried up at a diagonal angle, with tail ends threaded and bolted to engage with crank ended 4" x ⅝" iron plates, which were in turn coach bolted through the main beams. These plates also served as a bearing for suspension rod nuts, and those to the alternate rod ends were fitted with 6" x 4" x ⅝" plates.

Tension induced by the bracing rods, within the general triangle of forces, in relation to the main beam did make for greater stiffness of the platform, but because the elimination of the 'run-bars' was in some way felt to be too much a loss of rigidity at the extreme edge, a 15" x 3" timber plank was recessed within the beam edge and bolted through to tie-in with the suspension rod bearing plates at the underside. Getting rid of the deep decorative fascia obviously did not upset anyone, for in its passing both weight was reduced and maintenance lessened, yet, it seems Mr Smith was concerned that something was being amputated that had a value. This may be why he thought of the system of diagonal bracing, that was to be located and interlaced between the main beams, at each side of the platform near to the suspension rods. It consisted of one inch diameter rods in unit lengths that spanned over two platform bays (10 feet), their ends swollen out, flattened and cranked to form eyes for uniting with bolts to make a continuous element. This diagonal interlacing had no positive fixing to the structure, it simply lodged in position.

The general principle of a raised footwalk was retained, and a double layer deck planking was stopped against a foot-walk curb, or ribband, instead of the base layer carrying across the whole platform width as previously. The footwalk was decked with 3" thick planks, transversely arranged, spiked to the ribband member and a pole plate at the extreme edge.

An inherent fault in this scheme of changes was the failure to recognise the value of the 'run-bar', and the continuity of structure that it provided, The bolted beam end edge-plank was no substitute for the underslung bearing. However, the work was done, and lasted for another thirty years.

In 1881 the approach road down to the bridge on the English side was causing the Trustees some anxiety. For all their care about quality of stone to be used in its construction, the road was slipping down the bank. The Trustees, in an attempt to obtain good advice, put their problem to the County of Northumberland, and the Clerk of the Peace replied on October 28th 1881:

'...Sir,

Union Suspension Bridge
With reference to your letter of 3rd inst. I beg to inform you that at the last Michaelmas Quarter Sessions an Order was made authorising the County Surveyor to render assistance and advice if desired by the Trustees of the Norham and Islandshires Trust, with respect to the road to the approach to the bridge, but I should add that in doing this it is not to be understood that the County in any way admits responsibility for any work that may be determined on.

Your obedt. St:
Steph. Sanderson
C.P.

W Willoby Esq.'

Mr. Willoby was ordered to reply and inform the County Surveyor that the Trustees wanted this advice and assistance, and that the county would not be held responsible for costs.

The County Surveyor investigated the problem and presented proposals to the Trustees on January 21st 1882. Ground movement had been induced by inadequate sub-soil drainage and the surveyor's scheme proposed a new retaining wall with drain conduits, the design of which he illustrated. The Trustees deferred work until the month of May.

The Turnpike road system ended in the following year. Payment of toll dues was a disagreeable process and its eventual demise welcomed, but it carried the sting that money was nonetheless required for roads, bridges etc., and a 'property rate' was to be instituted, so that all and everyone contributed to the common good. Overall social well-being was not the accepted practice of the day, and the new rate levy idea met with stormy reaction through the columns of the local press.

The *Berwick Advertiser* reported the end of the Turnpike Gates on March 16th 1883:

> '. . .The system of turnpike tolls came to an end within the bounds of the Berwick, Norham, and Islandshires Turnpike Trust on Monday, and the gates and turnstiles were wholly removed. By the private Act of 1861, which was passed for the purpose of clearing off the debt which had accumulated under the old Trust, and at the same time giving powers to levy contributions from the townships as well as continue the tolls, it was enacted that on the complete redemption of the debt, the management of the roads within the municipal borough should pass into the hands of the Urban Sanitary Authority. This consummation has now been arrived at, and for the future the roads will be maintained by a rate levied upon the occupiers of property. By this system the expense of toll-keeping is saved, but it has the serious defect that it throws the expense of the roads directly upon those parties who do not contribute to their tear and wear, while those who do so use up the roads by riding and driving, escape by paying at the same rate as simple pedestrians. The injustice and absurdity of this system are evident; but it is nevertheless the system now adopted wherever it can be carried into effect. The property of the expiring Turnpike Trust, in the shape of toll-houses, etc., will not, it is understood, be handed over to their successors in the management of the roads. Such portions of the toll-houses as abut upon the roads will require to be cleared away.'

Removal of road tolls required the gates to be dismantled, but not necessarily the toll-houses. However, if the houses were to be left they needed maintenance, and the house attached to the bridge posed a possible structural problem. On March 10th 1883 a Meeting of Trustees considered the matter:

> 'Union Bridge. The meeting having been informed that the taking down of this Tollhouse might endanger the Bridge they directed the Clerk to draw the attention of the County Surveyor to this alteration, and reminded him that the Trustees will cease to take charge of the Bridge after the 25th inst. and to intimate that the Trustees will be glad to transfer to the County their Title to the Tollhouse for the reasonable consideration if he is of the opinion that the Toll House is necessary to the support of the Bridge.
>
> It was resolved that permission be granted to the present occupiers of the Tollhouses to

continue therein until the next May term, subject to their signing an acknowledgement and paying nominal rent.'

It should have been obvious to the surveyor that the bridge tollhouse was nothing more than an appendage, and this much he should have realised, but for some reason saw fit that it should remain. The tollhouse remained occupied for another seventy years by succeeding generations of council employed road-men, who raised families in the little two-roomed dwelling. Its eventual evacuation and removal was due to the problem of preventing water penetration through the natural rock face that formed the rear wall, and the almost impossible task of providing a supply of piped drinking water. This detail story will be dealt with later.

The future role of the Trustees was to be decided by the Secretary of State; their original duty of getting things done and raising the necessary funds through tolls was past. Their assets had to he declared and at a meeting held on December 18th 1883 the clerk reported:

> '....the sum of £230 10 8 being in the hands of the Treasurer and being an accumulation of the annual sum set apart for the repair of the Union Bridge and not expended at the 25th March last and that the disposal of this sum awaits the decision of the Secretary of State in an Order to be made by him in pursuance of the Roads and Bridges (Scotland) Act I878.'

The Trustees found that the time needed to wind-up their affairs took longer than envisaged, and an application by them to the Secretary of State to '. . .have a further prolongation of the time...' was granted, but contained within the various ramifications '....a determination made by him as to the future maintenance of the Union Bridge.' - became fact on April 7th 1884. As from this date a new Trust was to be constituted '.... to be called the Tweed Bridges Trust, for the management, maintenance, repair and if need be re-construction of the said Three Bridges (Ladykirk and Norham, Coldstream and Union) that the Trustees shall be six in number of whom three shall be nominated by the County Road Trustees of Berwickshire and three by the Northumberland Court of Quarter Sessions and that the Trustees shall hold their first meeting on this date.' Sept. 1st 1884.

The inaugural meeting of Trustees was soon followed by another on September 9th 1884 which dealt with their inheritance from the former Trust and appointment of a surveyor. From now on the name Clerk to the Trustees becomes Secretary, and he reported the state of finances that existed from the three Bridges '...that had been furnished to him...':

	£	s	d
From the Coldstream Bridges Trust	10,858	13	3
From the Ladykirk and Norham Bridges Trust	2,072	1	2
From the Union Bridge Trust	203	9	10
Making a total, Of	13,134	4	3

This was a considerable sum of money and the Union Bridge account clearly showed it the poor relation of the three bridges family, and to an extent indicated the continual claim on financial resources that its increasing maintenance demanded.

The meeting was initially concerned with the appointment of a surveyor and set down '....the conditions on which that officer should hold his appointment.

1. The appointment to be during the pleasure of the Trustees.

2. The ordinary duties of the Surveyor to be to inspect as often as occasion shall arise, or the Trustees require (and at least 4 times in each year) each of the three Bridges comprised in the Trust, and to make a written report on the same to the Trustees twice in each year or oftener if necessary.

3. To prepare specifications and advertisements having reference to ordinary repairs and maintenance, and to superintend the due execution of all such works and issue certificates for payment, said certificates to be addressed to the Treasurer.

4. To advise the Trustees generally on all engineering matters connected with the Trust.

5. The salary for the above duties to be £30 per annum payable quarterly.

6. With regard to new works specified by the Trustees as being such before being entered upon, the Surveyor, if required by the Trustees, to prepare all necessary specification, plans and drawings - to take the superintendence of the works if entered upon, and to report thereon periodically to the Trustees - to issue Certificates for payment to the Contractors and to discharge generally all the duties of superintending engineer.

7. In respect of services such as last specified the remuneration to be as follows:
For the preparation of plans etc. if the same are not adopted and put in execution either wholly or partially such a sum as the Trustees shall award. If the plans be adopted and either wholly or partially put into execution, a Commission of 5 per cent on the first estimated cost of the works ordered to be executed, such commission to include all travelling and other expenses and also the Salary of the Clerk of the Works when one is deemed necessary, unless the Trustees shall sanction the employment of one at the cost of the Trust.'

Mr. H.F. Sneyd-Kynnersley was appointed surveyor to the Trust, and in his Report of January 13th, 1885 he expressed concern about the 'constant attention required' to maintain the 'rapidly decaying' flooring. He continued to report about general matters:

'With regard to the current years expenditure it will be necessary to cover the Roadway at the Union Bridge with Asphalt and to repair the woodwork of the foot-paths. It will also be advisable to clean and paint the anchor chains within the masonry of the south Tower. I am not at present prepared to lay before you any scheme or estimate for stiffening this

Bridge, but I am convinced that something should be done as soon as possible to diminish its excessive oscillation as the strain which high winds produce upon parts of the structure exceeds the limit of safety.'

The Surveyor's ideas to reduce oscillation by stiffening the structure were sensible, but the necessity for laying asphalt to the roadway was a mistake, as it is a semi-rigid material that would crack with movement and allow water penetration, and thereby accelerate the process of rotting. This is what happened over the years after the asphalt was put down, and the condition has not been realised until now 89 years later!

The recommended painting was done in the summer of 1885 and the platform coated with creosote after 'necessary repairs to the decayed timber.'

The Treasurer's Statement of February 1887 recorded expenditure for the year 1885 and 1886:

Union Bridge

Nov 25	John Bruce for laying creosote on decking	£1. 9. 4
1886		
Jany 7	James Lowrie, Horncliffe for repairing footpaths	£2. 19. 2
Mch 16	S. Riddle & Sons, Engineers, Tweedmouth for repairs	£2. 3. 3
		£6. 11. 10

The Surveyor reported to the same February meeting the need for repairs to decking '. . .at each end of the platform, where there is at present an objectionable difference of level between the surface of the bridge and of the road on the approaches. The cost of these works should not exceed £35.'

Nothing resulted from the Surveyor's first report about the structure that he gave in January 1885, and on August 24th 1887 his views were qualified and posed worry for the Trustees:

'I have made careful investigation into the condition and strength of Union Bridge with a view of giving you a definite opinion as to the propriety of increasing its rigidity and stability. The condition of the ironwork is so far as can be seen, satisfactory, although some amount of corrosion has undoubtedly occurred at the points of suspension.

The woodwork of the platform is very much worn and decayed and apparently the timber which was laid down in 1871 was not of the best quality as it certainly should not have failed to so great an extent in so short a time.

As to the strength and stability of the main structure it is my duty to report that in these respects the bridge is according to modern practice deficient. In 1820 the designers of suspension bridges had very little practical experience, and the calculations of the strains in such structures which were then generally accepted have since been materially modified. At that time either by design or from ignorance no provision was made for securing such bridges from the excessive undulations which high winds are liable to occasion, or from undue vibration from loads passing at a high rate of speed.

There are now several methods by which these unequal and excessive strains can be modified, but as all these methods add considerably to the weight of the structure I am unable to recommend the adoption of any of them in the case of the Union Bridge on account of the want of strength in the main chains to bear any additional load.

According to the rules of the Board of Trade, the bridge will not safely bear a greater moving load than 28 tons and even this load must not be allowed to produce excessive undulation.

Consequently, I beg to recommend that a Notice should be fixed at either end of the bridge giving specific regulations as to the number of persons or cattle, and the number, weight, and speed of vehicles which may be allowed upon the bridge. These regulations I append below.

I do not think these limitations will cause any great amount of practical inconvenience and I am of opinion that they should be enforced as apart from all considerations of the safety of the public, there is no doubt that the continued recurrence of excessive vibration has a distinctly injurious effect upon iron.

Yours faithfully,

H. F. S. Kynnersley.

Moot Hall, Newcastle   24th March 1887 . . .'

REGULATIONS

Not more than 370 persons to be allowed on the bridge
30 cattle or horses
60 sheep
6 loaded carts

No horses drawing vehicles or otherwise shall be allowed to cross except at a walking pace.
Bodies of troops and processions must 'break step' in passing.

Fig 95 - Union Bridge Regulations and Walk notice 1887
(Print taken from a negative discovered by Mr James Scott of Chain Bridge House.
Neither the photographer nor date when the photograph was taken is known, but the Notice relates to Regulations
recommended by the Surveyor on March 24th, 1887)

'Midsummer 1887   Surveyor's Report

Gentlemen,

The condition of the Masonry of Coldstream Bridge is at present satisfactory.

The long continuance of dry weather has to some extent broken up the surface of tile roadway, and it has been difficult to keep it free from loose stones.

The repairs to the platform of Union Bridge have been carried out, and the roadway is now in fair condition. At my last inspection I found that two of the keys in the caps of suspension rods were loose: these I have ordered to be refixed.

Yours faithfully,   H.F.S. Kynnersley.

The Tweed Bridges Trustees, Berwick on Tweed
20th Aug. 1887

Although the Surveyor was critical of Samuel Brown's 'practical experience' and means of determining safe loads, his own calculations, which provided for a maximum moving moving load of 28 tons, was almost the ultimate load the bridge was capable of carrying even when built.

As the Surveyor's figures of 28 tons agrees with present day assessment of the original realistic load limits, then he was virtually confirming the bridge to be as good as new after sixty years of use. His anxiety about 'excessive undulation' through inadequate deck stiffness was justified, but he also pointed out that the suspension chain strength was insufficient to support any extra structural dead load, and left the matter at that.

The Surveyor's 'Regulations' proved a little too optimistic, for one year after their adoption he reported:

'During the passage of five loaded carts over Union Bridge one of the suspension rods broke, and the cap fell into the river where water is very deep. All attempts to recover it have been futile and I have been obliged to order a new cap to be cast....'

Apart from this mishap, the year 1888 was uneventful, and the surveyor informed the Trustees that the bridge should be painted in 1889, which work was duly carried out by a Mr. Richardson who submitted the lowest tender, but no costs have been recorded. The Surveyor's Reports of October 30th. 1889, March and October 1890 were collectively presented to the Meeting of Trustees on January 14th 1891 and included the following:

'...Part of the platform is very much worn, but I consider it will be best to make it last as long as it will and then renew it entirely as it is impossible to make a watertight joint by replacing a few planks here and there.'

Fig 96 - Union Chain Bridge, circa 1905, with WALK sign

'The tenant of the Toll House is dead and the family has left the house. It will be remembered that he was allowed the free occupation of the house on the condition that he kept the roadway of this bridge clean. Unless another tenant can be found it will be necessary to pay one of the roadman to look after the bridge.'

Apart from his report to the meeting, matters put forward were some months old, and the Surveyor brought the issues up to date:

'...It may also be necessary to replace portions of the planking of the platform but I do not propose this year to do more of this than is absolutely required to enable the traffic to be safely conducted. I hope this year to make some arrangements with the County Surveyor of Northumberland by which the repair of the roadway over the bridge may be more satisfactorily performed in connection with the main road of that County.

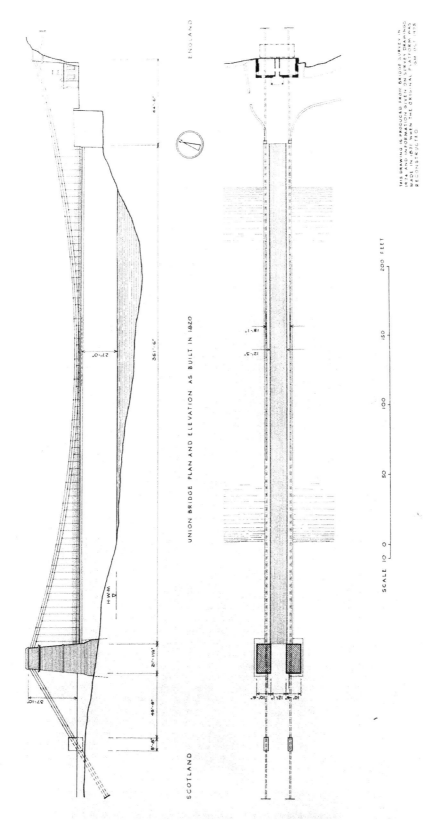

UNION BRIDGE PLAN AND ELEVATION AS BUILT IN 1820

SCOTLAND

ENGLAND

THIS DRAWING IS PRODUCED FROM BRIGHT SURVEY IN 1974 AND INFORMATION GIVEN ON SURVEY DRAWING MADE IN 1871 WHEN THE ORIGINAL PLATFORM WAS RECONSTRUCTED

SCALE 10 0 50 100 150 200 FEET

Fig 97 - Author's drawing of Bridge from 1974 Northumberland CC survey

SAMUEL BROWN AND UNION CHAIN BRIDGE

It may be my duty to report that the Toll House at Union Bridge has been unoccupied during the winter and that probably the painting and woodwork have suffered in consequence. I have not myself received any application for the tenancy of the house, which is a wretched building considered as a dwelling house.

I append my estimate of the amount which should be provided to meet the probable cost of the maintenance of the bridges, roads, and other works in connection with the bridge.

Maintenance of Road . . .
    Union Bridge   3. 0. 0.
    Cleaning Platform

Repairs to Structure
    Union Platforms   6. 0. 0.
    Coating Chains   30. 0. 0.'

More serious matters were beginning to emerge as a result of the Surveyor's enquiring mind as his report of October 1890 recorded:

'....After removing the masonry over the chainways of the English tower I found that the chains had lost a considerable amount of sectional area through corrosion.

They have probably not been examined since the bridge was built seventy years ago and during all this tine have been exposed to the action of the atmosphere. The original sectional area of the chains was 37.67 inches, but now the point where they leave the saddles and enter the chainway, their total area is not more than 28.86 inches.

This is a very important loss of strength, and is particularly serious at this point, when, according to modern calculations the original strength of the bridge was considerably weaker than it should have been. To express this more clearly, the designer of the bridge made the sectional area of the chains uniform throughout their whole length, while they should have been 12% stronger over the saddles than at the middle of the bridge.

It is necessary, I think, that I should trouble you with any technical observations on the essential defects in the original design. The bridge has carried the traffic with safety, and being in good condition elsewhere, there seems no reason for making it stronger than it originally was. It is however obviously desirable that this original strength should be maintained, and it will therefore be necessary either to attach supplementary chains over the saddles to make up the section which has been lost, or to replace the defective links with new ones of full strength. There are several ways of doing this, but I am unable at present to state which would be the most economical and satisfactory.

The operation, however it may he carried out, is a difficult one and though as an interesting piece of engineering I should like to take it in hand, I feel that personally I cannot, consistently with the proper performance of my other work, devote to it the time and thought it requires.

In these circumstances I am willing either to place my resignation in your hands, or should you, under the 6th and 7th clause of my appointment, specify that the necessary operations are new works, I would take charge of the undertaking and engage what assistance I require, both in designing and in supervision of its execution . . . '

Coming at the end of a lengthy meeting such observations must have stupefied the Trustees, for they concluded by merely fixing the Surveyor's salary '...for the past and current year...at £30.'

Here was a matter about which the Surveyor clearly thought the clauses of his appointment were ambiguous. Clause 3 required him to deal with 'ordinary repairs and maintenance and clauses 6 and 7 related to '...new works...'. Without doubt defects arising from corrosion were a maintenance item, but were major structural innovations to be regarded as ordinary The Surveyor had now been acting for the Trustees over a period of six years, and he acknowledged the considerable age of the bridge. It is therefore surprising that a seemingly alert and experienced engineer did not make a thorough bridge survey soon after his appointment. However, his discovery should not have surprised him, in which event, why was deterioration of the bar-link section area out of the ordinary? The Surveyor's thinking obviously revolved around the fact that repairs to that existing were out of the question and a completely new linkage over the bearing was needed. The work involved was well outside the scope of his annual salary, but in offering his resignation he must have been in doubt about the Trustees reception of his views.

Fig 98 - Union Chain Bridge circa 1890 before addition of strengthening cables (Mrs E Purvis)

The outcome of events favoured the Surveyor's retention, and the designation of bearing-chain repair as 'new works' was accepted by the Trustees. Accordingly, estimates obtained through the surveyor's proposals were laid before the Trustees at their meeting on July 17th 1891:

'... 1. Teesside Iron Co.   £290
    2. Cleveland Bridge Co.   £285
    3. Robertson & Co.   £200

And the Trustees on consideration thereof are of opinion that the tender of Messrs. Robertson & Co. should be accepted.

The Surveyor further reported that an expenditure of from £20 to £80 would be required for concrete and other work which he recommended to be done under his own supervision....'

The proposed work was carried out, and the Surveyor outlined the course of events at the Trustees meeting on May 20th 1892:

'The work of strengthening the main chains over and near the saddles at the English end of this bridge has been satisfactorily completed.

I have also carried out some work at the back of the chain-ways by which any loss of strength the land chains may have sustained by corrosion will be compensated for any additional anchorage.

The cost of providing and fixing these additional plates and encasing the chains between them and the saddles in concrete has been £55.17.3.

The main structure of the bridge may now be relied on to carry ordinary traffic with safety, but it must be remembered that it is not adapted to stand heavy gales, and probably owes its continued existence to the fact that it is remarkably well sheltered on almost every side.

The structure of the floor is very defective in design and by additional bracing the excessive oscillation could be, to some extent, reduced. This should be remembered when the lower decking and joists are worn out and require renewal.

There is also a grave constructional fault at the English end which causes most objectionable shocks to vehicles entering the bridge. This fault cannot be altogether remedied except at great cost but the bad effect can be reduced by fixing cast iron bed plates at the top of the abutment and attaching bearing plates to the run bars, and by constructing a new hinged deck at this end of the bridge.

I should recommend that the bedplates and bearing plates should be provided and fixed this year and that the hinged deck should be postponed until the effect of the improved bearing has been ascertained. The cost of this (i.e. the bed plates and bearing plates) I should estimate at £24.

Some of the flooring boards, about 50 in number, should be taken out and replaced at a cost of £18.0.0.

I have let the toll house to a roadman, rent free, on condition that he keeps the platform of the bridge clean and lays sand and ashes in frosty weather.

I have had to call the Secretary's attention to the fact that the maximum loads on the bridge are, according to report, frequently exceeded, and I propose, with your permission, to fix two short and clear notices in more prominent positions at each end of the Bridge - I should recommend that the maximum load should now be fixed at four loaded carts instead of six, not because I consider the bridge weaker than it was formerly, but in consequence of the Peculiarity of the traffic. I find that the rule is for 8 loaded carts to leave Velvet Hall station together (the contents of one railway truck) – at present (either all or six) go on the bridge together. It would cause less wear and tear if this cavalcade was equally divided and I don't think that any appreciable loss of time or obstruction to the traffic would be caused by this alteration in the regulations.

The roof of the toll house was found by the new tenant not to be watertight, and I have expended 16/1 in attempting to make it so but without success. The lead gutters are worn out and should be entirely renewed, and the slating repaired:- this will cost not less than £7.

My annual estimate is as follows:

Union Bridge, repairs to platform	18.0.0
new bed plates & bearers	24.0.0
repairs to toll house	7.0.0
notice boards	1.10.0. . .'

The meeting then discussed matters of finance,

'In view of the expenditure necessary for carrying out the repairs above referred to, the Secretary was instructed to make application to the Rent Authorities of the Counties of Northumberland and Berwick for permission to encroach upon the capital Fund to the extent of £200, and to intimate that the Trustees proposed, with the consent of those Counties, to exhaust the Capital Fund remaining in their hands before asking for a contribution from the Rates for the purpose of the Trust.'

The toll house was let to a Mr. Edward Roxburgh, rent free, on the understanding that in return he would carry out specific duties and services. These conditions were set out in a letter from the surveyor:

'County Surveyor's Office
Moot Hall
Newcastle upon Tyne

30th Sept. 1891.

Sir,
Union Bridge Toll House

The Trustees would be willing to let you have this house rent free on condition that you will sweep the platform of the Bridge when required, and exercise a general supervision over the structure of the bridge, reporting to me at all times when any defect is visible in the ironwork, or mason-work, or platform. In frosty weather, ashes or sand should also be laid on such places as may be slippery.

It would also be a condition of your occupancy that you should exercise a control over the traffic, and prevent the crossing of the bridge by locomotives or a number of carts or cattle in excess of that stipulated on the notice boards.

In the event of drivers persisting in crossing, it would be your duty to report to me giving particulars of the occurrence, with the names and addresses of the drivers.

The Trustees would be willing to do any necessary repairs to the house during your tenancy.

Yours faithfully,
H. S. Kynnersly

Mr. Edward Roxburgh
Loanend
Berwick-on-Tweed...'

Having dealt with the bearing saddles and back chain anchorages the Surveyor had again expressed concern about the deck oscillation and suggested that something should be done when deck repairs are carried out. What he envisaged is not evident - but he may have been thinking about increasing the number of longitudinal members under the deck, possibly at the extreme edges.

The meeting authorised the recommended action that the bed plates and bearing plates should be renewed during the year, and the new roadman was to be instructed to report any contravention of bridge loading regulations.

The bridge gave no particular trouble for almost a year, other than some minor repairs to the deck which cost £16, but on November 17th 1893 a gale brought down a tree on the Scottish side that damaged the 'land chain pillars'. The surveyor also reported that '...the running bars which carry the platform were also displaced from their resting places on the west abutments. The damage has been repaired, and the platform replaced . . . '

On May 15th 1894 the Surveyor announced to the Trustees that '...the upper decking of this bridge is now much worn, and it will be necessary to relay it entirely next year...' Then continued on April 26th 1895:

'I estimate the cost of laying a new creosoted redwood deck with a camber to throw the water to the sides at £200.
It is also desirable that bed plates should be fixed at the west abutment to carry the run bars, which have cut deep grooves in the masonry

During the year the following sums are required for maintenance and repair:

....Union New Platform	£175
Repairing footpath and fascia	25
New bed plates and angle irons to run bars	16....'

A more decisive statement was presented to the Trustees on May 18th 1895:

'At Union Bridge the upper decking is now worn out.'

So that was that; but for some reason '...nor have bed plates been fixed under the running bars at the north end of Union Bridge.' (He meant west end) and continues -

'I have recommended that ... works should be executed during the current financial year, and that Union Bridge, last painted in 1890, should be repainted. I estimate the total expenditure necessary for the maintenance ...during 1896-7..

Painting Union Bridge	£40
Bed plates etc. at Union Bridge	16....'

The platform was renewed at a cost of £210.4.3

An uneventful two years passed by until the Surveyor's report of March 22nd 1898:

'I have inspected the Tweed Bridges from time to time during the last six months.

The damage done by the gale of November 28th to the Union Bridge has been satisfactorily repaired at a cost of £6.10.5., and the structure of the bridge itself and the platform are now in good condition. The fence walls at the English end are however in bad repair and require pointing and other repairs. The roof of the toll hose is defective, the lead gutter being worn out, and many of the slates being broken and misplaced.. The cost of the necessary repairs, provided the timber is found to be sound, should not exceed £8 …'

During the following year the retaining walls were repaired at a cost of £30.0.0., and £20.0.0. was spent on repairs to decking and 'protecting main chains.' This last item may refer to permanent weather protection of the chains at the pier head bearings.

On March 10th 1900 the Surveyor reported:

'I have to report that the Bridges and Roads maintainable by the Trust have been kept in good condition …..'

His recommendations and estimates for the year ending March 31st 1901 were accepted, and simply included for 'Painting £50 - Repairs to platform £8.'

Mr. H.F. Sneyd-Kynnersley, Surveyor to the Trust, died on October 15th 1900, and the Trustees at their meeting on March 9th 1901 minuted 'an Acknowledgement of the value they attached to his services....' They then turned their attention to a successor, and 'resolved' upon the same conditions of appointment that had been originally determined on September 9th 1884. The Trustees 'unanimously agreed to offer the appointment of Surveyor ….Mr. Joseph Alfred Bean, the County Surveyor of Northumberland.'

The expert care of the bridge continued to be the responsibility of the County Surveyor and this new appointment was to prove invaluable in the future life of the bridge.

Mr. Bean had already inspected the bridge and reported some unwelcome information to the meeting:

'There is an indication of deflexion of the platform on the upstream side of this bridge, and in my opinion a minute examination of the suspension chains or links is necessary.'

He also raised the question of the painting; which had been deferred, and urged that it should be done. Tenders for this work had been obtained and presented to a Meeting on May 4th 1901:

... the tender of Mr. R. Hume.... be accepted.'

Mr. Bean expanded upon his thoughts:

'You requested me at an interview to thoroughly overhaul the Bridge and give an opinion as to its condition and strength. In order to give you this information it will be necessary to clear the ironwork of all existing paint and corrosion which I will carry out when the Bridge is being painted. It would be a great advantage to place a camber on the Bridge, than an incline from the centre to each and, so that water may not accumulate and saturate the timber floor. I need hardly point out the life of the floor is very short under present circumstances.'

On October 5th 1901 Mr. Bean reported the completion of painting to the Trustees:

'The amount of the tender was £69.10.0. There are, however, certain extras amounting to the sum of £7.10.0. They comprise the painting of the cottage on the bridge (which I was not aware was a part of the bridge property at the time the tender was let).

Supplying, painting and fixing new notice boards, the old ones being rotten.

Fixing twelve new squares of glass to windows broken by a hailstorm.

The cottage will require pointing next year.'

Mr. Bean's explorations had taken him to the chain bearings over the Scotch tower:

'....The ironwork of the bridge generally is in a better condition than I expected to find it. I have, however, to draw your attention to a very serious defect. The six cables on either side of the bridge pass through small openings in the tower on the North side of the river. It was

Fig 99 - Union Chain Bridge, general view from the Scottish side (Jim Walker)

impossible to ascertain the condition of the links, there being no access to them. I therefore cut four manholes in the top of the tower in order to examine and paint them. Evidently they had not been painted or ever examined since the bridge was erected. The four bottom cables are much corroded and I estimate at least 25% of the section has rusted away. It will be necessary to strengthen the defective portion by new links. With your instructions I will prepare plan and obtain tender from a reliable firm for this work.'

Nine years previously Mr. Kynnersley had the corroded chains over the bearing on the English side repaired and why he failed to examine the Scottish counterpart is not known. Maybe it was a case of "out of sight out of mind", but just such a condition and knowledge of the earlier work prompted Mr. Bean into action, and during November 1901 he prepared detailed requirements, obtained an-estimate from the Cleveland Bridge Engineering Co. Ltd., received the Trustees' approval and had the necessary work started. The following is the letter estimate that was received:

'...Darlington, November 16th 1901

J.A.Bean Esq.,
Newcastle on Tyne

Dear Sir:
Union Bridge over River Tweed

In accordance with your instructions we have had under consideration the proposal for the renewal of the two pairs of lowermost chains over the Tower at the Scotch end of this Bridge, and we now beg to submit our offer for executing the work. We enclose a sketch showing what we propose and this comprises the introduction of new central bars each in three parts to allow of entering them into place, the ends of these being made to embrace coupling boxes of wrought iron or steel plates. These are made in halves bolted together and filled each with four pairs of gibs and cotters which can be separately adjusted to their places so as to bear truly on the existing side links. The sketch shews approximately the position of the present rods, the new bars would have to be made to exact templates taken from site and arranged to bear at the centre on the present links over the central roller, and towards each end with bearing blocks on to the cast iron saddles. The sketch is intended to shew the arrangement proposed, but this; as well as all details would be submitted to you for approval before proceeding with the work. We propose 'Whitewells Special Admiralty Cable Iron' if this be preferred to mild steel. The gibs and cotters would perhaps need to be in steel to obtain the requisite bearing areas. We include with this work for the removal (by scraping or burning) of all paint from the present rods, and the coating of both new and old work (over the Tower) with three coats of an approved bitumastic solution.

Our price for supplying and fixing this work (including the coating) all to your satisfaction and approval would be £150 nett, and if you entrusted us with the work it should have our best attention.

We are, Yours faithfully,
For the Cleveland Bridge Engineering Co,. Ltd.

A.Q. Hancock
Assistant Manager …'

The Trustees, in accepting the tender of £150, also agreed the sum of £10 for mason's work and £10 for pointing and repairs to the cottage on the bridge. All necessary work was quickly done and the account agreed at the Trustees' meeting on April 12th 1902 and they made an application '…to the County Councils of Northumberland and Berwickshire respectively under Section 8 of the Determination of the Secretary of State for contributions to enable the Trustees to meet the expenditure consisting of works of ordinary maintenance and repair and the general expenses of management during the year ending 31st March 1903 …'

Deterioration of the timber platform became an emergency matter for the Surveyor, and the overall strength of the chain cables was causing him worries, On June 21st 1902 he confronted the Trustees with a form of ultimatum: either 'replacing the existing cables with new cables of a strength sufficient to meet the requirements of the Board of Trade or to build a new Bridge.'

The Surveyor was clearly aware of deficiencies in the bridge which could not be completely rectified, and from a practical point of view he obviously favoured a new bridge. However, he placed all the facts before the meeting including his action of preparing details and inviting tenders for the entire platform renewal.

Tweed Bridges Trustees
Union Chain Bridge

Gentlemen,

Report upon the condition of the Timber Floor

Having received a report on the 27th May that some of the timber joists, which carry the planking and support the floor of the bridge, were defective and giving way I at once made a close investigation and found the timber joists and planking throughout in so rotten a condition that I considered it absolutely essential (with the sanction of your Chairman) to immediately close the bridge to vehicular traffic.

It appears the flooring or surface was renewed about six years ago and today is in fair order, but I gathered from a resident near the Bridge that the joists and planking were renewed 31 years ago. The floor having no proper means of drainage or camber or asphalt covering, the life of this timber may be considered to have been very good.

I was instructed by your Chairman, in order to avoid delay, to obtain tenders for renewing the defective timbers. Plans, specifications and Bills of Quantities were prepared and tenders invited by advertisement. It is proposed to adopt pitch pine joists and fir planking specially treated so as to preserve the life of the timber. I have deemed it advisable not to adopt steel joists or flooring as this would materially increase the weight to be carried by the chains. At present a very sensible deformation of the structure takes place when a load passes over the Bridge, in consequence of the weight not being distributed uniformly over the twelve chains. I have therefore devised a method of stiffening the floor which will render the structure a little more rigid.

The floor will be covered with asphalt, which if maintained watertight, should indefinitely prolong the life of the timber.

The road surface at present falls to the centre of the river, consequently water accumulates, stands in pools or penetrates thro' and rots the timber. It is proposed to shorten the suspension rods so that the road surface may be at a gradient of 1 in 90 from the centre to each end, thus allowing the surface water to drain away properly.

I estimate the cost of this work to be £350.

With reference to the chains supporting the superstructure of the bridge I think it advisable to inform you that under present circumstances it is impossible for me to give you any assurance that the Bridge or chains may be considered absolutely safe. These chains have always been under excessive strain and when such is the case no surprise should be felt if the Bridge collapsed under certain conditions which may arise, such as a gale of wind with a snowstorm or a rolling load passing over at a considerable velocity or a crowd of people upon the Bridge. You have notices upon the Bridge providing against the latter. The Bridge chains are one third of the strength required by the Board of Trade. The question for your consideration is, would it be wise to spend the sum of £850 upon repairs or to erect a new Bridge sufficiently strong to carry all heavy traffic including a crowd of people? Such a Bridge may cost £10,000.0.0.

Yours faithfully,

J.A. Bean
Engineer to the Trust

Moothall
Newcastle on Tyne
19th June 1902   '

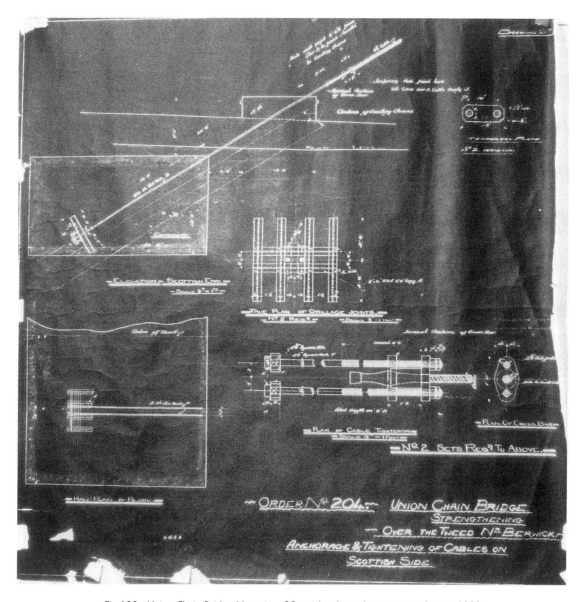

Fig 100 - Union Chain Bridge, blueprint of Scottish side anchorage strengthening 1902

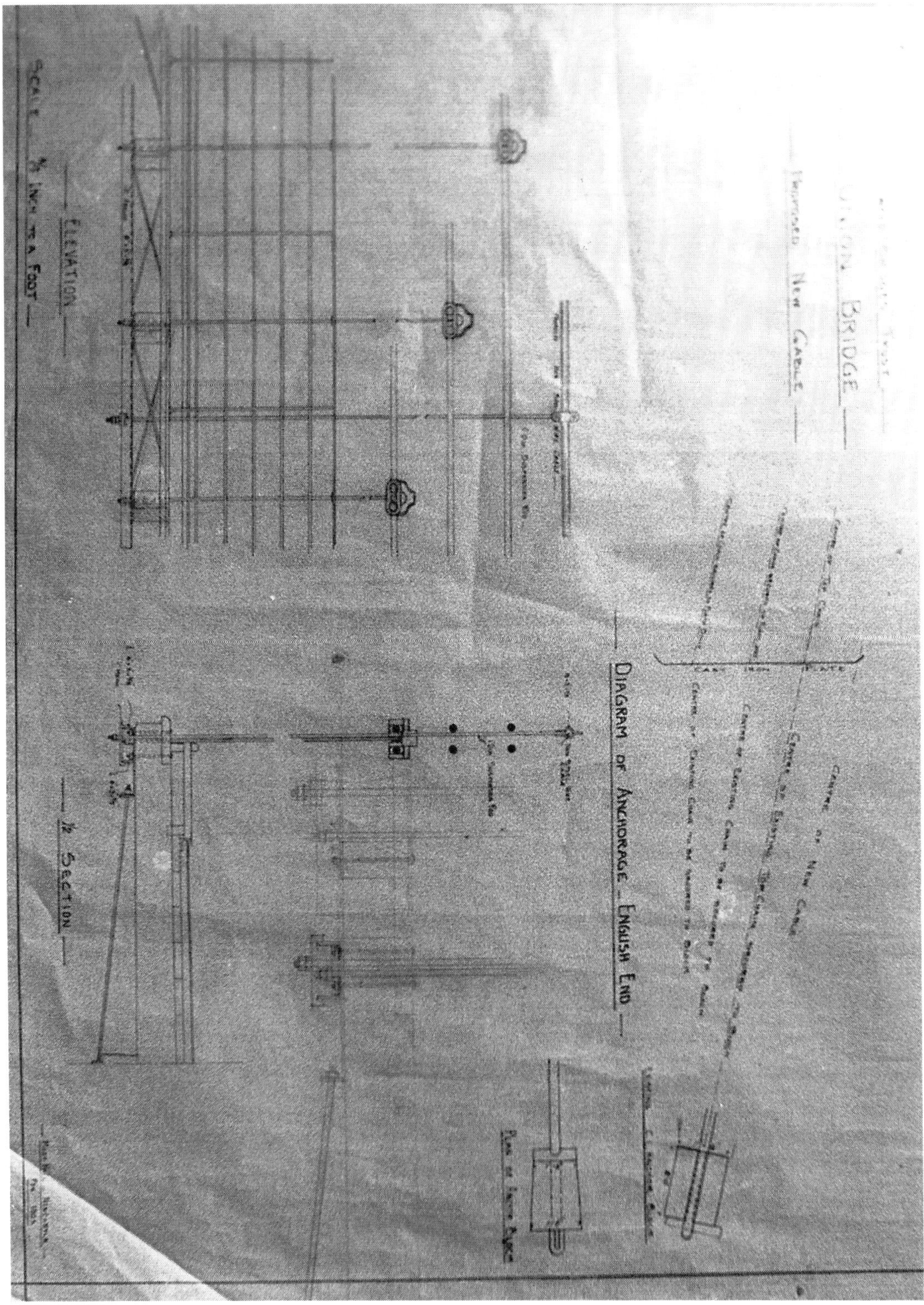

Fig 101 - Union Chain Bridge, diagram of English side anchorage

The Bridge was undoubtedly in jeopardy, possibly through a lack of maintenance and keen observation of the structure generally. This reflected on the competence of the late Mr. Kynnersley, former surveyor, who through illness, may have relied too much on the advice of his assistants. The overall circumstances of the situation are not clear, but the complete breakdown of the platform was relatively sudden. Mr Kynnersley was always concerned about the strength of the chains, and the loading to which they could safely be subjected, yet he never produced a scheme whereby they could be reinforced, particularly when his reason for not stiffening the deck was because the extra load could not be carried by the chains.

Complete replacement of the bridge platform preceded the addition of supplementary steel wire rope cables, and the design changes that Mr Bean proposed, and carried into effect, gave consideration to the problem of new cable attachments. Suspension rods were to be placed centrally between every third bay of those existing (15 feet centres) and to provide some continuity of support between the old and new rods, a pair of 4" x 3" x ½" rolled steel angles were located as 'run-bar' under the main beam ends at each side. These angles would not only provide a fixing for suspension rods but, by their positive attachment to the platform, introduced additional stiffening that Mr Bean was anxious to obtain.

New 13"x6" main beams were now to be tapered along their top edge, from the centre to 12" deep at the extreme edge, to effect a small cross fall for improving deck drainage.

New 13"x6" main beams, tapered down from their top centre to each end by one inch, gave a small transverse camber for assisting deck drainage.

The main beams were now more sensibly positioned beside the suspension rods, as they had been at the beginning in 1820, and up to the major changes in 1871. The ends of each beam were now to be bolted to the steel angle sections 'run-bar' with ½" diameter bolts, through their whole depth. The outer end fixing bars, of the old underslung bracing arrangement, to alternate main beams provided a packing between the angle and underside beam faces, that was compensated for in the other situations with 10" x 6" x ½" steel plates.

The old platform stiffening member was renewed, and the related bracing ironwork refixed. Also, as before, two 7" x 3" timber planks were sunk within the top surface level of the main beam ends, and secured by the ½" diameter bolts that connected with the pair of 'run-bar' angles. Although Mr Bean probably doubted the value of the old diagonal iron bar linked bracing, it was duly refurbished and replaced. Road decking and footwalks were renewed exactly as that previously existing, in which some of the sound old material was reused.

The threaded tail-ends of the original suspension rods were now passed through steel plates 8" x 4" x 1", drilled and located between the inner faces of the steel angle 'run-bar', but not otherwise fixed, other than a pair of nuts to the rod end. The new series of suspension rods, being located between beam bay spaces, were terminated by the use of 'U' shaped plates 4" x 1" in section, with 3" upturned ends that embraced the steel angle flanges. These bars were therefore free to move independently from the old suspending members, and the threaded tails of all rods were fitted with double nuts and washers.

An amount of discontent 'concerning vigilance over the bridge could well have prompted the Trustees' Secretary to ask Mr Kynnersley for a definition of the roadman's duties in January 1898, when he was sent a copy of a letter to Edward Roxburgh of September 30th 1891. The Secretary's reply was both snide and to the point:

> '....it seems to me that the letter of which you send me a copy makes sufficiently clear the conditions on which Roxburgh was allowed to enter the cottage at the Bridge. I suppose he has occasionally done something, or reported to you about the Bridge. When you repair the cottage that will be an act of ownership which the occupant cannot gainsay, but it would be well to get from him something in the shape of a report, and to call upon him from time to time to render some little service. . . '

The meeting of June 21st closed with a resolution seeking financial aid from the respective Counties concerning the proposed platform replacement and instructed the surveyor to 'take steps' and prepare a scheme, with approximate estimates for strengthening the chain cables.

> '...It was resolved that an application be made to the County Councils of Northumberland and Berwickshire respectively under Section 8 of the Determination of the Secretary of State, for contributions to enable the Trustees to meet the additional expenditure on Union Bridge for the year ended 31st March 1903 referred to in the Surveyor's Report, and the Trustees certify that the sum of £1,000 is necessary and direct that a Certificate to that effect under the hand of the Chairman be presented to the respective Authorities of Northumberland and Berwick accordingly.

> It was resolved that the Treasurer be instructed to arrange with the Bank for a temporary overdraft to meet the expenditure incurred pending the provision of the money by the respective County Councils.'

At the next meeting of Trustees on November 11th 1902 they received the Surveyor's proposal for strengthening the bridge structure '....by new and additional steel wire cables, which might be added without the Bridge being stopped for traffic and the practical effect of which would, in his opinion, be to strengthen the Bridge to such a degree as to provide an equivalent to a new Bridge, the cost of the proposed improvement being approximately estimated by the surveyor at £1450...'

The meeting was impressed with this proposal, for it offered a complete solution; retention of the existing Bridge, open to traffic during the course of the works; and all at minute cost in comparison to the alternative of total replacement. It was '...resolved that the Surveyor do prepare specifications and working plans and to obtain tenders from some selected Firms of good standing for the work....'

On March 28th 1903 the Surveyor reminded the Trustees that it was '.. four years since the bridge was painted and I would advise your committee to repaint the Bridge three coats for which I have obtained the following tenders:

A. Robertson & Son...........................£50. 0. 0.
Thomas Crow & Co ....£65. 0. 0.

He then presented the result of his invitation to tender for the new cables, and his estimation of expenditure for the year ending March 1904.(Items relevant to other bridges in his charge have been excluded).

'In accordance with your instructions I have obtained tenders for auxiliary cables to strengthen this bridge. Six building firms were requested to send tenders but I have only succeeded in obtaining one tender, that of the Cleveland Bridge Engineering Coy. for the sum of £1000. I consider this tender is satisfactory. I have also obtained a tender for the anchorage for the cables from Messrs. Henry Elliot and Son. Such tender comprises taking down of the fence walls and rebuilding them, the necessary excavation and concrete anchorages forming manholes and re-asphalting the whole of the bridge with rock asphalt, also a contingent sum of £50. The tender amounts to £531.16.6, therefore the total tenders of the Cleveland Bridge and Engineering Coy. and Messrs Henry Elliot & Son amount to £1,450. I should also state that the Bridge Keeper at Union Bridge has requested me to bring to your notice the fact that there is no W.C. or earth-closet in connection with the house in which he lives. I think it is desirable that this sanitary convenience should be provided. Should you think it necessary, it will be advisable to include in the Annual estimate the sum of an additional £10.

J. A. Bean
Surveyor to the Tweed Bridges Trust.

The Moothall
Newcastle on Tyne 27th March 1903.'

Surveyor's Estimate for the year ending March 1904 Union Bridge

New steel cable £1531. 16. 6

The Charges to be met by the Trustees during the year 1903-4 are estimated as follows:

1. Balance due to Messrs. H. Elliot & Son in respect
of repairs to the Union Bridge during last year...£86. 19. 6

2. Amount of Cleveland Engineering Co. Tender for
new cables for Union Bridge £1000. 0. 0

3. Messrs. H. Elliot & Son's Tender in connection with
new cables for Union Bridge £531. 6. 6

4. Surveyor's commission in connection with new cables for Union Bridge.................£80. 0. 0

5. Earth Closet for cottage at Union Bridge £10. 0. 0

All the works of repair and strengthening were carried out during 1903, and the Surveyor's Report of events given to the Trustees on January 1st 1904 explains the events. Unfortunately for the Roadman the provision of a 'sanitary convenience' presented a problem of some magnitude which matter is also dealt with in the report. Relevant accounts and estimated charges for the year ending March 31st 1905 were included:

'....   **Union Bridge**

I have to report the tenders for the anchorage for the new and old cables, comprising excavation, concrete anchorages, rebuilding walls and asphalting the whole bridge with rock asphalt and the supply of new steel cables to strengthen the bridge, have been successfully carried out. The amount or the tenders was £1531.16.6. and the expenditure has been £1594.14.1 or £62.17.1 in excess. This excess was in consequence of the defective condition of an existing anchor on the English end. The six cables on each side of the bridge are secured to large cast iron plates about 7 feet by 5 feet square which are anchored by two rods into the solid rock. On excavating down to fix the new cable rods the existing anchor rod on one side was fractured in consequence of the enormous strain upon it; therefore the weight of the bridge was brought upon the cast iron plate and masonry tower of the bridge.

The stability of the masonry is undoubtedly very good or the whole structure would have failed and precipitated the bridge into the river. New anchor rods into the solid rock have been placed down to support and take the strain off each cable at the English end in order to render the bridge secure.

It will be necessary during the coming year to paint the new steel cable with two coats of paint, also to provide for fine gravel and tar for the road surface over the bridge, which I estimate to cost £23.

I should also bring to your notice that you instructed me to provide a sanitary convenience for the bridge keeper by the side of the cottage but in commencing the work, I was requested not to proceed by Mr. Dunbar who claims the land as his property. I have been through the old minutes of the Trust and cannot ascertain the boundaries of the bridge but I am rather of the opinion that the land in question has been purchased by the Trust.

I have to request the payment of the following accounts:

Union Bridge   The Cleveland Bridge & Engineering Coy £1054. 15. 2

--do--   H. Elliot & Son balance.....................................169. 18. 11

--do--   John Rule (Hadfield & Coy.)................................120. 0. 0

J.A. Bean
County Surveyor
27th Jan. 1904

The estimated charges to be met by the Trustees for the year ended 31st March 1905 are:

Estimated cost of work authorised..£155. 0. 0

Earth closet at Union Bridge not yet provided 10. 0. 0

Add for Secretary's (£12.10.0)
      Treasurer's (£ 7.10.0)
      and Surveyor's (£30) Salaries... 50. 0. 0

Commission to Surveyor on Union Bridge
as ordered at last meeting 80. 0. 0
Add for contingencies 49. 19. 3

The meeting concluded with a resolution of application to the respective County Councils for finance.

Strengthening by additional catenary cables, carried out in 1903, gave the bridge a new lease of life, and up to the year 1908 only the sum of £30 was spent in repairing the deck timbers and surface, and £5 on small items of maintenance. In 1908 the surveyor optimistically reported to the Trustees '... generally speaking, this bridge is in good order. I think it would be wise to tar paint the road surface which would have the effect of filling up worn places and so prevent water standing on the bridge. It would also tend to prevent the sleepers of the roadway from being worn away so rapidly...'

The roadman and his family, who occupied the bridge cottage, became a subject of concern by the Surveyor and Trustees in 1909, for they lacked both sanitary and fresh water facilities. Although efforts were made over many years to provide a supply of fresh piped water, it was never obtained. This and other matters which offended the Housing Act, and Public Health Acts, led to the cottage abandonment in 1952, and its final demolition in 1953. Demolition was a regrettable incident in the bridge history, and the details of its demise will be dealt with later.

From the days when the first Tollgate keeper occupied the bridge cottage until Mr. Cockburn and his family left one hundred and thirty four years later, water for drinking and other purposes was collected from a spring down the river bank. As the years passed by, even this spring dried up in the summer months and the River Tweed became the only source of supply. In 1893 Margaret Roxburgh was born in Chain Bridge Cottage, and well remembers those dry summer days, when, with her brother and sister, she climbed down the steep bank with buckets, and '...didn't find it any bother.' Miss Roxburgh's memory is of '....happy days - we all liked it very much there, it was warm and comfortable with an open range fire, and I helped to control the traffic.'

Returning to 1909, when the Surveyor started the ball rolling, about the need for a 'closet', at a Trustees' Meeting on March 20th:

> 'The surface of the road requires repairing in certain parts of the carriageway. Attention has been given to the cottage, the kitchen chimney of which smoked badly and a new curb has been placed upon it and the caretaker informs me it has been of great benefit to the residents. You will remember we reviewed this bridge in the autumn and discussed the question of providing an earth closet for the caretaker. At the present time, they have no convenience at all. It will of course be necessary to rent or purchase a piece of land from the adjoining landowner. If it can be obtained at a reasonable price, I would advise that a convenience be erected for this house. The Rural District Council have drawn attention to the fact that the house is without any convenience. I have included the sum of £30 for the repairs to the roadway and the provision of this convenience.'

The roadman and his family were to become long suffering, for the surveyor was to make little progress about the earth closet during the year as his report of February 12th 1910 explains:

'This Bridge requires painting. I am obtaining tenders for the work which I will lay before you at your meeting.

The road surface is in bad order at the present time. I fear this surface is a difficult matter to keep in repair, in consequence of the thin wearing surface of metal that may be applied owing to the limitation of weight. In order to reduce the weight of a lasting wearing surface to a minimum it would be necessary to use a rock asphalt or cork asphalt but this material would be too costly to adopt. I therefore propose to remove the remainder of the present asphalt on the bridge and to allow the three inch cross timbers to act as the wearing surface. At the same time it will be necessary to tar the timbers and sprinkle them with shingle or gravel.The main timbers of the bridge are Haskinized and will take little harm from the weather.

Certain small repairs to the cottage were found essential and have been carried out. With regard to the earth closet for the caretaker, your Chairman has been at some trouble with Sir. H. Jerningham as to the purchase or rent of a small piece of land but unsuccessfully. I would therefore suggest that as land is most difficult to obtain at a reasonable price that you authorise me to erect this building on a portion of the roadside opposite the house but lowered into the ground, which involves no payment to anyone. The position is not the best but under the circumstances I cannot advise you to adopt a more advantageous one.'

Estimates of cost covering the year ended March 31st 1911 were presented to the Meeting:

'... **Union Bridge**
Repairs to road £12. 0. 0
Convenience 15. 0. 0
Painting .... 70. 0. 0   ...'

Deterioration of the road surface remained a continual problem: in 1908 the surveyor was reporting the bridge to be "....in good order", and now in 1910 all was not well again. However the idea of removing the asphaltic wearing surface because replacement with natural rock asphalt would be 'too costly' was a blessing in disguise. At that time the process of Haskinising (creosote pickling) was an excellent method of delaying timber decay, but it did not prevent mechanical damage.

Coating the road decking with fine shingle on tar was a good idea but the tar as binding agent was readily soluble in hot weather and would not effectively support a sufficient wearing surface thickness. These ideas were nevertheless good as present day resin based binding agents were unfortunately not available.

The adjoining land owner Sir H. Jerningham was not to help over the land required for the closet, and the surveyor pursued the idea of its provision adjacent to the cottage. He reported to the Trustees a year later, February, 4th 1911:

'....I have obtained at suggestion from the Clerk to the Norham and Islandshires Council that the earth closet for the cottage should be erected next to the house and I have given Messrs. Henry Elliot & Son instructions to proceed with the works.'

The bridge was painted during the year 1910 and repairs to roadway only amounted to £5. 0. 0. In 1911 the surveyor's ideas for the road surface had been carried out, but the closet remained an enigma. He reported to the Trustees on February 17th 1912:

'...the tar macadam has been removed from the road, leaving exposed the timber sleepers which appear to give good foothold to the horses and with a more satisfactory result. Messrs. Henry Elliot & Son had not proceeded with the work of erection of the earth closet. I have given them instructions for immediately proceeding with the work which I hope will be carried out during the next fortnight....'

Eventually the closet was provided according to the plan agreed.

In 1915 the bridge was again painted and on February 12th 1916 it was reported that the '... road surface is in good condition and timber work is in good order.' This same Meeting dealt with the value of both bridge and land under the Finance (1909-10) Act, 1910, a copy of which had been served on each of the Trustees '....the original gross value of the bridge was to be fixed at £3650 and the original full site value at £40 was submitted.'

Even in the middle of the First World War the final sum of £3690 was ridiculously low, for the bridge could not have been replaced for many times that figure. The extension of bridge life given by the 1903 catenary cables was obviously not viewed with optimism. By the end of 1916 the road deck sleepers with their new type surface treatment was 'being gradually worn away...' The Bridge itself was in a good state of repair, and the surveyor reported on February 3rd 1917 'the traffic over this bridge has increased during the past year, I believe it is in consequence of the War....'

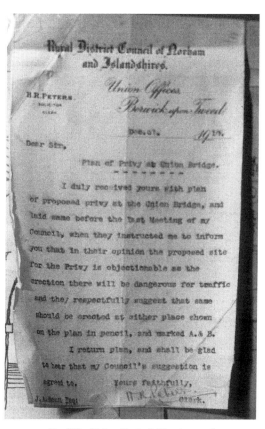

*Fig 102 - Union Chain Bridge, letter of
31st Dec 1910 re proposed privy*

James Straughan recalls:

'Many a farmer used to have cattle delivered to Velvet Hall Station near Horncliffe and drive them down over Chain Bridge - two head once broke loose and charged across the

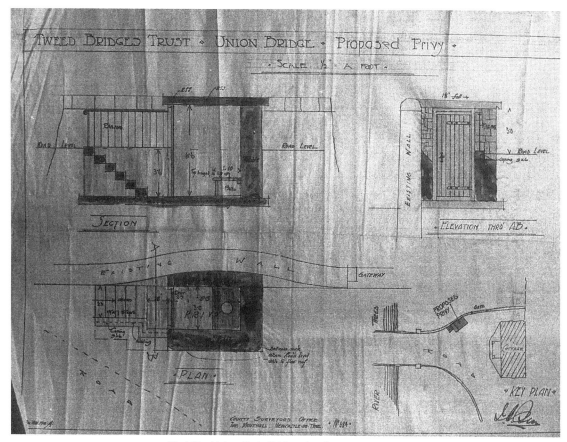

Fig 103 - Union Chain Bridge, plan for proposed privy

bridge and it bounced and rocked. On the south side the tensions on chains needed urgent attention to balance tension (top steel wire cables), and a pair of iron spanners was used - here is one...'

Traffic that the surveyor referred to was mainly cattle being driven from the Scottish Borders to Velvet Hall railway station, destined for the south. No actual record exists about these movements but 'memories' speak of '....large numbers of rampaging cattle....' which must have given the bridge quite a jolting.

The volume of traffic over the bridge continued to increase, and the surveyor reported on March 2nd 1918 '...it becomes essential to save the road surface as far as possible, and I estimate the tar painting of the surface will amount to £14.0.0.'

It seems absurd that the road surface could be 'saved' by the expenditure of £14.0.0. However, the deck was duly tarred and saved but not for long. Two years later, on February 7th 1920, the surveyor told the Trustees about a new threat by heavy timber waggons crossing the bridge. He reported:

'I think it very desirable to tar paint the surface of this bridge again and I must draw the attention of the Committee to the fact that two or three timber hauliers are carrying timber by horses and timber waggons over this bridge. I am carefully watching the timber platform and, if I consider that any structural deterioration is likely to take place, I would ask your committee to give me power to stop this traffic over the bridge. There is an alternative route, about one mile longer, via Norham Bridge.

Small repairs have been carried out in consequence of the breaking of the suspension rod in one or two instances which may be expected as the metal has been in use for so many years'.

Tar painting of the road deck was carried out in 1920, and thereafter annually until 1925, together with retouching the paintwork of ironwork, but the timber decking was deteriorating and on January 1st 1926, the surveyor reported to the Trustees:

'Early in September, it was found that the longitudinal wooden sleepers had deteriorated and it was unsafe to retain them on the bridge.

Your Committee will remember accepting the lowest tender, viz. that of Mr. S. Davidson, amounting to £416.6.3. The work however cost the sum of £372.11.5. It was rather difficult at the time to ascertain the amount of work to be carried out.

The old sleepers were advertised for sale and were purchased by Mr. R. Roxburgh for £4. 5. 0, his offer being the highest received, and this amount was paid to your Treasurer....'

The urgent replacement of the 'longitudinal wooden sleepers' must have referred to the underlayer planking that spanned the primary wooden transoms, and not the transverse surface layer. Continual tar painting of the surface had obviously caused excessive saturation of the underlayer and its consequent rotting, a matter which the surveyor had not recognised as he continued with the coating process.

During the same year, the ironwork was completely painted at a cost of £150.

For some years the bridge remained in good condition except for the renewal of a few footpath battens touching up of paintwork, and the continuing tar painting of roadway deck.

Roadman Mr. Edward Roxburgh died in December 1929, and the engineer

Fig 104 - Winter in 1905; from a photograph album
(Miss D Somervail)

reported his death to the Chairman of the Trustees:

'Dear Sir Francis,

Mr. E. Roxburgh, who resided in the cottage at the Chain Bridge, Horncliffe, died last month and his widow has asked to be allowed to remain in the cottage. They have lived there so long that she knows what to do if anything happens and will report to my office at once. I think, in any case, she should be allowed to remain for twelve months until your new engineer takes office, when he may consider the whole question.

I believe you intend holding a meeting of the Tweed Bridges Trust Committee in the near future to consider the appointment of an engineer, and no doubt this question could be brought up then.

Yours faithfully,
(sgd.) J.A. Bean

Sir Francis Blake, Bart., C.B., D.L.,
Tillmouth Park, Cornhill on Tweed.'

This was also the year of Mr. J.A. Bean's retirement, and he was succeeded by Mr. Alex. Cheyne as engineer to the Tweed Bridges Trust.

Fig 105 - Union Chain Bridge, washing day at the Toll House circa 1930 (Jim Walker)

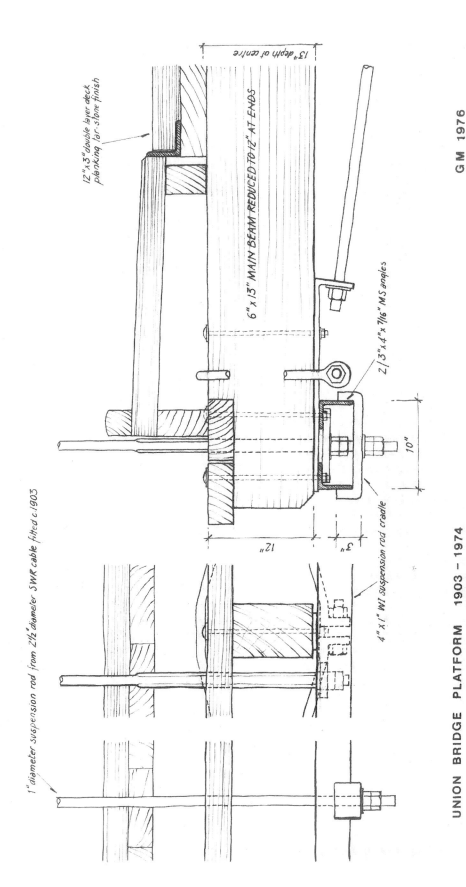

UNION BRIDGE PLATFORM 1903 – 1974

IN 1933 ALL PLATFORM TIMBERING WAS REPLACED AS EXISTING BUT WITH THE ORIGINAL SUSPENSION RODS AGAIN PASSED THROUGH THE MAIN BEAMS

GM 1976

Fig 106 - Detail: Union Chain Bridge platform 1903-1974

The bridge remained in good condition and was painted during the summer of 1930 at a cost of £77.8.0.

On December 12th 1930, the engineer reported:

> '…Mrs. Roxburgh vacated the cottage on the 6th September 1930, and T. Cockburn moved into the cottage on the 12th September 1930. This man is a roadman employed on the Northumberland County Roads, in the area and is in almost daily touch with the County Divisional Surveyor in the area.'

The spraying of the deck continued, and in 1932 'one of the main beams near the north end of the bridge is failing and it will be necessary to have it replaced...' This incident made the engineer take a closer look at main transoms, to discover that all were rotten. The outcome was reported to a Trustees Meeting on December 2nd 1933:

> 'It will be remembered that a special meeting of the Trustees was held on December 31st 1932, to consider a report by me on the serious condition of the cross beams of this bridge.
>
> Tenders were obtained for carrying out the necessary work of renewing the cross beams and that of Messrs. E. Henderson and Sons of Pentland, amounting to £767.16.10 was accepted. The actual cost of the work was £763.2.0 and whilst the contractors were on the site, I arranged for some repairs to be carried out to the towers at a cost of £18.14.0.
>
> The structure is now in good condition . . . '

The entire timber platform was therefore replaced, and although the work was contracted, a gang of roadmen employed by Northumberland County Council assisted, including the new cottage tenant, Mr. Cockburn. Mr. J. Turner of Horncliffe was among their number, and remembers the event as a 'very interesting job; it was a change from the usual work.' One of the gang took a photograph during the restoration, also one of Mrs Cockburn with baby Tom and friends at the entrance to Chain Bridge Cottage - both reproduced here.

Tom Cockburn remembers the cottage as being 'warm and comfortable' but his mother and father thought differently about the damp, which the engineer was trying to prevent and cure, the subject of which he reported to a Trustees' Meeting on December 1st 1934:

Fig 107 - Union Chain Bridge, Mrs Cockburn (wife of toll keeper) with baby and friends circa 1930

'This structure is in good condition. As requested I have examined the cottage at this bridge which belongs to the Trust and which is occupied by the caretaker named Cockburn, and have to report as follows -

The Cottage is built against the rock in the south side and consists of two rooms, a kitchen and a bed-living room, each about 12 feet square. Some six or seven years ago the walls of both rooms were stripped to the level of the window sills and replastered with Pudlo to resist dampness from the foundations. At the present time, there are no signs of dampness in the kitchen but in the other room, there is some dampness shewing above the partition treated with Pudlo, particularly on the west wall. A short down spout should be extended to a properly formed channel, to prevent splashing against the wall and this would probably prevent some of the dampness. The roof is in good order. The house is occupied by Cockburn, his wife and three children aged 15, 12 and 3 years, none of whom have, I understand required the services of a doctor since their arrival at the bridge cottage.

I have received an application from Mr. R.W. Cairns, the owner of the property adjoining the Bridge on the south west side, for permission to attach the stern-mooring rope of his boat to the Bridge. There does not appear to be any objection to the request and I recommend that permission be granted subject to Mr. Cairns paying an acknowledgment of 1/- per annum and agreeing to the following conditions:

That he will cease to tie his boat to the structure when called upon...'

The engineer's reference to 'services of a doctor' typified the contemporary relationship between good health and living conditions. Some repairs to the cottage were offered at a cost of £5.0.0, which 'considerably improved conditions.'

Nothing of consequence was now happening to the bridge, but the local Sanitary Authority became interested in the fact that the occupants of the toll house were 50 per cent in excess of that permitted, and that the building was sub-standard. The engineer's remarks about the occupants were not kind, but just how the family managed with 269 sq. ft. of usable floor space has to be imagined. At a Meeting of Trustees on December 5, 1936, the engineer reported:

Fig 108 - Union Chain Bridge, deck renewal 1934 Box Brownie Record taking by Mr J Turner (Top Right next to Mr T Cockburn, the Bridge cottage tenant)

'This structure is in good condition except that some of the paintwork requires touching up and I am arranging to have this done. It was last painted in 1930 and the paintwork has lasted very well.

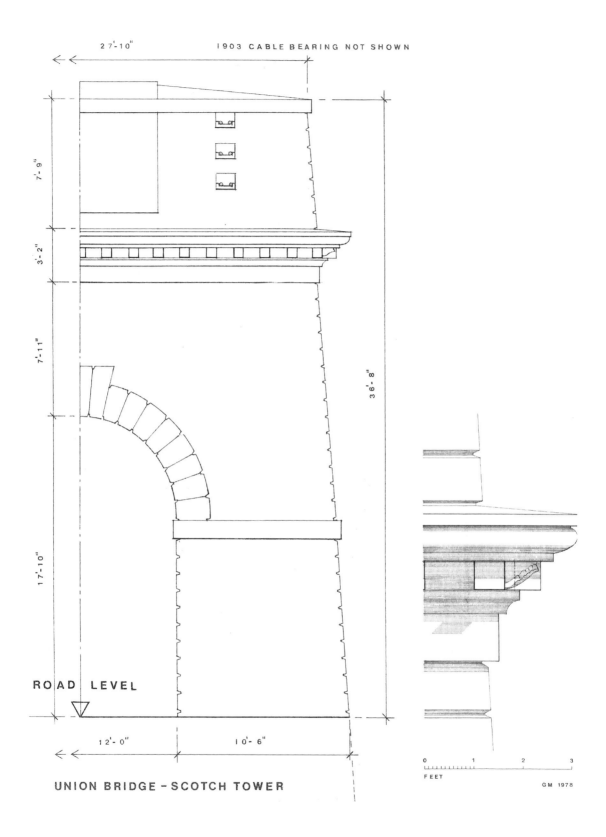

27'-10"   1903 CABLE BEARING NOT SHOWN

7'-9"

3'-2"

7'-11"

17'-10"

36'-8"

ROAD LEVEL

12'-0"   10'-6"

UNION BRIDGE - SCOTCH TOWER

0   1   2   3
FEET

GM 1978

Fig 109 - Drawing of Scottish Tower 1978, with detail

I received a notice dated the 24th August last from the Sanitary Inspector to the Norham and Islandshires Rural District Council under the Housing Acts 1925-35 stating that the house at the Union Chain Bridge was overcrowded, the number of occupants being 4½ adult units whilst the permitted number was 3.

I took the matter up and ascertained that as no rent was paid it would require special consideration.

I received a further notice dated the 15th November 1936 to the effect that the previous notice had been withdrawn and that the further notice would most likely fix the date as the 1st July next.

In a further letter I have received from the Sanitary Inspector, he states that its condition is below the required standard. The walls are damp, the floor is defective and the food store is not properly ventilated.

I am afraid that the present occupiers do not help matters and, in any case, I think it desirable that they be given notice to terminate their tenancy.

I think that the Trustees should visit the house as in my opinion it will be difficult to bring it up to modern standard without extensive alterations ...'

The cottage was becoming a real worry to the Engineer and the Trustees. They had to accept that the building was sub-standard and were exploring possibilities of re-housing the tenant, Mr. Cockburn, but without success. In December 1937 he reported the situation:

'No further notice with regard to the Bridge Cottage has been received from the Rural District Council and the tenant, Mr. Cockburn, is still in occupation. I approached Messrs W. J. Bolam & Son, the agents for Mrs. Allenby, with regard to the land adjoining the present bridge cottage on the east side, with a view to its acquisition for the purpose of erecting a new cottage, but Mrs. Allenby was not prepared to sell the site. It is desirable that, if a new cottage is to be built, that it should be erected as near as possible to the bridge.

There are no alternative sites near the Bridge on the south side and on the north side the bridge is approached by an embankment and the only suitable site is some distance from the bridge, unless a considerable amount of dead walling is provided to bring the floor level up to road level.'

Acquisition of a site for a new cottage was the only practical solution, but it was never to materialise, and Mr. Cockburn and his family continued in occupation, although he was being asked to find alternative accommodation.

The bridge continued to be trouble-free and remained in good condition, except for the cottage, which Mr. Cockburn had left by 1943, and damage through vandalism had started. Slates had been stripped off the roof, and replaced at a cost of £15.0.0., but the damage had revealed the roof timbers to be rotten, and the whole roof was in danger of collapse. Its renewal would have been costly and without any good reason, for the building was virtually condemned, and the Trustees had to accept that unless sanitary facilities and a water supply was to be provided, and the building made to resist damp, then all was lost. A sub-committee of Trustees met at the Bridge on Monday, February 14th 1944, and the engineer recorded:

'I was instructed to prepare plans for putting the cottage into habitable condition and I proceeded with the necessary drawings. It became apparent that no reconstruction of the cottage could be complete without a proper piped water supply.

In the past, the tenants have got their water for drinking and household purposes from a well in the garden at the south west corner of the bridge. This garden is owned by Mrs Cairns and whilst our tenants have always used the water from this well, I am not clear to what our legal rights are in this matter.

I ascertained that the owner of Chainbridge House, Mrs. J. Cairns, has an excellent source of water in her garden, and as this could be readily piped to the Cottage; I approached her to see if she would be prepared to let us take the overflow from her tank. She would not, however, agree to this.

I feel that it would not be advisable to spend a considerable sum of money on the Cottage without an adequate piped supply of water.

I submit a plan showing proposals for reconditioning and altering the cottage for your consideration...'

At the December 1944 Meeting of Trustees, the engineer presented a scheme for reparations but the ideas were deferred for the want of a water supply, and the engineer was instructed to approach Mrs. Jessie Cairns, the owner of Chain Bridge House "...to ascertain whether the Trustees might be permitted to take the surplus water therefrom..."

Another year passed by, and in December 1945 the engineer was again reporting about the matter:

'Since the last meeting, I have spent a considerable amount of time investigating the possibilities of providing a piped water supply to the cottage but so far, I have not found any source which is completely satisfactory. The possible sources are:

1. Well in garden to the south west of cottage
This was the source of supply for the cottage when occupied. It is on land belonging to Mrs Cairns, and the quantity was never fully adequate and the tenants of the cottage had, at times, to get some of their water elsewhere. It is not adequate to justify pumping to the cottage.

2. Surplus water from Chain Bridge House

Following the last meeting of the Trustees, Mr. Fleming and I had an interview with Mrs Cairns at which she again refused to allow us to take the surplus water. Later, however, she wrote to me stating she wished to help and at another interview, I ascertained that at periods there was barely sufficient water for her own purposes. There does not seem to be much purpose in pursuing this matter further.

3. Water supply to Horncliffe House and other properties

A supply of water to Horncliffe House and other properties is rammed from an abundant sourcenear Horncliffe Mill. The nearest point that the supply main comes to the Bridge Cottage is Bank Head Cottage, about 400 yards away. This is a private supply and is the subject of an agreement between a number of owners who share the cost of maintenance in varying proportions. To share this water supply would involve lengthy negotiations and perhaps a not very satisfactory agreement in the end.

4. Public Supply to Horncliffe Village

This would involve laying a supply pipe along the Highway from the Village to the Bridge Cottage, a distance of 1500 yards (approx.)

I have made enquiries from the Land Agents to adjoining properties but have not heard of any source which would be available...'

During the 1939-45 War it had been the practice to 'patch paint' the ironwork and generally make good woodwork, but at the end of 1946 the engineer reported to the Trustees '...the time has arrived when the whole structure should be properly cleaned down and painted, at least two coats where necessary. It may be difficult to obtain tenders for this work, but the work should be done by direct labour if necessary.'

The importance of Chain Bridge and the road network it served was on the downgrade, and the engineer continued:

'I have to report that the Ministry of Transport have classified the Union Chain Bridge approach roads as Class III Roads, and the expenditure upon Bridge and Road works will call for a 50 per cent Grant...'

Although the road was no longer regarded as vital, possible grant aid was a good omen for the bridge. In 1948 the engineer became concerned about the weight of traffic using the bridge and a special Meeting of Trustees was called to deal with the matter:

'...the Trustees, having regard to the fact that they themselves are not a highway authority under the Road Traffic Act 1930, resolved that the County Councils of Northumberland and Berwick respectively be requested to make orders under S.47 of the said Act, that the use of such parts of the road over the Union Chain Bridge as are respectively situated in Northumberland and Berwickshire be restricted to vehicles the weight of which, whether laden or unladen, does not exceed two tons from and after the earliest possible dates to be fixed by the respective County Councils....'

Plans were produced at this same meeting for the reconstruction of the Toll House but their consideration was deferred until the Annual Meeting.

The 'Surveyor's worries had been intensified because of an increase in traffic that resulted from the destruction of the Whiteadder Bridge in August 1948 floods. Union Bridge itself only just survived, for the Tweed rose to within touching distance of the platform and the scene after many days of torrential rain was aptly described in the *Berwick Advertiser* on August 10th:

> '...As dawn broke with a blink of sunshine on Friday morning over the stricken areas, the scenes of devastation surpassed anything in living memory. Great tracts of land were completely inundated. In places only the chimneys of houses were seen above the rooftops.'

Fig 110 - Union Chain Bridge, Aug 1948; River Tweed in flood

Mr. James Scott of Chain Bridge House well remembers the event when brother and sister, 86 year old James Gilchrist and 80 year old Mrs. Rogerson, were marooned in the Boat House and refused to leave. Eventually, when they had been forced to take to the roof through the attic windows, Mr. Scott and others rescued them with ladders. Across the river at the Shiel, fishermen managed to secure all their gear, and hauled their boats high up the bank, and people spent anxious moments fending off trees that tended to become entangled in the platform understructure.

The proposed bridge painting was deferred, but because of the Surveyor's concern about excessively heavy traffic, he started two men working on patch painting, with the secondary task, and possibly most important, of checking and controlling vehicles. This unofficial system of control was necessary because the order under the Road Traffic Act, imposing a weight restriction, became effective from March 10th 1950, after which two persons were prosecuted and fines of £5 and £1 imposed.

The water subsided, the bridge survived another threat to its somewhat charmed existence, and in 1949 the bridge cottage and bridge strength became important issues. At a Meeting of the Trustees on February 12th the Surveyor reported his findings about the cottage reconditioning, with the proviso that everything depended upon an adequate main supply, but he made no progress. The new owner of Chain Bridge House, Mr. Scott, had agreed that the cottage could be supplied from his tank overflow, but investigation by a plumber confirmed the previous owner's view that the supply was inadequate for the House, let alone the cottage. Because it was also impractical to draw water from a nearby well owing to the lack of electricity supply, the Surveyor had decided against proceeding with the cottage restoration plans. The services of a water diviner had been suggested, and dismissed on the grounds that such tactics were 'a somewhat speculative matter.'

The Surveyor had put forward his views about the strength of the bridge. It was a familiar story that reflected back to 1902, when the Surveyor of the time was not unreasonably fighting shy of responsibility for the safety of the bridge. Now, with another forty seven years of bridge life, the surveyor carefully spelled out the situation:

'I have given consideration to the proposal that the Ministry of Transport should be approached with a view to the above bridge being strengthened to take the normal weight of traffic of the district, and have the following observations to make:

1. I have made a careful inspection of the structure of the existing bridge, and am satisfied that the present weight limit of two tons should not be exceeded.

The strength of the old chains is theoretically indeterminate, as the exact composition of the metal is not known, nor is it known what structural changes may have taken place by reason of its age and the stresses to which it has been subject in its long life.

Further, many of the joints have corroded to the extent that they are completely solid. The steel cables which were put up in 1903 are rather more determinate, but even with them, a certain amount of straining and fixity has occurred, particularly where the cables pass over the saddles.

It is also well nigh impossible to ascertain what exact division of the load there is, between the chains and cables.

2. In view of the last consideration, any strengthening works would involve the complete scrapping of the existing cables and chains, and also the decking. The latter is already light for the present load limit.

3. If strengthening works were undertaken, practically the only part of the existing structure which could be retained would be the tower at the northern end. The anchorages would have to be removed to provide for new anchorages for new cables.

4. If a completely new structure has to be provided then I consider that it should be constructed to take Ministry of Transport Standard loading. The difference in cost would not be great between that and a bridge to take a weight up to 10 tons load units and I am confident the Ministry would not agree to anything below their standard.The question also arises as to whether a new bridge should not be on a new site.

5. It is difficult to give a reliable estimate without preparing full details, but a bridge designed for standard loading and making use of the present tower, would not cost less than £70,000.

6. Under present financial restrictions, there does not appear to be any likelihood of the Ministry being prepared to give a Grant towards the work. The road is classified as a Class III road, so any grant would be on a 50 per cent basis.

7. The Highway Committees of the two County Councils have supported the proposal to strengthen the bridge, but I feel that I should point out that in Northumberland, we already have on the waiting list, a number of bridges for strengthening and reconstruction, which would have a much higher priority than the Union Chain Bridge.

8. I submit a map of the area on which I have indicated the roads within a radius of six miles of the Union Chain Bridge.

I think it can be assumed that heavy traffic, whose origin and destination is beyond this limit would not have any real necessity to use the Union Chain Bridge as its needs could be equally well met by the Berwick and Norham Bridges. Berwick Bridge is 4 miles in direct line from the Union Chain Bridge, and Norham Bridge 3½ miles.

I consider that even if the Union Chain Bridge were strengthened, it would only serve a very limited number of heavy vehicles. The existing bridge serves pedestrians, cyclists, cars and light tradesmen's vans, which I think would be 75 per cent of all traffic using a standard bridge.

9. The Divisional Road Engineer of the Ministry of Transport and the Chief Bridge Engineer of the Ministry have inspected the Bridge when they were in the area recently so they are familiar with the conditions should an approach be made to the Ministry.

10. A full investigation will be made by the Ministry into the strength of the existing bridge, in connection with the Order under Section 46 of the Road Traffic Act, 1930, restricting the use of the bridge to vehicles weighing not more than two tons...'

One of the Surveyor's last records about the bridge at the end of 1950, before he retired in 1951, was ominous:

'...I felt a little concern at the movement which is taking place between the deck timbers which seem to indicate excessive weight and excessive speed of vehicles some of the decking timbers are showing signs of deterioration and I am arranging to replace about half a dozen. I am hopeful that this does not indicate a general deterioration...'

Constant troubles with the cottage and general unsuitability as a dwelling house sealed its fate. It had been vacated and was being damaged, and demolition seemed to be the only sensible solution; but as part of a building listed as a structure of historical and architectural interest, difficulties were encountered in obtaining the necessary planning consent. The general idea of the Trust was that the Northumberland County Council should demolish the cottage in return for the materials, but the situation was not so simple, as reported by the surveyor in December, 1952:

'. ...it was found that the rock face behind the cottage was in a very unsightly condition, with steel props inserted to support the rock face. The alternatives appear to be to demolish the cottage and build a masonry facing to the rock, or to leave the cottage standing, build up the doors and windows and remove the brick chimney and outbuildings.

The estimated costs are:
Demolish cottage and provide facing to the rock   £600. 0. 0.
Build up doors and windows, remove the brick chimney
and outbuildings   £160. 0. 0...'

These costs were favourable towards the cottage being retained, but unfortunately the portico was struck and damaged by a vehicle of some sort that cracked one pillar and the lintel. As the portico was an essential cottage feature, its demolition and reconstruction reversed the order of costs which the surveyor put forward on December 10th 1953:

'...1. Build up doors and windows, remove brick chimney and out-buildings, take down portico and make good, underpinning rock face at back of building and encasing steel props in concrete   £350. 0. 0.

2. As above but rebuilding portico in its present form   £430. 0. 0.

3. Demolish building, using removed stone to provide
masonry faced concrete wall at back of site, level up
floor with concrete, widen carriageway with kerb and
refix name plate on front of new wall   £630. 0. 0.'

This last proposal was accepted, and it only remained for the design of the anchorage pier rock face to be agreed by the Northumberland County Council and the Ministry of Housing and local Government. The Surveyor prepared and presented a scheme to the Trust in December, 1953,

showing the cottage as existing: cottage with portico removed, door and windows walled up and cottage demolished and forecourt provided. The three illustrations arranged side by side on a single sheet substantiated the architectural strength of the cottage, and the weakness of the two alternatives, in particular the chosen scheme. However, an amendment was later suggested which incorporated the form of doorway portico as a bass relief, and this was agreed by all concerned.

It is to be regretted that neither Trustees nor authorities valued the cottage as an essential element in the bridge design. Something obviously had to be done to overcome the continuing damage, but it would have been possible to blank up the windows and door and provide a concrete flat roof, and thereby keep the original structure complete, but this was not to be, and the demolition and changes were completed during 1955.

On January 31st 1953 the bridge nearly suffered the fate of most of its contemporaries, which 'whistled, oscillated and tore themselves apart from the effects of the wind...' The 'severe gale' during that day and night caused the bridge to heave and sway, and fortunately, the damage only amounted to a repair sum of £155. 0. 0. By good fortune the bridge survived, and many local people remember its 'dynamic antics'.

Fig 111 - (Top Left) Union Chain Bridge, toll cottage before demolition 1955

Fig 112 - (Top Right) Union Chain Bridge, toll cottage before demolition 1955

Fig 113 - (Left) Union Chain Bridge, exposed rock face following toll cottage demolition 1955

Fig 114 - (Above) Union Chain Bridge, re-facing exposed rock face 1955

At the November 1955 Trustees' Meeting, the Surveyor considered the bridge to be in a fair condition. The approach roads on both sides of the bridge and the upper part of the south anchorage were cleaned and pointed and the openings for the cables at the top of the tower on the Scottish side were covered with a wooden framework and the masonry slabs replaced by concrete because of weathering. Although the Surveyor said nothing at the Meeting to arouse anxiety, members questioned the future policy to be adopted in relation to the bridge and asked the Surveyor, Mr G. F. Garnett, to report at the next annual Meeting in December 1956, and this he duly made:

'... The distance between Berwick and Coldstream, measured along the Berwick-Cornhill road, A698, is 14 miles and the following table shows the various crossings of the River Tweed and the estimated volume of traffic using these crossings:

Miles	Crossing	Estimated average number of vehicles per day	Road Classn
0	Royal Tweed Bridge	2500	Trunk
5	Union Chain Bridge	50	'C'
9	Norham Bridge	150	'B'
14	Coldstream Bridge	1700	'A'

The next crossing is at Kelso, 9 miles to the west of Coldstream.

The general main road pattern of the area shows the roads running very roughly east-west, parallel with the River Tweed and radiating from Berwick, with the two main north-south routes, A1 and A697, crossing the River at Berwick and Coldstream. There is, therefore, no real potential for cross-river traffic at points between Berwick and Coldstream, any crossing between these places serving only very strictly localised needs.

This is borne out by the very small amount of traffic which uses the Norham and Union Chain Bridges and with this small volume of traffic I consider that it would be very difficult to justify the expense of a completely new road bridge between Coldstream or Berwick or between Norham and Berwick and I take it that such a project would only be contemplated if a Government grant was made towards the cost.

The Royal Tweed Bridge was opened in 1928 and it now forms part of the Trunk Road, A.1, for which the Minister of Transport is the highway authority. If the Ministry were to be contemplating such a crossing today I have no doubt they would at least give consideration to the possibility of avoiding Berwick and the obstruction caused by the Scots Gate and I think that if a proposal for a new road bridge was put forward it would have to provide a convenient by-pass to Berwick if it was to be considered for Government grant and the approaches to such a bridge would involve the authorities on each side of the river.

At present the Union Chain Bridge is restricted to vehicles of under 2 tons weight and with careful maintenance it should last for a considerable time. The main maintenance costs would be regular painting and the renewal of the decking and any partial failure of the chains or anchorages could be repaired without unduly straining the financial resources of the Trust.

If the danger of a complete failure arose then the Trustees would have to consider:

(a) The abandonment of a crossing at this point
(b) The building of a new bridge on a different site
(c) The rebuilding on the present site.

(a) The total abandonment of a crossing would no doubt be strongly opposed by local interests as it would involve the use of either Norham or Berwick.

(b) The building of a new bridge on a different site would depend on the attitude of the Ministry of Transport to a new crossing of the Tweed and would also involve approach roads.

(c) The rebuilding on the present site could be contemplated if it was decided that a crossing for only very local interests should be maintained.

The very approximate estimated costs of (b) and (c) are:-

(b) A new bridge on a new site	£250,000
(c) Rebuilding the bridge on the existing site	£85,000

The approach to the Union Chain Bridge on the English side would not be satisfactory if the Bridge was to be considered as a principal traffic route, but would be adequate for the small volume of local traffic. In any rebuilding, the existing towers could be retained but adequate strength and stiffening could be provided to take all commercial vehicles and it is on that basis that the estimate has been made.'

In relative terms the use of Union Bridge was small, but to local people it was a vital artery. The surveyor was taking the pessimistic view that the bridge was nearing the end of its days, and that a new bridge would be difficult to justify. He made the point to the Trustees that if they wished to pursue the subject it would be necessary for them to discuss the matter with the Ministry of Transport and obtain their views about the possibility of any new bridge being considered as a diversion of the Trunk Road A1, at Berwick. This possibility was of considerable importance, for the building of the bridge at Berwick in 1928 penetrated the town within the Elizabethan Walls and has always been regarded as idiotic. The size and volume of traffic now carried by this bridge, and its effect on Berwick, was now proving a threat to the town, and the question of a new bridge and possible re-routing of the A1 (T) was now in planners' minds, and if such a decision was made, then large investments in prolonging the life of Union Bridge would be questionable, but fortunately nothing was decided. The usual items of maintenance continued to be done until a routine inspection revealed serious deterioration of the steel angles that support the road deck platform, which prompted the surveyor to make a detailed inspection of the entire bridge in March, 1973.

'A very handsome suspension bridge, executed by Captain Samuel Brown of the Royal Navy, here connects England and Scotland, and at some distance below, the Tweed receives the Whiteadder as its tributary from the left bank.'

Scottish Rivers
Sir Thomas Dick-Lauder, Bart.
of Fountainhall   1890.

Fig 115 - Union Chain Bridge, view from English side tower in 1974 before platform restoration

The Surveyor's report was presented to the Trustees on November 28th 1973, and contained unwelcome information:

'The investigation into the condition of the lower timbers and supports for the bridge deck, maintained in the last Report, was carried out in March, 1973, and disclosed extensive and severe corrosion to the steel angles which are the essential connection between the vertical hangers and the bridge deck. Emergency repairs were immediately carried out to the worst of these members, but these are of a temporary nature and I conclude as an Appendix to this Report a <u>detailed</u> report on the Condition of the Union Chain Bridge, together with proposals for repair. These repairs are of a major nature, estimated to cost £30,000 and would involve closure of the structure for approximately six months...'

The Surveyor's detailed report confirmed that the deck supporting angles at every suspension point were severely corroded, and that removal of the suspension rod nuts was impossible. A repair scheme that avoided removal of the nuts was therefore proposed:

'(a) Repairs
The following members of the bridge require renewal

(i)   All four longitudinal steel angles
(ii) All lateral deck timbers
(iii) At least half of the longitudinal deck timbers
(iv) Possibly some of the cross bearing timbers (until the deck timbers are removed it is impossible to determine the state of these beams). Superficial inspection does, however, suggest that the majority are satisfactory.

Fig 116 - Union Chain Bridge,
platform and decking before restoration 1974

Fig 117 - Union Chain Bridge,
decking before restoration 1974

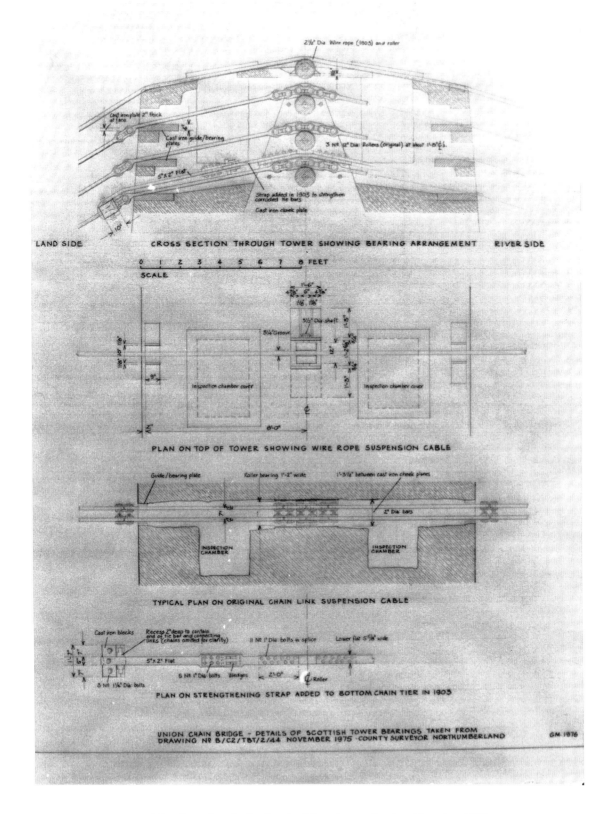

Fig 118 - Union Chain Bridge, Details of Scottish tower bearings November 1975

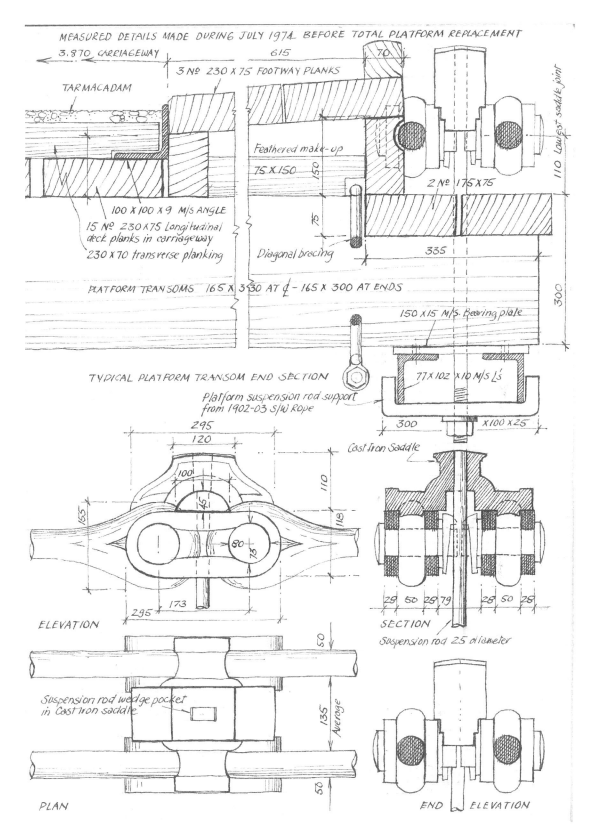

MEASURED DETAILS MADE DURING JULY 1974 BEFORE TOTAL PLATFORM REPLACEMENT

3.870 CARRIAGEWAY

615

70

TARMACADAM

3 N⁰ 230 X 75 FOOTWAY PLANKS

Feathered make-up
75 X 150

150

75

2 N⁰ 175 X 75

110 Lowest saddle joint

335

300

100 X 100 X 9 M/S ANGLE
15 N⁰ 230 X 75 Longitudinal deck planks in carriageway
230 X 70 transverse planking

Diagonal bracing

PLATFORM TRANSOMS   165 X 330 AT ℄ - 165 X 300 AT ENDS

150 X 15 M/S. Bearing plate

TYPICAL PLATFORM TRANSOM END SECTION

Platform suspension rod support
from 1902-03 S/W Rope

77 X 102 X 10 M/S L's

300   X 100 X 25

295

120

Cast Iron Saddle

100

45

110

118

155

80

73

173

295

ELEVATION

SECTION

28 50 28 79   28 50 28

Suspension rod 25 diameter

50

Suspension rod wedge pocket
in Cast Iron saddle

135 Average

PLAN

50

END   ELEVATION

Fig 119 - Union Chain Bridge, drawings of measured details made July 1974

(b) New Work

In the past the only method which could be found to provide a non-skid, light-weight-wearing surface has been a thin coat of tarred stone, but because of the inherent flexibility of the structure, this has proved difficult to maintain, irregular and unsightly. It is proposed, therefore, to surface the deck with a form of epoxy resin type anti-skid surface, supplied by Acme Flooring Ltd., as resin bonded plywood panels'

The Surveyor concluded that the extensive nature of the proposed works would require complete possession of the bridge for not less than 24 weeks.

Work started on Tuesday May 28th 1974, and preliminary dismantling revealed the need for more extensive repairs than had been anticipated. The main cross beams were found to be rotten and their entire replacement recommended. The suspension rods that had been provided in the 1902-3 reconstructions were found to be severely corroded where they pass through deck timbers, and this meant their removal, cutting off the corroded end and re-positioning on the cable to allow for their reduced length.

Because of everyone's concern, a special meeting of the Tweed Bridges Trust was held at the bridge on June 19th 1974, when members could see for themselves the extent of deterioration not previously revealed or possible to foresee. Costs of materials were also increasing, and the surveyor presented an additional account the amount of which was within the agreed contingency sum of £5,000.

"Additional steelwork costs £2,000
Increase in timber prices 1,000
Inceased cost of 'Acme' surface panels.....................1,290
Enforced charge of scaffolding contractor..................210

Total £4,500

In addition to which, the extra work is estimated as follows:

Main beam timbers £3,500
Repairs to 1902 hangers 750
End walls and expansion joints 1,250

Total £5,500

Considerable expertise, skill and care was exercised by both engineers and workmen in the deck restorations and the work was completed at the end of 1974. During the course of the work, opportunity was taken to release a number of the original suspension rods and saddle from their chain link connections. Although deterioration at these points was expected, the surveyor reported:

" ...This deterioration gives no cause for immediate concern, but it will be necessary to renew the defective washers and links during the course of the next few years and, while the joints are dismantled, the opportunity of cleaning and galvanising all the other parts should be taken".

The tower and rock anchorages were not forgotten.

"Some of the stonework is seriously weathered and the present condition of the pointing and growth of vegetation can only hasten deterioration. The method of protecting the chains and cable bearing saddles is not satisfactory and since it is impossible to carry out routine inspections and painting without completely dismantling and replacing the protective covering it is recommended that these coverings be replaced by properly constructed concrete chambers and steel covers."

'The Surveyor told the Trustees that a further expenditure of £40,000 was required for maintenance of the Bridge and '...even though spread over seven years', questioned whether the structure was 'worthy of preservation'. He outlined the pros and cons and mentioned that the June 1972 census showed an average of 307 vehicles a day using the bridge and the historically important fact that "... it should be borne in mind that the bridge is unique. As far as I am aware it is the only chain suspension bridge remaining in the United Kingdom that carries a public highway used by road vehicles and it is also the first of this type of bridge ever to be constructed'

The 1972 Union Bridge vehicle use figures of 307 a day was a considerable increase over the 1956 estimate of 50 vehicles a day, and which obviously reflected the national increase in road traffic.

The surveyor presented a long term maintenance programme to the Trustees which, if implemented, would extend the bridge life by 50 years, apart from routine maintenance, now costing £40 per year.

The recommended programme and costs was given as follows:

Year		Estimated Costs	

English Abutment

1975-76		Item £	Annual £
Renew bearing arrangements, and provide lateral restraint and repair abutment stonework.			
Regrade approach road		4,000	
Make good repair and paint prospects		2,000	
Residual expenditure from 1974-75		2,000	8,000

1976-77   None

1977-78   None

	Item £	Annual £
Anchorage		
Provide sealed chambers, inspect paint	2,500	
Clean and point all masonry	5,000	7,500

N.B. These operations should be done concurrently to economise on scaffolding costs

1978-79 None

1979-80
Remove, clean and galvanise saddles and
Hangers, renew defective links and washers 17,500 17,500

1980-81 None

1981-82
Maintenance painting 7.500 7,500

TOTAL **£40,000**

Even for 1974, a cost of £40,000 to cope with forseeable reparations was a high figure, and although grants were possible through the Ancient Monuments Secretariat, it was doubtful if a very great percentage could be obtained.

The climate for securing grant aid is never ripe, particularly in a situation of increasing need to deal with an expanding list of works and worsening economy.

The total costs expended on Union Bridge during 1974-75 amounted to £37,000 plus £5,000. This sum, together with the forecast requirements totaled £82,000, which was a sobering thought in relation to the importance of the bridge in the roadwork pattern, but its very unique position in civil engineering warranted high priority.

During the investigation made in the Autumn of 1973, the County Surveyor made a detailed measured survey of the bridge platform, including its levels and those of the catenary chains at points of suspension. The curve shape of both chains and platform proved to be irregular and unrelated, and during the reconstruction, necessary adjustments were made to correct the shape, including the 1903 steel wire rope cable. The centre of platform span was raised to produce a level difference of 0.337m with the Scottish pier road level, and a difference of 0.186m with the English end road level. This increased longitudinal fall was considered essential to improve surface water drainage, and an additional feature being the provision of 1½" diameter polypropylene drain tubes, 2' - 4" in length, located at the carriageway edge at 3" centres off the curb face; 14 in number at each side, spaced equally.

Because the threaded tails of suspension rods attached to the steel wire rope cable were found to be almost corroded through, their entire thickness, it either meant their replacement, or moving the connection point of rods down the cable slope to gain length and allow new threads to be cut; and this method was adopted. Visually the resulting irregular bar spacing is not very evident, and the method was an economic way of overcoming the problem.

Another design change was the method of engaging the 1903 suspension rods to the pairs of ledger angles. Originally they passed through the centre of 4" x 1" bars with 3" upstand ends, and washer and nut that locked around the downstanding ends of the ledger angles. The replacement was simply a 3" x 7/8" section plate, attached to the rod as before; bolt located between the downstand ledger flanges.

All the existing 4" x 3" x 3/8" ledger angles were replaced by 5" x 3" x ½" angle sections with plated splice and bolted connections.

Suspension hangers were now positioned to provide a one inch space between their face and transoms, except the single case of the Scottish end transom where hangers passed through the centre. At the English end an articulated deck flap, or hinged section 5'0" in length was provided to take up the deflection created when vehicles moved on or off the bridge, which resulted from the suspended platform ending while the chain cables continued for another 65' to their point of contact with the abutment pier. In September 1975 the road approach was lowered in relation to the hinged joint sections and now provided a level situation before loading.

All the platform timber was also renewed, and the opportunity was taken to modify transom shape. They became 13" x 6" in sections for their whole length, without camber, and the previous sinking at transom ends to accommodate a continuous riband of 12" x 3" overall sections, was sensibly abandoned.

The general form of the new decking remained the same as before, but considerably improved in detail. Primary

Figs 120 to 123 - Union Chain Bridge, platform and decking during 1974 reconstruction

SAMUEL BROWN AND UNION CHAIN BRIDGE

Fig 124 & 125 - Union Chain Bridge, English tower – reinforcement of original chains

Fig 126 - Union Chain Bridge, English tower –
View of linkage inside tower chamber

Fig 127 - Union Chain Bridge, English side pier cable
showing bar and clamp reinforcement 1974

Fig 128 - Union Chain Bridge, view towards Paxton during platform reconstruction 1974

longitudinal timbering consisted of 9" x 3" deals with 1½" gaps between. Of the fifteen members that make up the width, the four outer planks are twenty feet in length; thereby spanning over four transom spaces, and the seven inner deals vary between ten and fifteen feet in length, and all fixed with ½" x 6" coach screws with their heads recessed half an inch. Transverse planking is 9" x 1⅞", butt jointed and secured with 3/8" and 4" coach screws, also recessed head.

At long last, the tar and former asphalt surfacing was rejected in favour of a compound ply and resin finish. One inch thick, 'Acme' Anti-skid Plyboard Panels with a surface of bauxite chippings in epoxy resin, set in hot rubberised bitumen and attached with 3" x 18g countersunk wood screws, was the practical surfacing that proved both durable and protective to its substructure.

The footpath, each side of the bridge, was raised as previously; structurally simplified, yet giving greater platform stiffness. A 9" x 6" kerb member was fixed to transoms with mild steel cleats, and plate splice jointed in the respective continuous length. Arranged level with the kerb top, footpath decking consisted of 9" x 3" planks spiked transversely to longitudinal bearers that raised the level, 6¾" x 3" on the outside and 6" x 3" - 4" on the inside, with a 3" x 3" toeboard at the outer extremity. Bearers were likewise secured with mild steel angle cleats, screw fixed.

Running continuously under the centre line of transoms, the earlier 12" x 6" deal was replaced, and all related bracing ironwork cleaned, galvanised and re-fixed.

Diagonal bracing, that intertwines between transoms, was also treated and returned to its original position.

A number of details from the Surveyor's drawings are illustrated, as they tell the story more clearly, and also show the care to detail that was exercised in this phase of restoration.

Fig 129 - Bronze plaque affixed to English side pier wall

Fig 130 - Union Chain Bridge, view towards the Scottish side following platform reconstruction 1974

The Chainworks of Brown Lenox

Stephen K. Jones

Although established as Samuel Brown & Co., the company name of the chainworks soon changed to reflect the important input made by Samuel Lenox, continuing as Brown Lenox through variations of Brown, Lenox & Co., and Brown & Lenox. A multi-stranded business story, it covered the development of iron chain cables, the early suspension bridge and more, and figuring strongly in the industrial history of south Wales and beyond. First and foremost it was a commercial undertaking, led by Samuel Brown and his Welsh born smith and works manager; Philip Thomas, to manufacture iron chains for the anchoring, mooring and even rigging of ships. It would lead to the establishment of purpose built chainworks at Millwall and Pontypridd, the latter works being the source of round eye bar suspension chains for Brown's chainbridges. The early phase of the story of Brown and Thomas perfecting the correct manufacturing techniques and chain cable shape has already been covered and this chapter is a brief attempt to examine the two chainworks, in particular Pontypridd, otherwise known as the Newbridge or Ynysangharad chainworks. To avoid confusion with the Monmouthshire town of Newbridge, Pontypridd was officially adopted in 1856 as the place name, originating from the description of William Edwards's famous bridge across the Taff here; the 'Pont y ty pridd'.

To briefly recap this story, Samuel Brown had joined the navy as an able-bodied seaman on *HMS Assistance* at the age of nineteen and worked his way up to acting lieutenant. He served with distinction during the Napoleonic wars and on return to peaceful waters, turned his mind to improving the efficiency of the Royal Navy taking rigging and mooring cables as a starting point. The Royal Navy had begun to dominate the high seas as the greatest naval power in the world from 1774 with 'wooden-wall' sailing ships which, apart from improved hull designs, were based on technology little changed for centuries, 1774 was also the year that Samuel Brown was born. Clear British naval dominance however dates from 1759 with the success blockade of the French fleets at Toulon and Brest, followed by decisive victories over these fleets at the battles of Lagos and Quiberon Bay. The French navy was powerless to prevent the loss of their colonies of New France (Quebec) and Guadeloupe, the latter figuring in Samuel Brown's 'proving' expeditions for his chain cable. By 1799 Samuel Brown had was making a name for himself in terms of his naval career, in 1796 he was Midshipman of *HMS Assistance* at the capture of the French frigate *Elizabet*.

Commissioned in 1800 he served as lieutenant on *HMS Royal Sovereign* in 1803 and in 1805, as first lieutenant, he was present on *HMS Phoenix* during her action with and in the capture of the *Didon*. The following year Brown was appointed to *HMS Imperieuse* and this was followed by service aboard the *HMS Flore* and *HMS Ulysses*, during this time he began testing wrought iron chains, using them as rigging and cable for a vessel of 400 tons; the *Penelope*, on a voyage to Martinique and Guadeloupe in 1806 which returned four months later to London. To this end he had spent several months developing his ideas, shut away in two rooms in a house in Dove Court,

Lombard Street, London. His first chain cable was made up of twisted wrought iron links and he engaged smiths based in Narrow Street, Ratcliffe, and in the Borough near Waterloo Bridge, to manufacture it. In need of further capital, he turned to his cousin Samuel Lenox and enlisted his financial aid. Brown and Lenox formed a partnership in 1808, trading under the name of Samuel Brown & Co. A successful merchant, Lenox provided a stable financial basis on which to build up a thriving chain cable and anchor manufacturing business. In 1808 Brown took out patents for twisted open chain links, joining shackles and swivels. The trial voyage prompted the Admiralty to equip four vessels of war with chain cables.

The year 1808 marks a significant turning point in the replacement of chain cable and also the emergence of a competitor's wrought iron chain cable used on the 221 ton ship; *Anne and Isabella*. Built at Berwick-upon-Tweed, the ship carried a chain cable made by Robert Flinn of North Shields using, it was reported, rectangular Welsh iron. Flinn set up his works on the Tyne with Brunton and Brown's first chainworks being centred on London. Within a few years chain cable manufactories and associated testing machines had spread to most ports and dockyards in the country. Flinn's voyage was a success but the development and promotion of chain cable was to be dominated by Samuel Brown who was by no means the first in this field, indeed, the first recorded patent for chain cable was taken out by Phillip White, a Northumbrian blacksmith, in 1634 whilst another smith, listed as a whitesmith, would take out a patent in 1791, Colin Mackenzie of Oxford Market, Marylebone, London, patented a new design of link; 'for a chain and a certain way and method of making a chain of such links by uniting the same and which may be used as a mooring chain, ship cable...'

The reason for the delay in producing chain cable was the difficulty of obtaining iron in sufficient quality and quantity. It was not until the iron industry could meet this demand by technological improvement that iron cable could replace the traditional means of mooring ships. Hempen cables, which for a ship like Nelson's *Victory*, required as many as eleven cables of up to 20 inches in diameter each which had a short life due to its alternate wet and dry state, providing an ideal medium for fungal and bacterial growth. It was vulnerable to the cutting action of rocks, ice and enemy action. It also took up valuable space on ship, having to be stored in cable tiers by the most able men on board so that it could be run out quickly without jamming. It is likely that Brown was well versed in this activity during his naval career. Getting a cautious Admiralty to try out iron chain cables was no easy task in spite of the overwhelming superiority of chain cables giving increased security and cable life,

Fig 131 - Brown established his first purpose-built chainworks at Millwall on the Thames. It was still manufacturing marine-related products such as buoys when the photograph was taken in 1977 but would close in the early 1980s. (SKJ photograph)

their storage in lockers gave a space saving of almost 50% over hempen cable. The cost of chain cable was only slightly more than hemp, making it extremely competitive through its longevity. Disadvantages included the difficulty with handling chain in deep water and the need to reinforce the ships' hawse-holes and riding-bits.

In his proposition to the Navy and as a practical demonstration; Brown chartered the *Penelope*, a 400-ton sailing vessel, and at his own expense, fitted it out with chain cable for both mooring and rigging cables. Brown then captained the *Penelope* on a four-month voyage to Martinique and Guadaloupe in the West Indies. This voyage was a complete success as regards proving the merits of chain cable, and a favourable naval report induced the government to order the re-equipping of four warships with iron chain cable. Brown's main competitor; Brunton, Middleton and Co., had also recognised the value of such voyages for promoting their chain cables. By 1811 chain cables were in general use on His Majesty's ships with one cable to each ship but in the same year a number of failures on naval vessels caused the Navy Board to temporarily suspend the adoption of chain cable. Probably because of the full complement of hempen cable would still be carried, indeed, some thirty-six years later ships of the line were still carrying two hempen cables in addition to their complement of four chain cables. By 1840 the superiority of iron chain cables was beyond dispute and commonplace for all maritime uses and hempen cables were completely replaced.

Brown had been promoted to master and commander in recognition of his work, and the patents were an important factor in being sole supplier of chain cables to the Navy. With regular naval contracts assured and merchant fleet orders coming in, Brown was pressed to look for a site to establish a purpose-built chain works. A suitable site was found in 1812/3, at Millwall on the Thames, convenient to Deptford Naval yard and within easy reach of the India and London docks. By 1823 a co-partnership was agreed between Samuel Brown of Billiter Square, City of London, Captain in the Royal Navy; Samuel Lenox of Billiter Square, London, and of Plaistow (co. Essex), merchant; James Thomas Walker of Bethnal Green, gent.; and George William Lenox of Millwall (co. Middx.), gent.; 'who agreed to manufacture and sell iron chain cables and anchors, under the firm of 'Samuel Brown and Company', for nine years. The proportion of profits shared by the partners being 3:3:1:1. There was however, a change of name shortly afterwards to Brown, Lenox & Co.

With regular naval contracts coming in, and the Millwall works now fully engaged, Brown decided on a second manufactory at Newbridge. Brown had considered establishing a chainworks in every principal port but eventually settled on building his second purpose-built chainworks at Newbridge to be closer to his main source of iron. Between 1788 and 1815, Britain's bar iron output rose from 32,000 tons to 150,000 tons, while pig iron output rocketed from just under 70,000 to 390,000. The demand created by orders from the Board of Ordnance was to create enough work to keep ironworks, such as the Cyfarthfa ironworks of Merthyr Tydfil, operating at maximum output throughout the wartime period. Merthyr Tydfil rose as the leading industrial centre of its kind, making it well-placed to meet engineering demands for structural iron. Iron chain cable supplied to the Navy had to be consistent in strength and the introduction of testing and the determination of proof stresses for iron used in the manufacture of chain cable owes much to the pioneering work carried out by Brown. In 1816 Brown installed a testing machine at

Millwall that acted on the principle of a weigh-bridge, being manually-powered through a system of wheels and axles, while the stress was estimated by weights suspended through a system of levers at the other end of the cable.

The reason behind the choice of Pontypridd is intriguing especially regarding Brown's talk of establishing a chainworks in every principal port, but when Brown was looking for a new site, Cardiff, the nearest port to Pontypridd, could hardly be termed a principal port. Access to the sea had been greatly improved in 1798 with the Glamorganshire Canal's sea-lock, the first on the Severn Estuary which allowing ships of up to 200 tons access to the mile-long floating basin through the 97ft by 27ft sea-lock near the mouth of the river Taff. The sea-lock at Cardiff freed the port from the constraints of the tidal estuary but not completely

Fig 132 - Brown Lenox's Millwall chain testing machine. This illustration appeared in Discoveries and Inventions of the Nineteenth Century by Robert Routledge (1876) and although indicating that it was originally designed by Samuel Brown, this is a hydraulic testing machine and possibly a refurbishment of the 1816 machine based on weigh-bridge principles (SKJ Collection)

as the winding two-mile approach channel constrained access and was completely dry for three hours a day. Cardiff's first major dock was not opened until 1839, although the Glamorganshire Canal Company had called for improvements to the sea-lock for enlarged wharfage accommodation since 1814. The principal cargo going down the canal to Cardiff was iron sent down by Merthyr ironmasters, Brown being familiar with and had used Welsh iron, primarily Cyfarthfa iron obtained through the Crawshays' London outlet. Crawshay iron had been found entirely satisfactory for Brown's purposes, and as the Cyfarthfa works were turning out 12,000 tons of bar iron annually, the Newbridge site had a major advantage in being less than ten miles away from the ironworks on its main supply route. Coal was for the smith's forges also being available locally.

The Newbridge site may have been brought to Brown's attention through this source also, or more likely, by the local knowledge of one of his smith foremen - Philip Thomas. Thomas was involved with the development of chain cable design and his contribution led to a joint patent with Brown in 1816. The exact extent of his involvement in the development of chain cable is uncertain but as Thomas was to become the first manager at Newbridge his part must have been by no means insignificant. Philip Thomas was born at Drumau near Neath, in 1771, the son of Philip Samuel Thomas, a weaver, who had become the steward of the Drumau estate after marrying the head servant of John Popkin, the estate owner. Popkin died in 1774 or 1775, leaving Drumau to an absent heir and vesting much authority in Philip and Margaret Thomas. Some income was derived from the leasing of minerals on the Drumau estate and it would seem that Philip Samuel Thomas was able to establish himself as an ironmaster in London by the 1800s. Presumably Philip Thomas was employed at his father's business when Brown was looking for skilled smiths to manufacture his cable. There is also evidence that he was working, indeed managing, a Liverpool chainworks; probably Crawford Logan, at this time.

Whatever the circumstances of Philip Thomas's contact with Brown, it led to a working partnership which lasted until Thomas's death in 1840. Philip Thomas is remembered in Pontypridd today as the man

Fig 133 - Aerial view of the Newbridge works at Ynysangharad occupying the centre ground. Taken before the construction of the A470 trunk road, the derelict Glamorganshire Canal can be seen running diagonally from bottom left to top right; Lenox's former home, Ynysangharad House at bottom left.
(SKJ Collection)

with two gravestones. The first stone intended for his grave now stands on Pontypridd Common, overlooking the Newbridge works and the town of Pontypridd. The inscription on the stone was the cause of it being rejected from Thomas's resting place in Glyntaff churchyard:

> *Stranger halt*
> *I am placed here to commemorate*
> *The virtue and abilities of (Philip Thomas)*
> *Who after managin the chainwork*
> *On my right side for the space of*
> *21 years much to the benefet of all*
> *Mankind died and was buried*
> *1840*
> *Age 69*

Philip Thomas's name was deleted from the stone due to the somewhat awkward phrasing and this may have been done by his relatives or the eccentric Dr William Price of Llantrisant (1800-1893). A more conventional tombstone now covers Thomas's grave in Glyntaff churchyard, which is also the resting place of a later Newbridge manager; George James Penn, and of George William Lenox. Unlike Brown, who had no children, Samuel Lenox had a son, the above-mentioned George William Lenox, who took a very active role in the running of the works, developing many successful designs of anchors and buoys. G W Lenox's main residence for the works was Ynysyngharad House, largely demolished during the construction of the A470 trunk road through Pontypridd.

Another one of Brown's foremen also assisted in the promotion of chain cables, but with a rival company! This was John Fuller, who decided to branch out on his own with the experience of many of Brown and Thomas's experiments and manufacture cables with the backing of a Wapping ship chandler by the name of Thomas Brunton. Brunton set up a company in the Commercial Road area of London, trading as Brunton, Middleton & Co., with John Fuller as manager (Thomas Brunton's brother William had also been in the employ of Brown). Brown's first chain cables were composed of twisted wrought iron links which were welded on the ends. This end-welding was an inherent weakness of the design and was found to be the cause of some early cables parting. However, Brown continued to improve the construction of the chain cables by devising side welding of the links and adopting stay-pins or studs which maintained the shape of the link and prevented its collapse. Before Brown introduced these improvements Brunton enrolled a patent in 1813 for improvements to chain cables, the major improvement being the use of broad-ended studs (to be fair to Brunton, Brown's first ideas on the shape of studs had been towards pointed-end pins). Brunton supplied his new patent chain cable as bower and stream chain cables to the East Indiaman; *Java*, a 1200 ton ship that sailed in March 1814 to Batavia, Bombay, and back. There had been somewhat erroneous news that the ship had lost its anchor and chains but Bruntons sought to correct this in a letter to *The Times*, attaching a letter from the captain of the *Java*; Henry Templer; '…they have had trails sufficient to place their strength and utility beyond all doubt in my mind.'

Brown continued to supply the Navy, a monopoly which lasted until 1916 when war demands outstripped Brown Lenox production. By 1816 Brown had restored the status quo in his joint patent, with Philip Thomas for 'chain manufactured by a new process ...' This patent covered the manufacture of cable composed of oval-shaped links, side-welded with broad-ended studs, the links being formed on special machinery, also covered by the patent. Concerns were raised by Brown in 1820 over newspaper reports implying Brown's patent was inferior to that of Brunton's 1813 and even William Hawk's 1804 patents, these alluded back to a trial made in 1816 between Brunton's 'plain' link cables and Brown's twisted links. It was also rumoured that Brown's orders were to be discontinued by the Navy Board. Representing the Board, John Knowles would confirm that the Navy Board had never discontinued their orders to Brown; 'Indeed, the form of the links of the cables now supplied to his Majesty's navy was submitted by you, and I have never heard any opinion than that your cables are at least equal to those manufactured by any other persons.' Brown's improved stud-link chain cable gave the world the design of chain cable which has remained almost unchanged to the present day and a process of manufacture which remained the same at the Newbridge works until the end of wrought iron chain production.

Newbridge marked the end of Samuel Brown's expansion plans in terms of establishments at every principal port and instead encouraged other companies to manufacture his patent chain cable under licence. Companies included Acramans of Bristol, Crawford Logan of Liverpool and Hawkes, Crawshay & Sons of Gateshead, the latter company associated with the Crawshay family at Cyfarthfa. In 1823 Daniel Wade Acraman had patented his own chain cable design and would later manufacture Brown's patent chain cable under licence, launched in 1837 Brunel's first steamship; the *PS Great Western*, had chain cable supplied by Acramans of Bristol. William Edward Acraman was one of the directors of the Great Western Steam Ship Co. and his company forged both paddle shafts for the ship. Acramans would also supply the Great Britain steamship in 1843.When asked at the 1860 Select Committee into the Manufacture of Anchors and Chain Cables for the Merchant Service; 'Were those cables made of the same description of iron as the *Great Britain*'s'? The Great Western Steamship Company's MD; Captain Christopher Claxton stated that; 'They were made of the very best iron that Acramans could find; we paid a high price for them; Acramans were great makers in those days.'

Fig 134 - Chainsmiths and strikers at work at Newbridge (SKJ Collection)

As already stated the Newbridge works was on the Glamorganshire Canal of which the Crawshays were the principal shareholders in the Glamorganshire Canal Company and preferential treatment was often shown to Cyfarthfa boats, much to the annoyance of other users and shareholding traders. The finished product could be subject to delays at the Cardiff end, due to congestion at the sea-lock. Newbridge was not a greenfield site as Samuel Brown would take over the Newbridge site then occupied by a nail factory and a blast furnace. The nail factory had been originally started by the Tappenden family of Faversham in Kent, Francis and James Tappenden having come to south Wales in 1802 as partners with Jeremiah Homfray and James Birch in the Abernant ironworks near Aberdare. The Tappendens were capitalists and brought investors' money with them from their bank at Faversham. However, they became involved in heavy expenditure outside the partnership, in the construction of a tramroad from the Abernant works to the Neath canal and Birch pulled out of the partnership leaving the Tappendens as sole owners of the works. Purchasing Homfray and Birch's shares put them into debt, and after losing a court action brought against them by the Neath Canal Company, they were forced into bankruptcy, along with their bank at Faversham, in 1814. Benjamin Hall became the assignee of the Abernant works estate after the bankruptcy and sold off the ironworks, but retained the Newbridge site.

Benjamin Hall had married Charlotte Crawshay, the daughter of Richard Crawshay of Cyfarthfa, in 1801, and had received the Rhymney ironworks as part of his marriage dowry. Crawshay may have been using the works at Newbridge after the Tappendens were forced to abandon the works and before Brown moved in. On the death of Benjamin Hall in 1817, his estate passed to his son, another Benjamin who was later to become Lord Llanover. Samuel Brown leased the site, buying or later treating with the assignees for the existing works, and by November 1817 had taken possession. He started building work on site and leasing further land for the chainworks from the canal company. Production started in the middle of new building and the adaptation of Tappenden's nail factory, the works expanding and removing, in time, all traces of the former manufactory. Both Brown and the company tried many times to acquire the leasehold, Lord Llanover's invariable reply being that as the firm were such excellent tenants he had no mind to lose them! The firm eventually acquired the leasehold from the Llanover estate in 1908, possibly by threat of the company moving to another site. After selling parts of his estate surplus to his requirements, Lord Llanover kept the Ynysyngharad estate, which included Newbridge and the present day Ynysyngharad Park, and maintained a patronising interest in the chainworks. On his English tour in 1822, the young Benjamin Hall visited Plymouth and noted that chain cable 'made by the patentee who rents my small ironworks at Ynys Llanharad (sic) in Glamorganshire, seems to be much in use'. He also noted at Portsmouth 'that chain cables were much in use' in the arsenal, and that 'some captains will not use any others'.

Towards the end of the nineteenth century the company's main chain cable competitors were mainly located in the Black Country, predominantly at Cradley Heath, Netherton and Tipton, near Dudley, in Staffordshire. The works of Noah Hingley of Netherton had been established in 1820 and over a hundred and forty years later it would become a subsidiary along with Brown Lenox in F H Lloyd and Co. The Black Country works adopted similar production techniques to Newbridge for heavy chain cable but made small chain in large quantities in 'outhouse' conditions by both men and women chainsmiths usually at the back of their homes. At Newbridge chain cable was produced by self-employed chainmakers and strikers, not directly employed by the company, but who like their Black Country counterparts, agreed to make a set amount of chain at a certain price. It was in their interests to produce it to the high standards imposed by Brown Lenox from the beginning, as any chain rejected by the company would put its smiths out of pocket, no payment being made for rejected work. The works for a long time relied on water for transport and motive power to drive machinery and to provide a blast for the furnaces. The works had two canal basins off the canal, one at a higher level for raw materials and one at a lower level to despatch the finished product. The head of water was also taken from the canal and returned below the works, its power being utilised on the way. After testing, chain and other iron components were lowered through the floor of the test shop into a waiting barge in the basin below. Brown Lenox continued to use the canal until the 1930's, even though chain could now be despatched by rail, but a breach of the canal at Nantgarw in 1942 effectively marked the end of trade beyond the Sea Lock at Cardiff. The canal basins are long filled-in but a section of the canal can still be seen at Newbridge and is known as the Nightingale's Bush nature reserve.

An independent water supply was later provided by the building of an aqueduct, taking water from the Nant Clydach two miles away, the remains of which are still visible along its route with a pier of the Berw aqueduct across the Taff, still visible. Waterwheels transmitted power to the machinery in the workshops, such as bending and scarfing machines which turned links ready for welding and making up into chain. Water power drove waterwheels which powered machinery in the workshops, such as bending and scarfing machines which turned links ready for welding and making up into chain. The waterwheels were replaced by American turbines at the turn of the century, but the remains of cast iron waterwheel feeders could still be seen in the works right up to final closure. A boiler plant providing steam power throughout the works was installed around 1853, although a Nasmyth forty-ton steam hammer with its own power plant was installed in 1845, and by the turn of the century a total of eight steam hammers were in operation. The work force at the time of opening would have been under a hundred.

Newbridge attracted skilled workers from the locality and from other industrial areas such as the Black Country, tempted by higher rates, all wages being in cash as no truck system operated at Newbridge, and later in 1866 a sick relief fund was established. Dr William Price would also perform a pioneering role at the chainworks as he was retained by the workers in a prototype medical aid society as their surgeon and physician. The works soon became the largest employers in the locality, employing up to 700 men in peak periods, even during the Rhondda coal boom period. There was also a movement of workers between other chainmaking districts and a tradition of skills being passed from father to son gave the workforce many generations of chainsmiths. The Holloway family, represented by the last manager of the chain and smiths shops; Ken Holloway, recalled that his father had come down from the Midlands: '...to join Uncle Dan and Uncle Albert in Pontypridd'. In 1907 Dan Holloway was the foreman smith at Brown Lenox under Horace Mark Gregory MD. To facilitate the movement of heavy machinery and materials from shop to shop, a works railway was put in running two small tank engines. Although the Taff Vale Railway, engineered by Brunel, was opened between Cardiff and Pontypridd in 1840, Brown Lenox relied solely upon the canal for transport until 1902, when a connection was made to the Pontypridd, Caerphilly and Newport Railway giving access to Newport docks and to the TVR and Cardiff docks via an exchange siding.

Over the years the chainworks used bar iron from most of the Merthyr ironworks, indeed all four Merthyr ironworks appear to have been involved; Cyfarthfa iron has already been mentioned, and it was also using Dowlais iron, and supplying chain cable back to Dowlais. By the 1850s the works were using Plymouth iron from the Merthyr ironworks of Anthony Hill and Thompson, Forman of Penydarren supplied some of Brown's flat-eye bar suspension bridge links such those for his Wellington Chainbridge at Aberdeen. Later the company started to produce its own iron; Trinity iron, and built rolling mills and foundries for cast iron, crucible steel and brass. The Chain Cables Act of 1864 caused much concern to other manufacturers of chain cable, due to the introduction of standard proof stresses. Brown Lenox, however, had no need to upgrade their standards, as shown by the following extract from *Engineering* for 22 February 1867:

> The Admiralty chain cables made from Brown Lenox and Co.'s Trinity iron are tested to more than 11-tons per square inch of the section of the iron in the links. The really good iron bears this strain without injury, but since it has been adopted under the authority of the Board of Trade for all chain cables used in the merchant service, it is well-known that many

cables made of iron of less strength are injured by it. For it is easy to make a cable which shall pass the test, and which at the same time is of inferior quality. One of the largest ship builders in the Kingdom informs us that out of the first seven ships which he sent out with cables tested under the new act, three parted their cables the first time their anchors were dropped.

The company's reputation saw not only merchant fleets of the world ordering chain cable, but also many foreign navies, including the German navy in the pre-first world war period. Chain cable and anchor manufacture continued well into the twentieth century and there were also various other engineering products such as colliery winding engines and a variety of castings and mouldings. There was a flourishing trade in iron buoys made on contract to the Trinity Corporation. Wrought iron anchors were produced, some designed and patented by members of the staff, the 'Lenox' anchor being a good example. In 1922 a foundry was installed at Newbridge to handle cast steel and set out to develop the manufacture of continuous cast steel chain cable. This research came to fruition when the company became the first company in the world to gain Lloyds approval for their cast steel chain in 1928. From this time wrought iron and high tensile cast steel chain were made side by side at Pontypridd, until 1958, when the Company installed the largest and most modern semi-automatic chainmaking plant in the world. With this development wrought iron chain ceased to be made at the Newbridge Chainworks at Pontypridd after 150 years of continuous production. The manufacture of steel chain by this process continued until 1968, when the chain-making resources of the Company were concentrated at F H Lloyd's Midland factories.

In the field of ships' chain cables the company built up their reputation as the premier manufacturers of chain cable. Regular orders came in from merchant and passenger lines with famous ships supplied including the Cunarders, such as the *Mauretania* and *Aquitania*, the White Star Line (*Titanic*) went to Noah Hingley's for its anchors and chains. The Royal Navy was the biggest customer and battleships included *HMS Lion*, *Dreadnaught*, *Hood* and *Rodney*. At the turn of the century the works were making mooring cables with 4½ inch square links for battleships

Fig 135 - The Great Eastern on the gridiron at Neyland with the tide under the hull. Photograph taken shortly after the ship was beached on the gridiron, Sept 1860 (Courtesy of the Institution of Civil Engineers)

which required hydraulic presses for shaping. One of their most famous orders was for chain cable to Brunel's *Great Eastern* steamship; even though Brown Lenox had ignored his request to tender for the Clifton chain links. Newbridge did undertake chain orders for Brunel after this, for example for use on his railways with chain needed in the erection of his Chepstow tubular bridge in 1851. In 1857 Brunel had to override his directors who were worried about escalating costs when he wanted Brown Lenox to undertake the order for the *Great Eastern* as they were, he said; 'Not the cheapest, but the best'. Brunel was to visit the works at Newbridge several times during the course of work on this order, the largest size being the largest chains made up to that date, fittingly for the largest ship yet built – a vessel weighing more than 10,000 tons.

George William Lenox was questioned at the Select Committee into the Manufacture of Anchors and Chain Cables for the Merchant Service, about the cables for the Great Eastern, stating that Brown Lenox made the whole of them; 'How did you test them?' - 'There were two sizes, $2^5/8$ and $2^7/8$; 124 tons was the test for the $2^5/8$, and 148 tons was the test for the $2^7/8$ in...' 'That was Plymouth iron?' — 'Yes; it was made by an understanding between Mr. Hill and myself; I went down and arranged the quality with him.' The chains for the *Great Eastern* were made by Newbridge and, after testing, were shipped down the Glamorganshire Canal and then on by coastal vessel around to the Thames-side Millwall chainworks of Brown Lenox which was next door to the yard of the builder; John Scott Russell. Lenox was invited to the Millwall yard during the first launch attempt and Brunel had arranged for the chaincable to be wound around two large wooden drums and used to control the descent of the *Great Eastern* into the water during the sideways launch. The position of the drums also offered a convenient backdrop to the photographs taken by Robert Howlett (1830–58). Brunel asked Lenox to stand with him in one of the photographs to be taken by Howlett with the chains as a background. The reluctance of Lenox to come into a photograph meant only Brunel was recorded by the camera on this occasion.

Appropriately, in the tradition of a Company that had supplied the anchor cables of many famous ships throughout the world, the last major chain cable order fulfilled by the Newbridge works was the cable for the Cunarder *Queen Elizabeth II* launched in 1969 before finally ending chainmaking although the smiths' shops were retained and continued traditional smithwork for items such as ships' cables ancillary gear. It was not just products employed in marine and colliery applications that the company produced, there were stationary steam engines, including a winding engine for Dinas Steam Colliery, and a replacement cylinder in 1861 for John Calvert's Newbridge Colliery winding and pumping beam engine of 1845 that is now re-erected at the University of South Wales campus in Pontypridd. The company was commissioned to produce a weighbridge in 1836 which was first installed at the Tongwynlais Lock of the Glamorganshire Canal this was later moved to different locations on the canal before going to the National Waterways Museum at Stoke Bruerne, Northants. It has now returned and is on display at the National Waterfront Museum in Swansea. The weighbridge consists of six cast-iron columns supporting a superstructure and an overhead system of levers to calculate the barge weight, no doubt drawing on the experience of the testing machine. A more unusual product was the mine ventilating fan constructed in the 1850s at Newbridge under the design of William Brunton.

Brown died in 1852, outliving Samuel Lenox who died in 1836 and his nephew George William Lenox passed away in 1868. The partners that followed included John Jones and Hugh M. Gordon with the Lenox line continued by George Charles Lenox and Lewis Gordon Lenox, with the last Lenox being represented at Newbridge up to the 1950s. On 22 April 1909 Brown Lenox & Co

Limited was incorporated as a limited company. In 1969 Brown Lenox became a wholly-owned part of the F H Lloyd Group and with the change of ownership came change into new products and quarry plant became the major product of the Company. After the demise of chainmaking other activities of the Newbridge engineering complex included a lifting gear division, marine and mining division, an aggregate test house, a proving house and heat treatment and testing facilities. The main activity of the works at the end was the manufacture, under licence, of ore and waste processing machinery, such as jaw and gyratory crushers, hammer mills and domestic refuse shredding machines. The last owner of the Newbridge site, and the Brown Lenox name, was the Terex Corporation of the USA in 1999. Part of the site had been sold off to form a retail estate in 1987 and the site finally closed in 1999 drawing an end to one of the longest standing and consistently successful companies in Wales with a history as celebrated as any in the country.

Millwall closed before this in the 1980s and had an equally varied history and range of products over the years. In the 1850s and 1860s the Millwall foreman William Roberts was a pioneer in the manufacture of fire engines. Roberts's most ambitious fire fighting vehicle was a self-propelling steam traction and fire engine made at Millwall in 1862 for Messrs. C. J. Mare and Co. Roberts was also a co-patentee with George William Lenox for letters patent for the invention of improvements in machinery for raising and lowering cables and other chains in 1852. From an early date chain cable production was largely concentrated at Newbridge leaving Millwall to concentrate on tanks, buoys, anchors and other vessels. In 1858 G W Lenox was experimenting with buoys to give forth a continuous peal of sounds when placed in a tide-way or other current of water resulting in Lenox's patent signal buoy. Much later Millwall entered the Air Ministry's competition for a non-crashable aeroplane fuel tank winning a Government competition and a prize of £1,400 in 1922.

In addition to chain cable production the Newbridge works also made a different kind of chain; long eyebar links for Brown's suspension bridges. In this field Brown was the first to erect iron suspension bridges with level road decks in this country, and the Newbridge works produced the major part of the chainwork for Samuel Brown's suspension bridges, a major undertaking that has been covered in this book. Brown largely used round eyebar links for his chainbridges, presumably out of economy, as links could be made from the same round bar iron stock as used for chainmaking, although he did design some with flat eyebars which as far as can be asserted, were not made at his works and it is known that the Wellington Chainbridge links were supplied by Thompson, Forman of Penydarren, Merthyr. An early chainbridge in Britain can be found at Llantysillio near Llangollen, which although rebuilt twice retains its original chains. Permission was granted in 1814 for the bridge with the chains forged at Pickering's coke ovens near Pontcysyllte. An Ellesmere & Chester Canal General Committee report dated 31 July 1817 implies that the bridge was then open, it was seen by the French engineer (and suspected industrial spy) Joseph-Michel Dutens in 1818 who surveyed the bridge. The following year, Dutens published detailed drawings of it in his *Mémoires sur les Travaux publics de l'Angleterre*. They are the only known plans of the original bridge still in existence. The experimental chain suspension bridge erected by Brown at Millwall is also recorded in this.

Only two suspension bridges of Brown's design have been recorded in Wales, both of which were erected under the personal supervision of Philip Thomas. One at Llandovery over the Towy and another over the Usk at Kemeys both now replaced. The Kemeys suspension bridge was erected at a point still known on the map as Chainbridge. Tenders were invited for the erection of a suspension bridge here in 1829 and a final tender from Brown Lenox & Co., signed by Philip Thomas, was accepted for a bridge:

> '...of 150 feet span, 22 feet wide with cast iron towers and wrought iron side railings, all masonry, carpentry, the bridge to be 24 feet above low water, strong enough to carry fifty-tons with safety for £1800 ... I beg further to add that the work will be on the principle we have always erected these bridges and which have in every instance answered the intended purpose, and given perfect satisfaction.'

Completed in 1830 the bridge was guaranteed for two years and lasted until 1906, when it was replaced by the present steel arch bridge. One of the principal shareholders of the bridge company was Lord Llanover, the Newbridge estate landlord who had taken a keen interest in his tenant's work, particularly the Union Chainbridge for which he went out of his way to see in 1822. Stating that this 'hanging bridge' over the Tweed some five miles from Berwick was designed by Captain S. Brown 'and made at my works near Pontypridd in Wales', adding, 'the appearance of the bridge is very light and neat, and the general opinion is that it is likely to last and is as durable as any other'.

Fig 136 - The famous photograph of Brunel against the checking drum,
wound with Brown Lenox chain cable
(Courtesy of the Institution of Civil Engineers)

Fig 137 - Union Chain Bridge, England and Scotland signs 1974

Following completion of the extensive works of restoration in the 1970s, and further refurbishment between 1979 and 1981 under the Tweed Bridges Trust's last Surveyor, Basil Arthur, and its last Clerk, William McCreath, when the majority of the links and pins in the chains were replaced, and the Bridge was repainted from a not-unattractive overall white to the original colour specification of 1820 – dark green bolts, black joints, stone colour hangers (see fig 86) – it was hoped that a maintenance-free period of 50 years might be possible.

The Tweed Bridges Trust, which had maintained the Union Bridge, together with its sister border bridges at Norham and Coldstream, for over 100 years, was wound-up in controversial circumstances in 1986 and ownership of the three bridges passed to the two riparian authorities – Northumberland County Council and Borders Regional Council (later Scottish Borders Council), the former assuming responsibility as lead authority for the maintenance and repair of the Union Bridge. There was concern amongst those who opposed the transfer, that the maintenance requirements of the three bridges - and the Union Bridge in particular - until then the sole responsibility of local trustees, would be weighed against the competing needs of hundreds of bridges and roads in the two Councils' areas – and so it has proved.

The almost inevitable consequence of the transfer was a steady deterioration of the structure of the Union Bridge, now listed as Grade 1 in England and Grade A in Scotland. Extensive flaking of the paintwork, revealing large patches of corrosion, together with erosion of the masonry and deck panels, presented a general impression of disrepair and neglect.

Matters came to a head in 2007 when one of the wrought iron hangers sheared and the Bridge was immediately closed to vehicular traffic. It remained closed for eighteen months while Northumberland County Council undertook stress tests and applied for Listed Building Consent to carry out temporary repair works. English Heritage required the preparation of a management strategy for the longer-term repair and maintenance of the Bridge as a condition of a reluctant grant of a temporary approval of the use of stainless steel rods to replace a number of hangers found to be broken or susceptible to breaking.

In compliance with English Heritage's condition, Northumberland County Council commissioned a Conservation Management Plan from AECOM Transportation and Alan Williams Archaeology, assessing the historical and architectural significance of the Bridge, and providing a workable regime for the inspection, maintenance and upgrading of the Bridge. The Plan, which was delivered to Northumberland County Council in November 2010, outlined an extensive restoration programme involving all the constituent components of the Bridge, including the ground anchors.

Two years later, in 2012, with the temporary hangers still in place (they remain there in 2017) a group of concerned members of the local communities on both sides of the border formed an action group, Project 2020, with the aim of securing the proper repair and restoration of the Bridge before its bicentenary on the 26th July 2020 – allowing the Councils what at that time appeared to be a comfortable eight year period to carry out the necessary works. Northumberland County Council convened a meeting of local "stakeholders" in September 2014, out of which was formed the Friends of the Union Chain Bridge, a Charitable Incorporated Organisation registered as a charity in England and Scotland, to establish community support for a Heritage Lottery Bid by the Council. Membership of the Friends grew rapidly to over 600, principally within north Northumberland and the eastern Borders of Scotland but also throughout the UK and in Australia, Japan, Norway and the USA.

The two Councils' original intention was to submit a full stage 1 application to the Heritage Lottery Fund in December 2015, for substantial grant aid to carry out a full programme of repair and restoration of the Bridge, in accordance with their consultants' and their own engineers' recommendations. A favourable stage 1 decision in March 2016 would have enabled a stage 2 submission to be made in June 2017 which, if approved, would have allowed work to start in or around September 2017; and an 18 month works programme would have secured the full restoration of the Bridge well in time to celebrate its bicentenary. Consultants were appointed to take the bid through the two stages.

A series of frustrating delays, some occasioned by onerous requirements by heritage bodies, resulted in several slippages in the bid submission dates but Northumberland County Council remained confident that, through the appointment of a construction partner which would obviate the need for a lengthy tendering process, the works would be completed by July 2020. In July 2017, they announced that they were preparing to submit the much-delayed stage 1 bid by the end of August 2017. However, days after making this announcement, the County Council undertook a basic review of the project, appointed new bid consultants and a project manager and revised the stage 1 submission date to December 2017, two years exactly after the first projected submission date.

As this book is prepared for publication it is not clear whether the Bridge will be restored in time for its bicentenary celebrations. While it is more likely that it will be closed to all users on what should have been its celebration day, the outcome, although frustratingly delayed, should be an engineering icon restored and refreshed to serve its border communities and an ever-increasing number of visitors, as a continuing memorial to its remarkable designer, engineer and builder, for a further 200 years.

November 2017

Fig 138 - Engraving: Union Chain Bridge; W H Lizars 1849

Index

*Page numbers in **bold** refer to illustrations*

SAMUEL BROWN AND UNION CHAIN BRIDGE